U0112295

美国短篇小说选读

SELECTED READINGS IN
AMERICAN SHORT STORIES

范小玫 编著

厦门大学出版社

序

改革开放 30 年来,高校"英语热"持续升温。非英语专业的同学们,不但认真练好英语基本功,刻苦学习专业英语,而且想读点美国小说,了解美国社会的方方面面,掌握英语的文化和历史背景,进一步提高英语水平。这是个良好的愿望,值得重视和支持。

为了满足同学们的需要,范小玫副教授编选了这部《美国短篇小说选读》。它将为非英语专业的同学了解美国短篇小说提供一个快捷的平台。

与其他同类书籍相比,我觉得本书具有下列特点:

(一)选材跨度大,题材多样化。全书精选 18 篇美国短篇小说,涵盖了从 19 世纪初的小说家华盛顿·欧文到当代女作家谭恩美的作品;入选作家时间跨度大,涵盖面很广,包括了主流作家马克·吐温、霍桑、爱伦坡、安德森、海明威、厄普代克、德里罗等,南方作家福克纳、韦尔蒂,犹太作家马拉默德,黑人女作家艾丽丝·沃克和华裔作家谭恩美等。他们的入选作品内容丰富多彩,艺术风格迥异,语言各具特色。编者仿佛为读者举办了一场令人赏心悦目的小说盛宴。

(二)重点突出,名篇主导。美国文学历史不长,但名家辈出。编者打破贪大求全的老框框,精选了一些很有价值的名篇,以飨读者。许多选文如欧文的《瑞普·凡·温克尔》、霍桑的《教长的黑面纱》、马克·吐温的《跳蛙》、欧·亨利的《麦琪的礼物》、福克纳的《献给艾米莉的一朵玫瑰花》、海明威的《白象似的群山》和艾丽丝·沃克的《日常家用》等都是脍炙人口的佳作,常常入选美国各类选集和教科书。这些作品内容涉及美国社会生活的各个方面,有的揭露教长的虚伪,有的讽刺贿选的丑闻,有的歌颂淳朴的真情,有的揭示个人的困惑和挫折等等,喜怒哀乐之情跃然纸上,文字优美,语句简练,表达准确自如,虽留有时代之痕迹,仍不失为读者习作之范例。

(三)思想性与艺术性的统一,知识性与可读性的结合。本书除精选上述名篇之外,特别选了爱伦·坡的侦探小说《红死魔的面具》和当代科幻小说家勒·魁恩的小说《她消除了它们的名字》以及另外一位科幻小说家吉卜森的《根斯巴克连续体》等。这在一般美国小说选集里是不多见的。科幻小说在美国小说园地里一枝独秀,二次大战后有显著的发展。吉卜森在科幻小说里展现了一个奇妙的电脑世界。这也许是理工科同学很感兴趣的。后工业化时代以来，美国走进了后现代主义文学阶段，通俗小说与严肃小说平起平坐。科幻小说和侦探小说被大量改编成电影电视，受到广大观众的喜爱。因此，读点这类小说，也能增加阅读的乐趣，扩大知识面。

（四）评介加注释，导读作用大。本书主要面向高校非英语专业的同学，在编写上考虑比较周到。每篇选文前面有作家简介和选文评点，后面有难词难句注释和思考题，有助于引导同学学习和理解选文。这是编者多年来从事大学英语教学和认真研读美国小说的结晶。所以，本书既可作为高校非英语专业的文学教材，又可供同等学历的青年自学之用。他们可以从中得到有益的启迪，为进一步阅读美国长篇小说创造条件。

已故的著名学者范存忠教授曾指出：英语的真正价值，就在于它是一种文学语言。它是莎士比亚、弥尔顿和华兹华斯等大作家的语言。从 14 世纪到现在，经过许多杰出的文学家的提炼，英语具有音乐性的语调和五光十色的词汇。这些东西都有它的"弦外之音"，因为英语具有丰富的文学背景。

这些话对学习美国英语同样适用。德国哲学家赫尔德说："必须从语言中学习语法，而不是从语法中学习语言。"学习美国英语，要读点美国小说。比如，通过阅读小说来掌握令人头痛的美国俚语（slang），比死记硬背单词的效果好得多。况且小说离不开社会生活，读点美国小说可以了解和认识美国社会，理解人文精神的深刻内涵，作为自己人生旅途的有益参照。

美国作家梭罗说："多少人把读书作为一生中一个新时期的开端！"读点美国小说，直接接触生动优美的英语，将会拓展视野，提高英语阅读和写作的能力，增加读书的兴趣和快乐，这将使你如虎添翼，飞向知识的新天地，成为你一生中新生活的开端！

学习贵在坚持。有了好教材，还要坚持不懈地努力，才能学有所得。我相信《美国短篇小说选读》将受到师生们的喜爱，在教学中发挥它应有的作用；同时，我希望编者在实践中不断总结经验，集思广益，使它更加完善，成为高校非英语专业同学的好伙伴。是为序。

杨仁敬

2009 年元月

于瑞景新居

Contents

Washington Irving

(1783-1859)

Washington Irving (1783—1859) was the first American writer of imaginative literature to gain international fame. To say that he was the father of American literature is not much exaggeration. He is a major figure in the history of the short story in America. The short story as genre in American literature probably began with Irving's *The Sketch Book of Geoffrey Crayon* (1819—1820) , a collection of essays, sketches, and tales, of which the most famous and frequently anthologized are "Rip Van Winkle" and "The Legend of Sleepy Hollow". The book marked the beginning of American Romanticism.

Irving was born into a wealthy New York merchant family in the final year of the Revolutionary War and named after George Washington. From a very early age he began to read widely and write juvenile poems, essays and plays. Later, he studied law and for a time led the leisurely life of a gentleman lawyer, but he loved writing more. In 1815, he went to England to take care of his family business there, and when it failed, he had to write to support himself. When he was about 50, after an absence of 17 years, he returned to America and lived a life of leisure and comfort, and writing *The Life of Goldsmith* (1849) and a five-volume *Life of Washington* (1859) and a lot of other works. He died in 1859. He was not married.

He was not only a story writer, a biographer, but also a historian. Apart from *The Sketch Book*, his major works include *A History of New*

1

York (1809). Many of Irving's works are distinctively European in content and style and exhibit the Gothic, the supernatural, and the longing for the good old days, which are romantic enough in subject if not exactly in style. His English is mostly British English. A folk-tale quality governs the overall meaning of Irving's fiction. Irving's style can only be described as beautiful. It is imitative, but he was a highly skillful writer. His writing is elegant and full of gentle humor and vivid descriptions. His characters are vivid and true so that they tend to linger in the mind of the reader. Another characteristic of Irving's writing is the musical language. Some people read Irving just for the music of his language.

"Rip Van Winkle" is based on old German folk tales which Irving adapted to the American setting. The central character, Rip Van Winkle, the hen-pecked and lazy husband who sleeps for twenty years and awakens to a greatly changed world and a long beard, is one of the best-known characters in American popular culture, widely recognized through his many appearances and references in books, movies, cartoons, and advertisements. "Rip Van Winkle" has been called the most popular story in the United States. An American actor played in a stage version of it for 45 years!

Rip Van Winkle

Washington Irving

Whoever has made a voyage up the Hudson[1] must remember the Kaatskill mountains[2]. They are a dismembered[3] branch of the great Appalachian family[4], and are seen away to the west of the river, swelling up to a noble height, and lording it over the surrounding country[5]. Every change of season, every change of weather, indeed, every hour of the day, produces some change in the magical hues and shapes of these mountains,

2

and they are regarded by all the good wives, far and near, as perfect barometers[6]. When the weather is fair and settled, they are clothed in blue and purple, and print their bold outlines[7] on the clear evening sky; but sometimes, when the rest of the landscape is cloudless, they will gather a hood of gray vapours about their summits[8], which, in the last rays of the setting sun, will glow and light up like a crown of glory.

At the foot of these fairy mountains, the voyager[9] may have descried[10] the light smoke curling up from a village, whose shingle-roofs gleam among the trees[11], just where the blue tints[12] of the upland melt away into the fresh green of the nearer landscape. It is a little village, of great antiquity, having been founded by some of the Dutch colonists, in the early times of the province, just about the beginning of the government of the good Peter Stuyvesant[13] (may he rest in peace!) , and there were some of the houses of the original settlers standing within a few years, built of small yellow bricks brought from Holland, having latticed windows and gable fronts, surmounted with weathercocks[14].

In that same village and in one of these very houses (which, to tell the precise truth, was sadly time-worn and weather-beaten), there lived many years since[15], while the country was yet a province of Great Britain, a simple good-natured fellow, of the name of Rip Van Winkle. He was a descendant of the Van Winkles who figured so gallantly in the chivalrous days of Peter Stuyvesant[16], and accompanied him to the siege[17] of Fort Christina. He inherited, however, but little of the martial[18] character of his ancestors. I have observed that he was a simple good-natured man; he was, moreover, a kind neighbour, and an obedient hen-pecked[19] husband. Indeed, to the latter circumstance might be owing that meekness of spirit which gained him such universal popularity[20]; for those men are most apt to be obsequious and conciliating abroad[21], who are under the discipline of shrews[22] at home. Their temper, doubtless, are rendered pliant and

3

malleable in the fiery furnace of domestic tribulation[23], and a curtain lecture[24] is worth all the sermons in the world for teaching the virtues of patience and long-suffering. A termagant[25] wife may, therefore, in some respects, be considered a tolerable blessing; and if so, Rip Van Winkle was thrice[26] blessed.

Certain it is that he was a great favourite among all the good wives of the village, who, as usual with the amiable sex[27], took his part in all family squabbles[28]; and never failed, whenever they talked those matters over in their evening gossipings, to lay all the blame on Dame Van Winkle. The children of the village, too, would shout with joy whenever he approached. He assisted at their sports[29], made their playthings, taught them to fly kites and shoot marbles[30], and told them long stories of ghosts, witches, and Indians. Whenever he went dodging[31] about the village, he was surrounded by a troop of them, hanging on his skirts[32], clambering[33] on his back, and playing a thousand tricks on him with impunity[34]; and not a dog would bark at him throughout the neighbourhood.

The great error in Rip's composition was an insuperable aversion to all kinds of profitable labour[35]. It could not be from the want of assiduity or perseverance[36]; for he would sit on a wet rock, with a rod as long and heavy as a Tartar's lance[37], and fish all day without a murmur, even though he should not be encouraged by a single nibble[38]. He would carry a fowling-piece[39] on his shoulder for hours together, trudging through woods and swamps, and up hill and down dale, to shoot a few squirrels or wild pigeons. He would never refuse to assist a neighbour even in the roughest toil, and was a foremost man at all country frolics for husking Indian corn, or building stone fences[40]; the women of the village, too, used to employ him to run their errands[41], and to do such little odd jobs as their less obliging husbands would not do for them. In a word, Rip was ready to attend to[42] anybody's business but his own; but as to doing family duty,

4

and keeping his farm in order, he found it impossible.

In fact, he declared it was of no use to work on his farm; it was the most pestilent[43] little piece of ground in the whole country; everything about it went wrong, and would go wrong, in spite of him. His fences were continually falling to pieces; his cow would either go astray[44], or get among the cabbages; weeds were sure to grow quicker in his fields than anywhere else; the rain always made a point of setting in[45] just as he had some outdoor work to do; so that though his patrimonial estate had dwindled away[46] under his management, acre by acre, until there was little more left than a mere patch of Indian corn and potatoes, yet it was the worst conditioned farm in the neighbourhood.

His children, too, were as raged and wild as if they belonged to nobody. His son Rip, an urchin begotten in his own likeness[47], promised to inherit the habits, with the old clothes of his father. He was generally seen trooping like a colt at his mother's heels[48], equipped in a pair of his father's cast-off galligaskins[49], which he had much ado[50] to hold up with one hand, as a fine lady does her train[51] in bad weather.

Rip Van Winkle, however, was one of those happy mortals, of foolish, well-oiled dispositions, who take the world easy[52], eat white bread or brown, whichever can be got with least thought or trouble, and would rather starve on a penny than work for a pound. If left to himself, he would have whistled life away, in perfect contentment; but his wife kept continually dinning in his ears about[53] his idleness, his carelessness, and the ruin he was bringing on his family. Morning, noon, and night, her tongue was incessantly going, and everything he said or did was sure to produce a torrent of household eloquence[54]. Rip had but one way of replying to all lectures of the kind, and that, by frequent use, had grown into a habit. He shrugged his shoulders, shook his head, cast up his eyes, but said nothing. This, however, always provoked a fresh volley from his

5

wife; so that he was faint to draw off his forces, and take to the outside of the house[55]—the only side which, in truth, belongs to a hen-pecked husband.

Rip's sole domestic adherent[56] was his dog Wolf, who was as much hen-pecked as his master; for Dame Van Winkle regarded them as companions in idleness, and even looked upon Wolf with an evil eye, as the cause of his master's going so often astray. True it is, in all points of spirit befitting an honourable dog, he was as courageous an animal as ever scoured the woods[57]—but what courage can withstand the ever-during and all-besetting terrors of a wo man's tongue[58]? The moment Wolf entered the house, his crest fell, his tail drooped to the ground, or curled between his legs, he sneaked about with a gallows air, casting many a side-long glance at Dame Van Winkle, and at the least flourish of a broomstick or ladle, he would fly to the door with yelping precipitation[59].

Times grew worse and worse with Rip Van Winkle as years of matrimony rolled on[60]; a tart temper never mellows with age[61], and a sharp tongue is the only edged tool[62] that grows keener with constant use. For a long while he used to console himself, when driven from home, by frequenting a kind of perpetual club of the sages, philosophers, and other idle personages of the village[63]; which held its sessions on a bench before a small inn, designated by a rubicund portrait of his Majesty George the Third[64]. Here they used to sit in the shade through a long lazy summer's day, talking listlessly[65] over village gossip, or telling endless sleepy stories about nothing. But it would have been worth any states man's money to have heard the profound discussions that sometimes took place, when by chance an old newspaper fell into their hands from some passing traveler. How solemnly they would listen to the contents, as drawled out[66] by Derrick Van Bummel, the schoolmaster, a dapper[67] learned little man, who was not to be daunted by the most gigantic word in the dictionary[68]; and how sagely

6

they would deliberate upon[69] public events some months after they had taken place.

The opinions of this junto[70] were completely controlled by Nicholas Vedder, a patriarch[71] of the village, and landlord of the inn, at the door of which he took his seat from morning till night, just moving sufficiently to avoid the sun and keep in the shade of a large tree; so that the neighbours could tell the hour by his movements as accurately as by a sundial[72]. It is true he was rarely heard to speak, but smoked his pipe incessantly. His adherents, however (for every great man has his adherents), perfectly understood him, and knew how to gather his opinions. When anything that was read or related displeased him, he was observed to smoke his pipe vehemently, and to send forth short, frequent, and angry puffs, but when pleased he would inhale the smoke slowly and tranquilly, and emit it in light and placid clouds; and sometimes, taking the pipe from his mouth, and letting the fragrant vapour curl about his nose, would gravely nod his head in token of perfect approbation[73].

From even this stronghold[74] the unlucky Rip was at length routed[75] by his termagant wife, who would suddenly break in upon the tranquility of the assemblage and call the members all to naught[76]; nor was that august personage[77], Nicholas Vedder himself, sacred from[78] the daring tongue of this terrible virago[79], who charged him outright[80] with encouraging her husband in habits of idleness.

Poor Rip was at last reduced almost to despair[81]; and his only alternative to escape from the labour of the farm and clamour of his wife, was to take gun in hand and stroll away into the woods. Here he would sometimes seat himself at the foot of a tree, and share the contents of his wallet[82] with Wolf, with whom he sympathized as a fellow-sufferer in persecution. "Poor Wolf," he would say, "thy mistress leads thee a dog's life of it[83]; but never mind, my lad, whilst I live thou shalt never want a

7

friend to stand by thee[84]! " Wolf would wag[85] his tail, look wistfully[86] in his master's face, and if dogs can feel pity, I verily believe he reciprocated the sentiment with all his heart[87].

In a long ramble[88] of the kind on a fine autumnal day, Rip had unconsciously scrambled[89] to one of the highest parts of the Kaatskill mountains. He was after his favourite sport of squirrel-shooting[90], and the still solitudes had echoed and re-echoed with the reports[91] of his gun. Panting and fatigued[92], he threw himself, late in the afternoon, on a green knoll[93], covered with mountain herbage[94], that crowned the brow of a precipice[95]. From an opening between the trees he could overlook all the lower country for many a mile of rich woodland. He saw at a distance the lordly Hudson, far, far below him, moving on its silent but majestic course[96], with the reflection of a purple cloud, or the sail of a lagging bark[97], here and there sleeping on its glassy bosom[98], and at last losing itself in the blue highlands.

On the other side he looked down into a deep mountain glen[99], wild, lonely, and shagged[100], the bottom filled with fragments from the impending cliffs, and scarcely lighted by the reflected rays of the setting sun. For some time Rip lay musing on[101] this scene; evening was gradually advancing; the mountains began to throw their long blue shadows over the valley; he saw that it would be dark long before he could reach the village, and he heaved a heavy sigh[102] when he thought of encountering the terrors of Dame Van Winkle.

As he was about to descend[103], he heard a voice from a distance, hallooing[104], "Rip Van Winkle! Rip Van Winkle!" He looked round, but could see nothing but a crow winging its solitary flight across the mountain. He thought his fancy must have deceived him, and turned again to descend, when he heard the same cry ring through the still evening air, "Rip Van Winkle! Rip Van Winkle!"— at the same time Wolf bristled up

8

his back, and giving a loud growl, skulked to his master's side[105], looking fearfully down into the glen. Rip now felt a vague apprehension[106] stealing over him; he looked anxiously in the same direction, and perceived a strange figure slowly toiling[107] up the rocks, and bending under the weight of something he carried on his back. He was surprised to see any human being in this lonely and unfrequented[108] place; but supposing it to be some one of the neighbourhood in need of his assistance, he hastened down to yield it[109].

On nearer approach he was still more surprised at the singularity[110] of the stranger's appearance. He was a short, square-built[111] old fellow, with thick bushy hair and a grizzled[112] beard. His dress was of the antique Dutch fashion — a cloth jerkin strapped round the waist — several pair of breeches, the outer one of ample volume, decorated with rows of buttons down the sides, and bunches at the knees[113]. He bore on his shoulder a stout keg[114], that seemed full of liquor[115], and made signs for Rip to approach and assist him with the load. Though rather shy and distrustful of this new acquaintance, Rip complied with his usual alacrity[116]; and mutually relieving each other, they clambered up a narrow gully[117], apparently the dry bed of a mountain torrent. As they ascended, Rip every now and then heard long rolling peals[118], like distant thunder, that seemed to issue out of a deep ravine[119], or rather cleft[120] between lofty rocks, toward which their rugged path conducted[121]. He paused for an instant, but supposing it to be the muttering[122] of one of those transient thunder-showers which often take place in mountain heights, he proceeded. Passing through the ravine, they came to a hollow[123], like a small amphitheatre[124], surrounded by perpendicular precipices[125], over the brinks of which impending trees shot their branches[126] so that you only caught glimpses of the azure[127] sky and the bright evening cloud. During the whole time Rip and his companion had laboured on[128] in silence, for though the former

9

marveled greatly what could be the object of carrying a keg of liquor up this wild mountain; yet there was something strange and incomprehensible about the unknown, that inspired awe and checked familiarity[129].

On entering the amphitheatre, new objects of wonder presented themselves. On a level[130] spot in the center was a company of odd-looking personages playing at nine-pins[131]. They were dressed in a quaint outlandish fashion[132]; some wore short doublets[133], others jerkins, with long knives in their belts, and most of them had enormous breeches, of similar style with that of the guide's. Their visages[134], too, were peculiar: one had a large head, broad face, and small piggish eyes; the face of another seemed to consist entirely of nose, and was surmounted by a white sugar-loaf hat, set off with a little red cock's tail[135]. They all had beards, of various shapes and colours. There was one who seemed to be the commander. He was a stout old gentleman, with a weather-beaten countenance[136]; he wore a laced doublet, broad belt and hanger[137], high-crowned hat and feather, red stockings, and high-heeled shoes, with roses in them. The whole group reminded Rip of the figures in an old Flemish painting[138], in the parlour[139] of Dominie[140] Van Shaick, the village parson, and which had been brought over from Holland at the time of the settlement.

What seemed particularly odd to Rip was, that though these folks were evidently amusing themselves, yet they maintained the gravest faces, the most mysterious silence, and were, withal[141], the most melancholy party of pleasure he had ever witnessed. Nothing interrupted the stillness of the scene but the noise of the balls, which, whenever they were rolled, echoed along the mountains like rumbling peals or thunder.

As Rip and his companion approached them, they suddenly desisted from their play[142], and stared at him with such fixed, statue-like gaze, and such strange, uncouth[143], lack luster[144] countenances, that his heart turned

10

within him, and his knees smote[145] together. His companion now emptied the contents of the keg into large flagons[146], and made signs to him to wait upon the company. He obeyed with fear and trembling; they quaffed[147] the liquor in profound silence, and then returned to their game.

By degrees Rip's awe and apprehension subsided[148]. He even ventured, when no eye was fixed upon him, to taste the beverage[149], which he found had much of the flavour of excellent Hollands[150]. He was naturally a thirsty soul, and was soon tempted to repeat the draught[151]. One taste provoked another; and he reiterated[152] his visits to the flagon so often, that at length his senses were overpowered, his eyes swam in his head[153], his head gradually declined, and he fell into a deep sleep.

On waking, he found himself on the green knoll whence he had first seen the old man of the glen. He rubbed his eyes — it was a bright sunny morning. The birds were hopping and twittering[154] among the bushes, and the eagle was wheeling aloft[155], and breasting[156] the pure mountain breeze. "Surely," thought Rip, "I have not slept here all night." He recalled the occurrences before he fell asleep. The strange man with a keg of liquor — the mountain ravine —the wild retreat[157] among the rocks — the wo-begone party[158] at nine-pins — the flagon — "Oh! That flagon! That wicked flagon!" thought Rip, "what excuse shall I make to Dame Van Winkle?"

He looked round for his gun, but in place of the clean well-oiled fowling-piece[159], he found an old firelock[160] lying by him, the barrel incrusted with rust, the lock falling off, and the stock worm-eaten. He now suspected that the grave roysterers[161] of the mountain had put a trick upon him, and, having dosed him with liquor[162], had robbed him of his gun. Wolf, too, had disappeared, but he might have strayed away after a squirrel or partridge[163]. He whistled after him, and shouted his name, but all in vain; the echoes repeated his whistle and shout, but no dog was to be seen.

11

He determined to revisit the scene of the last evening's gambol[164], and, if he met with any of the party, to demand his dog and gun. As he rose to walk, he found himself stiff in the joints, and wanting in his usual activity. "These mountain beds do not agree with me," thought Rip, "and if this frolic should lay me up with a fit of the rheumatism[165], I shall have a blessed time with Dame Van Winkle." With some difficulty he got down into the glen: he found the gully up which he and his companion had ascended the preceding evening; but, to his astonishment, a mountain stream was now foaming down it — leaping from rock to rock, and filling the glen with babbling murmurs. He, however, made shift to scramble[166] up its sides, working his toilsome way through thickets of birch, sassafras, and witch-hazel[167], and sometimes tripped up or entangled[168] by the wild grape-vines that twisted their coils or tendrils[169] from tree to tree, and spread a kind of network in his path.

At length he reached to where the ravine had opened through the cliffs to the amphitheatre; but no traces of such opening remained. The rocks presented a high impenetrable wall, over which the torrent came tumbling in a sheet of feathery foam[170], and fell into a broad deep basin, black from the shadows of the surrounding forest. Here, then, poor Rip was brought to a stand[171]. He again called and whistled after his dog; he was only answered by the cawing[172] of a flock of idle crows, sporting high in air about a dry tree that overhung a sunny precipice; and who, secure in their elevation, seemed to look down and scoff at the poor man's perplexities[173]. What was to be done? — the morning was passing away, and Rip felt famished[174] for want of his breakfast. He grieved to give up his dog and his gun; he dreaded to meet his wife; but it would not do to starve among the mountains. He shook his head, shouldered the rusty firelock, and with a heart full of trouble and anxiety, turned his steps homeward.

As he approached the village he met a number of people, but none whom he knew, which somewhat surprised him, for he had thought himself acquainted with every one in the country round. Their dress, too, was of a different fashion from that to which he was accustomed. They all stared at him with equal marks of surprise[175], and whenever they cast their eyes upon him, invariably stroked their chins. The constant recurrence[176] of this gesture induced Rip, involuntarily, to do the same — when, to his astonishment, he found his beard had grown a foot long!

He had now entered the skirts[177] of the village. A troop of strange children ran at his heels, hooting after him[178], and pointing at his gray beard. The dogs, too, not one of which he recognized for an old acquaintance, barked at him as he passed. The very village was altered; it was larger and more populous[179]. There were rows of houses which he had never seen before, and those which had been his familiar haunts[180] had disappeared. Strange names were over the doors — strange faces at the windows — everything was strange. His mind now misgave[181] him; he began to doubt whether both he and the world around him were not bewitched[182]. Surely this was his native village, which he had left but the day before. There stood the Kaatskill mountains — there ran the silver Hudson at a distance — there was every hill and dale precisely as it had always been. Rip was sorely perplexed. "That flagon last night," thought he, "has addled[183] my poor head sadly!"

It was with some difficulty that he found the way to this own house, which he approached with silent awe, expecting every moment to hear the shrill voice of Dame Van Winkle. He found the house gone to decay[184] — the roof fallen in, the windows shattered, and the doors off the hinges[185]. A half-starved dog, that looked like Wolf, was skulking about it. Rip called him by name, but the cur snarled[186], showed his teeth, and passed on. This was an unkind cut[187] indeed — "My very dog," sighed poor Rip, "has forgotten me!"

He entered the house, which, to tell the truth, Dame Van Winkle had always kept in neat order. It was empty, forlorn[188], and apparently abandoned. The desolateness overcame all his connubial fears[189]— he called loudly for his wife and children — the lonely chambers rang for a moment with his voice, and then all again was silence.

He now hurried forth, and hastened to his old resort, the village inn — but it too was gone. A large rickety[190] wooden building stood in its place, with great gaping[191] windows, some of them broken and mended with old hats and petticoats, and over the door was painted: "The Union Hotel, by Jonathan Doolittle". Instead of the great tree that used to shelter the quiet little Dutch inn of yore[192], there was now reared[193] a tall naked pole, with something on the top that looked like a red nightcap, and from it was fluttering a flag, on which was a singular assemblage of stars and stripes — all this was strange and incomprehensible. He recognized on the sign, however, the ruby face of King George, under which he had smoked so many a peaceful pipe; but even this was singularly metamorphosed[194]. The red coat was changed for one of blue and buff[195], a sword was held in the hand instead of a scepter[196], the head was decorated with a cocked hat[197], and underneath was painted in large characters, GENERAL WASHINGTON.

There was, as usual, a crowd of folks about the door, but none that Rip recollected. The very character of the people seemed changed. There was a busy, bustling, disputatious tone about it, instead of the accustomed phlegm[198] and drowsy tranquility. He looked in vain for the sage Nicholas Vedder, with his broad face, double chin, and fair long pipe, uttering clouds of tobacco-smoke instead of idle speeches; or Van Bummel, the schoolmaster, doling forth[199] the contents of an ancient newspaper. In place of these, a lean, bilious-looking fellow[200], with his pocket full of handbills[201], was haranguing vehemently about[202] rights of citizens —

14

elections — members of congress — liberty — Bunker's Hill[203]— heroes of seventy-six[204]— and other words, which were a perfect Babylonish jargon[205] to the bewildered Van Winkle.

The appearance of Rip, with his long grizzled beard, his rusty fowling-piece, his uncouth[206] dress, and an army of women and children at his heels, soon attracted the attention of the tavern politicians. They crowded round him, eyeing him from head to foot with great curiosity. The orator bustled up to him[207], and, drawing him partly aside, inquired "on which side he voted?" Rip stared in vacant stupidity. Another short but busy little fellow pulled him by the arm, and rising on tiptoe, inquired in his ear, "Whether he was Federal or Democrat?" Rip was equally at a loss to comprehend the question; when a knowing, self-important old gentleman, in a sharp cocked hat, made his way through the crowd, putting them to the right and left with his elbows as he passed, and planting himself before Van Winkle, with one arm akimbo[208], the other resting on his cane[209], his keen eyes and sharp hat penetrating, as it were, into his very soul, demanded in an austere[210] tone, "What brought him to the election with a gun on his shoulder, and a mob at his heels, and whether he meant to breed a riot[211] in the village?" — "Alas! Gentlemen," cried Rip, somewhat dismayed[212], "I am a poor quiet man, a native of the place, and a loyal subject of the king[213]. God bless him!"

Here a general shout burst from the by-standers — "A tory[214]! A tory! A spy! A refugee! Hustle him! Away with him![215]" It was with great difficulty that the self-important man in the cocked hat restored order; and, having assumed a tenfold austerity of brow[216], demanded again of the unknown culprit[217], what he came there for, and whom he was seeking? The poor man humbly assured him that he meant no harm, but merely came there in search of some of his neighbours, who used to keep about the tavern[218].

"Well — who are they? — name them. "

Rip bethought himself a moment, and inquired, "Where's Nicholas Vedder?"

There was a silence for a little while, when an old man replied in a thin piping voice[219], "Nicholas Vedder! Why, he is dead and gone these eighteen years! There was a wooden tombstone in the churchyard that used to tell all about him, but that's rotten and gone too. "

"Where's Brom Dutcher?"

"Oh, he went off to the army in the beginning of the war; some say he was killed at the storming of Stony Point[220] — others say he was drowned in a squall[221] at the foot of Antony's Nose[222]. I don't know — he never came back again. "

"Where's Van Bummel, the schoolmaster?"

"He went off to the wars too, was a great militia[223] general, and is now in congress. "

Rip's heart died away at hearing of these sad changes in his home and friends, and finding himself thus alone in the world. Every answer puzzled him too, by treating of such enormous lapses of time, and of matters which he could not understand: war — congress — Stony Point; — he had no courage to ask after any more friends, but cried out in despair, "Does nobody here know Rip Van Winkle?"

"Oh, Rip Van Winkle!" exclaimed two or three. "Oh, to be sure! That's Rip Van Winkle yonder, leaning against the tree. "

Rip looked, and beheld a precise counterpart of himself[224], as he went up the mountain: apparently as lazy, and certainly as ragged. The poor fellow was now completely confounded[225]. He doubted his own identity, and whether he was himself or another man. In the midst of his bewilderment, the man in the cocked hat demanded who he was, and what was his name?

16

"God knows," exclaimed he, at his wit's end; "I'm not myself — I'm somebody else — that's me yonder — no —that's somebody else got into my shoes — I was myself last night, but I fell asleep on the mountain, and they've changed my gun, and everything's changed, and I'm changed, and I can't tell what's my name, or who I am!"

The bystanders began now to look at each other, nod, wink significantly, and tap their fingers against their foreheads. There was a whisper, also, about securing the gun, and keeping the old fellow from doing mischief, at the very suggestion of which the self-important man in the cocked hat retired with some precipitation[226]. At this critical moment a fresh comely woman pressed through the throng to get a peep at the gray-bearded man. She had a chubby child in her arms, which, frightened at his looks, began to cry. "Hush, Rip," cried she, "hush, you little fool; the old man won't hurt you." The name of the child, the air of the mother, the tone of her voice, all awakened a train of recollections in his mind[227].

"What is your name, my good woman?" asked he.

"Judith Gardenier."

"And your father's name?"

"Ah, poor man, Rip Van Winkle was his name, but it's twenty years since he went away from home with his gun, and never has been heard of since — his dog came home without him; but whether he shot himself, or was carried away by the Indians, nobody can tell. I was then but a little girl."

Rip had but one question more to ask; but he put it with a faltering voice[228]:

"Where's your mother?"

"Oh, she too had died but a short time since; she broke a blood vessel in a fit of passion at a New-England peddler[229]."

There was a drop of comfort, at least, in this intelligence[230]. The honest man could contain himself no longer. He caught his daughter and her child in his arms. "I am your father!" cried he — "Young Rip Van Winkle once — old Rip Van Winkle now! — Does nobody know poor Rip Van Winkle?"

All stood amazed, until an old woman, tottering[231] out from among the crowd, put her hand to her brow, and peering under it in his face for a moment, exclaimed, "Sure enough! It is Rip Van Winkle — it is himself! Welcome home again, old neighbour. — Why, where have you been these twenty long years?"

Rip's story was soon told, for the whole twenty years had been to him but as one night. The neighbours stared when they heard it; some were seen to wink at each other, and put their tongues in their cheeks; and the self-important man in the cocked hat, who, when the alarm was over, had returned to the field, screwed down the corners of his mouth[232], and shook his head — upon which there was a general shaking of the head throughout the assemblage.

It was determined, however, to take the opinion of old Peter Vanderdonk, who was seen slowly advancing up the road. He was a descendant of the historian of that name, who wrote one of the earliest accounts of the province. Peter was the most ancient inhabitant of the village, and well versed in[233] all the wonderful events and traditions of the neighbourhood. He recollected Rip at once, and corroborated[234] his story in the most satisfactory manner. He assured the company that it was a fact, handed down from his ancestor the historian, that the Kaatskill mountains had always been haunted by strange beings. That it was affirmed that the great Hendrick Hudson, the first discoverer of the river and country, kept a kind of vigil[235] there every twenty years, with his crew of the Half-moon; being permitted in this way to revisit the scenes of his enterprise, and keep

18

a guardian eye upon the river, and the great city called by his name. That his father had once seen them in their old Dutch dresses playing at nine-pins in a hollow of the mountain; and that he himself had heard, one summer afternoon, the sound of their balls, like distant peals of thunder.

To make a long story short, the company broke up, and returned to the more important concerns of the election. Rip's daughter took him home to live with her; she had a snug, well-furnished house[236], and a stout cheery farmer for her husband, whom Rip recollected for one of the urchins that used to climb upon his back. As to Rip's son and heir, who was the ditto[237] of himself, seen leaning against the tree, he was employed to work on the farm; but evinced an hereditary disposition to attend to anything else but his business[238].

Rip now resumed his old walks and habits; he soon found many of his former cronies[239], though all rather the worse for the wear and tear of time[240]; and preferred making friends among the rising generation, with whom he soon grew into great favour.

Having nothing to do at home, and being arrived at that happy age when a man can be idle with impunity, he took his place once more on the bench at the inn door, and was reverenced as one of the patriarchs of the village[241], and a chronicle[242] of the old times "before the war". It was some time before he could get into the regular track of gossip, or could be made to comprehend the strange events that had taken place during his torpor[243]. How that there had been a revolutionary war — that the country had thrown off the yoke[244] of old England — and that, instead of being a subject of His Majesty George the Third, he was now a free citizen of the United States. Rip, in fact, was no politician; the changes of states and empires made but little impression on him; but there was one species of despotism[245] under which he had long groaned, and that was — petticoat government[246]. Happily that was at an end; he had got his neck out of the yoke of matrimony, and could go in and out whenever he pleased without dreading the tyranny of Dame Van Winkle. Whenever her name was mentioned, however, he shook his head, shrugged his shoulders, and cast up his eyes; which might pass either for an expression of resignation to his fate, or joy at his deliverance[247].

He used to tell his story to every stranger that arrived at Mr. Doolittle's hotel. He was observed at first to vary on some points every time he told it, which was, doubtless, owing to his having so recently awaked. It at last settled down precisely to the tale I have related, and not a man, woman, or child in the neighbourhood but knew it by heart[248]. Some always pretended to doubt the reality of it, and insisted that Rip had been out of his head, and that this was one point on which he always remained flighty[249]. The old Dutch inhabitants, however, almost universally gave it full credit[250]. Even to this day they never hear a thunderstorm of a summer afternoon about the Kaatskill, but they say Hendrick Hudson and his crew are at their game of nine pins[251]; and it is a common wish of all henpecked husbands in the neighbourhood, when life hangs heavy on their hands, that they might have a quieting draught out of Rip Van Winkle's flagon.

Notes:

1. the Hudson: 哈得森河(a river that runs through the eastern portion of New York State. It is named for Henry Hudson, an Englishman sailing for the Dutch East India Company, who explored it in 1609.)

2. the Kaatskill mountains: a range of the Appalachian Mountains in southeast New York just west of the Hudson River.

3. dismembered: 分离的(disjointed)

4. the great Appalachian family: 阿巴拉契亚山脉(the Appalachian Mountains, a mountain range in the eastern North United States extending from Quebec to the Gulf of Mexico)

5. lording it over the surrounding country：威武地俯瞰着周围的乡村（towering over the surrounding country）；lord it over sb.：向……逞威风（behave arrogantly toward sb.）

6. they are regarded by all the good wives, far and near, as perfect barometers：它们被所有远近的好主妇视为精确的晴雨表。

7. bold outlines：鲜明的轮廓

8. they will gather a hood of gray vapours about their summits：在山顶周围将积聚一层灰色的水雾。

9. voyager：traveler

10. descry：发现（discover by observation or investigation）

11. whose shingle-roofs gleam among the trees：村子里的木屋顶在树丛中隐约可见。gleam：隐约闪现

12. tint：色调（a variety of a color）

13. Peter Stuyvesant（1592—1672）：荷兰人,曾任北美洲荷兰殖民领地"新荷兰"（现为纽约）的最后一任总督（last Governor of the Dutch province of New Netherlands, in 1655 defeated Swedish colonists at Fort Christina, near what is now Wilmington, Delaware.）

14. having latticed windows and gable fronts, surmounted with weathercocks：花格窗,人字门墙,屋顶装着风信标。surmount：装在……顶上；顶上戴着……

15. since：ago

16. figured so gallantly in the chivalrous days of Peter Stuyvesant：在 Peter Stuyvesant 执政的骑士时代以勇敢著称。

17. siege：围攻

18. martial：勇敢的,尚武的

19. hen-pecked：惧内的,怕老婆的

20. to the latter circumstance might be owing... such universal popularity：使他到处受欢迎的温顺性格可能是由于后面这种情况而来的（即怕老婆）

21. apt to be obsequious and conciliating abroad：在外面往往顺从、和气；
    apt to：likely to

22. under the discipline of shrews：受到泼妇的管教

23. rendered pliant and malleable in the fiery furnace of domestic
    tribulation：在家庭磨难的熊熊火炉里变得柔软和有韧性。pliant：
    easily influenced；malleable：adaptable；tribulation：suffering.

24. curtain lecture：(妻子对丈夫的)床帷内教训

25. termagant：凶悍的

26. thrice：three times

27. as usual with the amiable sex：通常女人们都是如此。amiable：温柔
    的,友好的

28. squabble：争吵 (a noisy quarrel, usually about a trivial matter)

29. sports：games

30. marble：弹珠

31. dodging：躲避

32. skirt：男子外套的下摆

33. clambering：climbing

34. with impunity：不受惩罚地(withou punishment)

35. The great error in Rip's composition ... all kinds of profitable labour：
    瑞普性格中最大的缺点就是对于一切有好处的劳动都感到不可克
    制的厌恶。composition：性格；insuperable：不能克服的；aversion
    to：对……厌恶

36. want of assiduity or perseverance：不能刻苦勤奋或持之以恒；want：
    lack

37. Tartar's lance：鞑靼人用的长矛

38. nibble：轻咬

39. fowling-piece：猎枪

40. was a foremost man at all country ... or building stone fences：每逢
    村子里为剥玉米或修石墙而举行集会时，他总是第一个到的人。

foremost：最先的；Indian corn：玉米

41. run their errands：为她们跑腿

42. attend to：look after

43. pestilent：引起疫病的

44. go astray：迷路（go off the right path or route）

45. the rain always made a point of setting in：天总是要下雨。make a point of doing sth.：特别注意；set in：（疾病，坏天气等）开始来临

46. his patrimonial estate had dwindled away：他祖上传下来的田产不断地减少。patrimonial：祖传的；dwindle：减少；缩小

47. an urchin begotten in his own likeness：一个长得和他一模一样的淘气鬼。beget：生（儿、女），begotten 是 beget 的过去分词

48. trooping like a colt at his mother's heels：像小马驹似的跟在他母亲的脚后跟

49. cast-off galligaskins：丢掉不穿的宽大马裤。cast-off：被丢弃的（discarded）；galligaskins：16、17 世纪流行的一种男子的宽大马裤

50. had much ado：费尽力气

51. train：长裙拖地的部分

52. of foolish, well-oiled dispositions, who take the world easy：傻傻的、无所谓的性格，随遇而安

53. dinning in his ears about：在他的耳边絮叨……

54. a torrent of household eloquence：妻子一连串的数落。torrent：滔滔不绝的，连续的

55. This, however, always provoked a fresh volley ... and take to the outside of the house：然而这种办法总是引起他妻子的一阵新的痛骂，结果他只好认输，逃出了家门。volley：迸发

56. adhcrent：追随者（follower）

57. scoured the woods：在林子里大胆逐猎

58. withstand the ever-during and all-besetting terrors of a woman's tongue：抵挡一个女人喋喋不休、咄咄逼人的可怕舌头

59. his crest fell, his tail drooped to the ground, or curled between his legs
    ... he would fly to the door with yelping precipitation：他垂头丧气，
    尾巴拖在地上或夹在两腿之间，样子凄惨地在屋里偷偷地走来走
    去，不停地瞟着 Van Winkle 太太，只要扫帚柄或长柄勺微微一举，
    便狂吠着飞也似的冲向门口。gallows：受绞刑的；flourish：挥动；
    yelp：狗吠；precipitation：猛冲

60. as years of matrimony rolled on：随着婚姻生活一年一年地过去（as
    years of marriage passed）

61. a tart temper never mellows with age：尖刻的脾气绝不会随年龄的增
    长变得柔和。

62. edged tool：利器

63. frequenting a kind of perpetual club of the sages, philosophers, and
    other idle personages of the village：常去一个由村里德高望重的人、
    哲学家和其他游手好闲的人组成的永久俱乐部

64. designated by a rubicund portrait of his Majesty George the Third：小
    旅馆的突出标志是一幅乔治三世陛下脸色红润的肖像。George the
    Third (1738—1820)：英国国王，他在位期间，英国失去了美洲的
    殖民地。

65. listlessly：无精打采地

66. drawled out：慢慢地读出

67. dapper：衣冠楚楚的（neatly dressed）

68. who was not to be daunted by the most gigantic word in the dictionary：
    字典里最大最难的词也难不倒他。

69. deliberate upon：discuss

70. junto：也作 junta，小集团，派别，此处指这个常在酒店聚会的小集
    团

71. patriarch：族长，德高望重的人

72. sundial：（通过太阳知道时间的）日规，日晷仪

73. would gravely nod his head in token of perfect approbation：会庄重地

点头,表示完全认可。in token of:表示(as a sign of);approbation:认可(approval)

74. stronghold:要塞,堡垒(fort)

75. rout:赶出,驱逐(drive or force out as if by digging)

76. suddenly break in upon the tranquility of the assemblage and call the members all to naught:突然闯入,打破聚会的安宁,痛骂参加聚会的每一个人。break in upon:闯入(intrude upon);call all to naught:痛骂,辱骂

77. august personage:尊贵的名流

78. sacred from:免除,不受(safe from)

79. virago:泼妇(a loud-voiced, ill-tempered, scolding woman)

80. outright:不客气地(without reservation)

81. was at last reduced almost to despair:最后几乎陷入绝望。reduce ... to ...:使……陷于……(bring ... to the point of ...)

82. wallet:(旧时)徒步旅行者用来携带干粮、衣服的背袋

83. thy mistress leads thee a dog's life of it:你的女主人叫你过这样悲惨的日子。

84. whilst I live thou shalt never want a friend to stand by thee:只要我活着,你就不怕没有朋友支持你。(while I live, you shall never lack a friend to stand by you.)

85. wag:摇摆

86. wistfully:sadly

87. I verily believe he reciprocated the sentiment with all his heart:我肯定相信它也会衷心地可怜它的主人。verily:真正地,肯定地(truly);reciprocate:报答(return);sentiment:情感(feeling);with all one's heart:全心全意地

88. ramble:漫游

89. scramble:攀登(move or climb quickly, esp. over a rough or steep surface)

90. He was after his favourite sport of squirrel-shooting：他正在进行他最喜爱的猎松鼠活动。after：从事于（engaged in）

91. reports：猎枪击发时的枪声。

92. Panting and fatigued：喘着气，很疲劳

93. knoll：小山丘（a small rounded hill）

94. herbage：grass

95. crowned the brow of a precipice：位于悬崖峭壁的顶上

96. moving on its silent but majestic course：静静地而又庄严地流淌。majestic：庄严的（impressive，grand）

97. a lagging bark：缓缓而行的小船。bark：小船（a small vessel that is propelled by oars or sails）

98. on its glassy bosom：在它如镜的河面。bosom：（海、湖、河等的）宽阔的表面

99. glen：峡谷（valley）

100. shagged：covered with trees

101. musing on：thinking about quietly

102. he heaved a heavy sigh：他深深地叹了一口气。

103. As he was about to descend：当他正要下山时。be about to do sth.：正要做某事

104. hallooing：calling

105. Wolf bristled up his back, and giving a loud growl, skulked to his master's side："狼"竖起了背上的毛，嗥叫了一声，躲到了主人的身边。

106. apprehension：忧虑，担心（fearful or uneasy anticipation of the future）

107. toil：跋涉（move with great effort）

108. unfrequented：人迹罕至的（receiving few or no travelers or visitors）

109. he hastened down to yield it：他赶紧下山去帮忙。yield：给予（give）；"it"指的是前面提到的"assistance"

110. singularity：古怪（oddness）

111. square-built：身体宽阔而结实的

112. grizzled：grey or partly grey

113. His dress was of the antique Dutch fashion — a cloth jerkin ... and bunches at the knees：他的衣服是古代的荷兰装束——身穿一件布的紧身短上衣，腰间束着皮带，下穿几条马裤，外面的一条非常宽大，两侧装饰着两排纽扣，膝上打着褶。

114. a stout keg：一个结实的桶

115. liquor：酒，液体

116. Rip complied with his usual alacrity：瑞普像往常那样爽快地答应。comply：答应，遵从（act in accordance with an other's command, request, rule, or wish）；alacrity：乐意，爽快（eagerness）

117. gully：小峡谷（a small valley worn away by running water）

118. peal：隆隆声（a loud long sound or number of sounds one after the other）

119. ravine：深谷（a deep narrow valley with steep sides）

120. cleft：裂缝，裂口（a crack, opening, or split）

121. toward which their rugged path conducted：他们走的这条崎岖的小道正通向那里

122. mutter：发出低沉而持续的声音

123. hollow：山谷（a shallow valley）

124. amphitheatre：露天的圆形剧场

125. perpendicular precipices：陡峭的悬崖

126. over the brinks of which impending trees shot their branches：崖顶上的树枝垂在悬崖的边上。brink：边缘

127. azure：蔚蓝的（blue）

128. laboured on：艰难地往前走

129. that inspired awe and checked familiarity：令人生畏，不敢亲近。check：抑制（restrain）

130. level: 平坦的(having a flat, smooth surface)

131. nine-pins: 九木柱游戏

132. They were dressed in a quaint outlandish fashion: 他们穿着古怪的、外国样式的服装。quaint: 古怪的(odd, especially in an old-fashioned way); outlandish: 外国的(having a foreign appearance, bizarre)

133. doublet: 14至16世纪男子穿的紧身上衣

134. visage: 容貌(face, countenance)

135. was surmounted by a white sugar-loaf hat, set off with a little red cock's tail: 头上戴着一顶圆锥形的白帽子,帽子上插着一根小小的红鸡毛。sugar-loaf: 圆锥形的

136. with a weather-beaten countenance: 有一张饱经风霜的脸。

137. hanger: 佩剑(a short sword that may be hung from a belt)

138. Flemish painting: 西北欧佛兰德人的绘画

139. parlour: a room in a home for receiving visitors

140. Dominie: 牧师(Minister)

141. withal: besides

142. desisted from their play: 停止玩游戏。desist from: stop

143. uncouth: unfamiliar

144. luster: 光彩(radiance)

145. smote: smite的过去式,"重击"的意思

146. flagon: 酒壶

147. quaff: 痛饮(drink heartily)

148. By degrees Rip's awe and apprehension subsided: 渐渐地瑞普的恐惧和不安减轻了。

149. beverage: 酒,饮料(通常不包括水)

150. Hollands: 荷兰产的一种杜松子酒

151. He was naturally a thirsty soul, and was soon tempted to repeat the draught: 他本来是个贪杯的人,不久经不住诱惑又喝了酒。

152. reiterate：repeat

153. at length his senses were overpowered, his eyes swam in his head：最后他神智迷糊,头晕目眩。

154. twitter：(鸟儿)喊喊喳喳地叫

155. wheeling aloft：在高空盘旋。

156. breast：挺胸迎⋯⋯而上(push against with or as if with the breast)

157. retreat：隐蔽的场所

158. the wo-begone party：那伙愁眉苦脸的人

159. fowling-piece：猎枪

160. firelock：用火星引爆、击发的旧式猎枪

161. roisterer：闹饮者

162. having dosed him with liquor：用酒把他灌醉

163. partridge：山鹑

164. gambol：嬉戏(merry play, frolic)

165. if this frolic should lay me up with a fit of the rheumatism：如果这一次玩笑害我得了风湿病,卧床不起

166. scramble：climb

167. working his toilsome way through thickets of birch, sassafras, and witch-hazel：费劲地穿过长满桦树、黄樟和金缕梅的树<u>丛</u>。toilsome：辛苦的(hard, difficult)

168. tripped up or entangled：被绊倒或缠住

169. coils or tendrils：蔓条或卷须

170. over which the torrent came tumbling in a sheet of feathery foam：瀑布从岩石上飞沫四溅地奔流而下;torrent：激流(a quick-flowing, violent stream of water);tumble：倾泻而下(pour);foam：泡沫

171. poor Rip was brought to a stand：可怜的瑞普被迫停下来;stand：stop

172. cawing：发出哇哇地叫声(making the loud, harsh call of the crow)

173. scoff at the poor man's perplexities：嘲笑这个可怜人的茫然不知

所措;perplexity：困惑,茫然(the state or condition of being confused over what is not understood or certain)

174. famished：very hungry

175. with equal marks of surprise：同样吃惊的神态

176. recurrence：反复发生(happening again)

177. skirts：郊区,外围(suburbs, edge)

178. A troop of strange children ran at his heels, hooting after him：一群陌生的孩子跟在他后面奔跑,朝他喊叫。hoot：喊叫(shout)

179. populous：人口稠密的(heavily populated)

180. haunts：常去的地方(a place frequently visited)

181. misgive：使疑虑(make sb. feel doubt, uncertain or worried)

182. bewitched：被施了魔法的(affected by wtichcraft or magic)

183. addle：把……弄糊涂(make ... confused)

184. He found the house gone to decay：他发现房子已经塌坏。

185. the doors off the hinges：门的铰链都脱落了

186. but the cur snarled：但这恶狗却狂吠起来

187. cut：伤人感情的举动

188. forlorn：凄凉的(wretched)

189. The desolateness overcame all his connubial fears：这种荒凉感压倒了他对老婆的所有惧怕。connubial：婚姻的(matrimonial)

190. rickety：摇晃的(unsteady)

191. gaping：敞开的(wide open)

192. of yore：in the old days

193. rear：竖起(lift up)

194. but even this was singularly metamorphosed：但是甚至这个像也发生了奇怪的改变。singularly：奇怪地(oddly)；metamorphose：变形(cause to undergo a change in form or nature)

195. one of blue and buff：蓝黄色外套,美国独立战争期间殖民地起义军的军服;buff：浅黄色

196. scepter：国王或女王的权杖

197. cocked hat：卷边三角帽

198. phlegm：懒散

199. doling forth：reading aloud

200. a lean bilious-looking fellow：一个瘦瘦的、看起来脾气很坏的家伙

201. handbills：传单（a small printed notice or advertisement to be given out by hand）

202. haranguing vehemently about：就……作激烈的演说

203. Bunker's Hill：山名，位于马萨诸塞州波士顿地区。1775 年美国殖民地起义军在此曾被英国军队击败。

204. heroes of seventy-six：1776 年美国独立战争中的英雄们

205. Babylonish jargon：源自《圣经》中没有建成的通天塔典故，此处意为混杂的、莫名其妙的演说

206. uncouth：strange, awkward, and clumsy in shape or appearance

207. The orator bustled up to him：那个演说家赶忙走到他面前。

208. akimbo：叉腰

209. cane：拐杖

210. austere：严肃的，严厉的（stern, severe）

211. breed a riot：引起暴乱。breed：惹起（start, produce）

212. dismayed：害怕的（frightened）

213. a loyal subject of the king：国王忠实的臣民

214. tory：（美国独立战争时期的）亲英分子，保皇党

215. Hustle him！Away with him！：把他轰走！叫他滚蛋！hustle：推搡（shove）

216. having assumed a tenfold austerity of brow：装出比以前严肃十倍的样子

217. culprit：罪犯（one accused or guilty of a crime）

218. keep about the tavern：常待在酒馆一带

219. in a thin piping voice：用一种尖细的声音。piping：尖声的，高声

的（making a shrill sound）

220. at the storming of Stony Point：在猛攻斯托尼点的时候。斯托尼点是美国纽约州东南部城镇，位于哈得森河西岸。1779 年 7 月 15 日美国将军安东尼·威因（Anthony Wayne）曾在此攻占英军要塞。这次攻击是美国革命中的一次辉煌功绩。storm：猛攻（attack or assault）

221. squall：风暴（a sudden, violent wind, often accompanied by rain, snow, or sleet）

222. Antony's Nose：西点（West Point）附近的一座山，位于哈德森河东岸

223. militia：民兵，国民自卫队（a body of men not belonging to a regular army, but trained as soldiers to serve only in their own country if it is attacked or in times when there is violence and disorder in towns, cities, etc.）

224. beheld a precise counterpart of himself：看见一个和自己长得一模一样的人。counterpart：极相似的人或物（a person or thing very closly like or corresponding to another person or thing）

225. confounded：不知所措的，惶惑的（confused, bewildered）

226. retired with some precipitation：仓促地离开了

227. awakened a train of recollections in his mind：在他的脑子里唤醒了一系列的回忆

228. but he put it with a faltering voice：但是他问的时候声音颤抖 faltering：颤抖的（trembling）

229. she broke a blood vessel in a fit of passion at a New-England peddler：她跟一个新英格兰小贩发脾气时血管破裂（而死）。

230. intelligence：信息，消息（information, news）

231. tottering：踉跄，蹒跚

232. screwed down the corners of his mouth：撅着嘴。screw down：拧紧

233. well versed in：熟悉……的，通晓……的（well-experienced or well-

32

practiced in)

234. corroborate：证实（support by fresh information or proof）

235. kept a kind of vigil：守夜

236. she had a snug, well-furnished house：她有一所舒适、陈设体面的房子。

237. ditto：复制品（copy）

238. but evinced an hereditary disposition to attend to anything else but his business：但是显示了他父亲那样的性格，任何事情都肯干，唯独不管自己的事。evince：显示（show clearly）；hereditary：遗传的

239. crony：朋友,密友（a close friend esp. of long standing）

240. for the wear and tear of time：由于时间的磨蚀或折磨

241. was reverenced as one of the patriarchs of the village：被尊为村里的老前辈

242. chronicle：编年史（a record of historical events, arranged in order of time）

243. torpor：指 20 年的长睡

244. yoke：枷锁;统治（rule, control）

245. despotism：专制统治（tyranny）

246. petticoat government：女人的统治

247. which might pass either for an expression of resignation to his fate, or joy at his deliverance：他的这种神态可以看成是对命运的顺从,也可以看成因为得到解放而感到高兴。pass for：理解为,视为（understand ... as）；deliverance：被拯救（being saved）

248. not a man, woman, or child in the neighbourhood but knew it by heart：附近的人,无论男人、女人和小孩,都背得出来。

249. flighty：反复无常的（unsteady）

250. gave it full credit：对这回事深信不疑

251. they never hear a thunderstorm of a summer afternoon ... and his crew are at their game of nine pins：whenever they hear a

33

thunderstorm on a summer afternoon around the Kaatskill Mountains, they say Hendrick Hudson and his men are playing ninepins.

Questions:

1. How does Irving describe the landscape: the Kaatskill mountains, the river, and the weather? What figure of speech is used in his description? What specific details does he include? Does the landscape influence Rip's story in any way?

2. What kind of person was Rip Van Winkle? Was he a failure or success? Was he a symbol of America?

3. What was Dame Van Winkle like? In what way does Irving's portrayal of Dame Van Winkle help to illumine Rip's character?

4. Compare the town Rip left with the one he finds on his return. What has changed, and what do these changes say about the effects of the American Revolution?

5. Although "Rip Van Winkle" is a fictional tale, it presents truths that can teach the reader. Discuss the truths presented in the short story.

Edgar Allan Poe

(1809-1849)

Edgar Allan Poe (1809—1849) was a poet, a short story writer and a literary critic. He was born to traveling actors in Boston, Massachusetts. His father disappeared and his mother died when he was two years old. He was taken into the home of John Allan, a wealthy merchant, but he was never officially adopted. In fact, John Allan came to dislike him strongly. Poe was educated in Virginia and England and served two years in the army as an enlisted man. He entered West Point in 1830 and expelled after a year because he drank to excess and neglected his studies. Thus ended his school days. In 1836 he married his cousin, Virginia Clemm, who was then 13 years old. For a time, it seemed that Poe would find some happiness. But his wife was sick for most of their marriage. She died in 1847. After his wife's death, Poe's problems with alcohol increased. He died two years later, at the age of forty. He was found dead in Baltimore after days of heavy drinking.

Allan Poe was a successful editor. In 1835 he became the editor of the *Southern Literary Messenger* in Richmond. Over the next ten years, Poe worked hard as an editor with a number of other literary journals. Yet he was not well-paid. His life was difficult. He was poor, and he was troubled by sicknesses of the body and mind. Poe suffered from depression and madness. He drank a lot of alcohol which had a very bad effect on him. His tragically disordered life is reflected in his stories and poems. For example, the illness and early death of his wife led him to

35

write two famous poems: "Raven" and "Annabel Lee" and the themes in them are love, beauty, loss, sadness and death.

Poe's achievements were substantial. His work as an editor, a poet, a short story writer and a critic has had a profound impact on American and international literature. His poems, with their unreal atmosphere and musical effects, had a considerable influence on the late 19th century French symbolist poets. His stories mark him as one of the originators of both horror and detective fiction. Many anthologies credit him as the "architect" of the modern short story. The horror and detective stories Poe created remain popular in books and movies. His literary criticism was a major contribution to a developing theory of Romantic literature. He was one of the first critics to focus primarily on the effect of the style and the structure in a literary work. He has been seen as a forerunner to the "art for art's sake" movement. Poe argues that poetry is for pleasure, not truth, and that poetic inspiration leads to truth. Poe maintains that a poem must please the ear while expressing genuine emotion, or passion. "Unity of effect or impression" is of primary importance and the most effective story is one that can be read at a single sitting. As Poe sees it, the short story writer should deliberately subordinate everything in the story — characters, incidents, style, and tone — to bringing out of a single, preconceived effect.

Poe is also regarded as the forerunner of psychological writing. His short stories explore the inner, often irrational world of the human mind and reveal Poe's interest in human psychology. Among his major stories are "The Fall of the House of Usher", "The Black Cat", "The Cask of Amontillado", "The Masque of the Red Death", "Ligeia", "The Pit and the Pendulum", "The Tell-Tale Heart", "The Murders of the Rue Morgue", "The Golden Bug", "The Purloined Letter", "The Mystery of Marie Roget", "The Man of the Crowd" and "William Wilson". Some of them are tales of terror, the terror coming from the workings of an irrational or criminal mind. Stories like "The Purloined Letter" belong to the tales of reason in which the detective has the power to enter intuitively the mind of another person as a source of technique in solving a crime. Stories like "William Wilson", a tale whose main character has a split personality, explore the theme of divided self.

"The Masque of the Red Death" (1842) is a famous story of terror. In it a terrible disease—the Red Death—has killed half the population of a country. Prince Prospero, the ruler of the country, shuts his castle against the disease. He and his wealthy friends hide themselves inside. They pass the time by having parties. They believe they are safe from the Red Death. But to their great surprise, the Red Death himself comes to the dance and kills them all. Poe uses the castle setting as part of its allegorical statement about the inevitability of death. The story reveals that death knows no boundaries and often comes unexpectedly. The masquerade takes place in seven connected but carefully separated rooms, each with decorations of a different color. The color imagery and other Gothic elements—the blackness of the westernmost chamber, the "deep blood color" of the window, the striking of the ebony clock, the Red Death in the shroud, and the odd structure of the castle — all contribute to the single effect of terror.

The Masque[1] of the Red Death

Edgar Allan Poe

The "Red Death" had long devastated the country. No pestilence had ever been so fatal, or so hideous[2]. Blood was its Avatar and its seal[3]—the redness and the horror of blood. There were sharp pains, and sudden dizziness, and then profuse bleeding at the pores, with dissolution[4]. The scarlet stains upon the body and especially upon the face of the victim, were the pest ban which shut him out from the aid and from the sympathy of

37

his fellow men. And the whole seizure, progress and termination of the disease[5], were the incidents of half an hour.

But the Prince Prospero was happy and dauntless and sagacious. When his dominions were half depopulated[6], he summoned to his presence a thousand hale and light-hearted[7] friends from among the knights and dames[8] of his court, and with these retired to the deep seclusion[9] of one of his castellated abbeys[10]. This was an extensive and magnificent structure, the creation of the prince's own eccentric yet august taste[11]. A strong and lofty wall girdled[12] it in. This wall had gates of iron. The courtiers[13], having entered, brought furnaces and massy[14] hammers and welded the bolts[15]. They resolved to leave means neither of ingress or egress[16] to the sudden impulses of despair or of frenzy[17] from within. The abbey was amply provisioned[18]. With such precautions the courtiers might bid defiance to contagion[19]. The external world could take care of itself. In the meantime it was folly to grieve, or to think. The prince had provided all the appliances of pleasure. There were buffoons[20], there were improvisatori[21], there were ballet-dancers, there were musicians, there was Beauty, there was wine. All these and security were within. Without[22] was the "Red Death."

It was toward the close of the fifth or sixth month of his seclusion, and while the pestilence raged most furiously abroad, that the Prince Prospero entertained his thousand friends at a masked ball of the most unusual magnificence.

It was a voluptuous[23] scene, that masquerade. But first let me tell of the rooms in which it was held. There were seven—an imperial suite[24]. In many palaces, however, such suites form a long and straight vista[25], while the folding doors slide back nearly to the walls on either hand, so that the view of the whole extent is scarcely impeded. Here the case was very different; as might have been expected from the duke's love of the bizarre[26]. The apartments were so irregularly disposed that the vision

38

embraced but little more than one at a time[27]. There was a sharp turn at every twenty or thirty yards, and at each turn a novel[28] effect. To the right and left, in the middle of each wall, a tall and narrow Gothic window looked out upon a closed corridor which pursued the windings[29] of the suite. These windows were of stained glass[30] whose color varied in accordance with the prevailing hue of the decorations of the chamber into which it opened. That at the eastern extremity was hung, for example, in blue[31]—and vividly blue were its windows. The second chamber was purple in its ornaments and tapestries[32], and here the panes[33] were purple. The third was green throughout, and so were the casements[34]. The fourth was furnished and lighted with orange—the fifth with white—the sixth with violet. The seventh apartment was closely shrouded in black velvet tapestries that hung all over the ceiling and down the walls, falling in heavy folds upon a carpet of the same material and hue. But in this chamber only, the color of the windows failed to correspond with the decorations. The panes here were scarlet—a deep blood color. Now in no one of the seven apartments was there any lamp or candelabrum[35], amid the profusion[36] of golden ornaments that lay scattered to and fro[37] or depended[38] from the roof. There was no light of any kind emanating from[39] lamp or candle within the suite of chambers. But in the corridors that followed the suite, there stood, opposite to each window, a heavy tripod[40], bearing a brazier[41] of fire that protected its rays through the tinted glass and so glaringly illumined the room. And thus were produced a multitude of gaudy and fantastic appearances[42]. But in the western or black chamber the effect of the firelight that streamed upon the dark hangings through the blood-tinted panes, was ghastly in the extreme[43], and produced so wild a look upon the countenances of those who entered, that there were few of the company bold enough to set foot within its precincts[44] at all.

It was in this apartment, also, that there stood against the western wall, a gigantic clock of ebony[45]. Its pendulum swung to and fro[46] with a dull, heavy, monotonous clang[47]; and when the minute-hand made the circuit of the face[48], and the hour was to be stricken, there came from the brazen[49] lungs of the clock a sound which was clear and loud and deep and exceedingly musical, but of so peculiar a note and emphasis that, at each lapse[50] of an hour, the musicians of the orchestra were constrained[51] to pause, momentarily, in their performance, to hearken[52] to the sound; and thus the waltzers perforce ceased their evolutions[53]; and there was a brief disconcert of the whole gay company[54]; and, while the chimes[56] of the clock yet rang, it was observed that the giddiest[55] grew pale, and the more aged and sedate[57] passed their hands over their brows as if in confused reverie or meditation[58]. But when the echoes had fully ceased, a light laughter at once pervaded[59] the assembly; the musicians looked at each other and smiled as if at their own nervousness and folly, and made whispering vows[60], each to the other, that the next chiming of the clock should produce in them no similar emotion; and then, after the lapse of sixty minutes, (which embrace three thousand and six hundred seconds of the Time that flies), there came yet another chiming of the clock, and then were the same disconcert and tremulousness[61] and meditation as before.

But, in spite of these things, it was a gay and magnificent revel[62]. The tastes of the duke were peculiar. He had a fine eye for colors and effects. He disregarded the decora of mere fashion[63]. His plans were bold and fiery[64], and his conceptions glowed with barbaric lustre[65]. There are some who would have thought him mad. His followers felt that he was not. It was necessary to hear and see and touch him to be sure that he was not.

He had directed, in great part[66], the moveable embellishments[67] of the seven chambers, upon occasion of this great fete[68]; and it was his own guiding taste which had given character to the masqueraders. Be sure they were grotesque[69]. There were much glare and glitter and piquancy and

40

phantasm[70]—much of what has been since seen in *Hernani*[71]. There were arabesque figures with unsuited limbs and appointments[72]. There were delirious[73] fancies such as the madman fashions[74]. There was much of the beautiful, much of the wanton[75], much of the bizarre, something of the terrible, and not a little of that which might have excited disgust. To and fro in the seven chambers there stalked, in fact, a multitude of dreams[76]. And these — the dreams — writhed[77] in and about, taking hue from the rooms, and causing the wild music of the orchestra to seem as the echo of their steps. And, anon[78], there strikes the ebony clock which stands in the hall of the velvet. And then, for a moment, all is still, and all is silent save[79] the voice of the clock. The dreams are stiff-frozen as they stand. But the echoes of the chime die away—they have endured but an instant—and a light, half-subdued laughter floats after them as they depart. And now again the music swells, and the dreams live, and writhe to and fro more merrily than ever, taking hue from the many-tinted windows through which stream the rays from the tripods. But to the chamber which lies most westwardly of the seven, there are now none of the maskers who venture; for the night is waning away[80]; and there flows a ruddier[81] light through the blood-colored panes; and the blackness of the sable drapery appalls[82]; and to him whose foot falls upon the sable carpet, there comes from the near clock of ebony a muffled peal more solemnly emphatic than any which reaches their ears who indulge in the more remote gaieties of the other apartments[83].

But these other apartments were densely crowded, and in them beat feverishly the heart of life. And the revel went whirlingly on, until at length there commenced the sounding of midnight upon the clock. And then the music ceased, as I have told; and the evolutions of the waltzers were quieted; and there was an uneasy cessation of all things as before[84]. But now there were twelve strokes to be sounded by the bell of the clock; and thus it happened, perhaps, that more of thought crept, with more of time, into the meditations of the thoughtful among those who revelled. And thus, too, it happened, perhaps, that before the last echoes of the last chime had utterly sunk into silence, there were many individuals in the crowd who had found leisure to become aware of the presence of a masked figure which had arrested the attention of no single individual before. And the rumor of this new presence having spread itself whisperingly around, there arose at length from the whole company a buzz, or murmur, expressive of disapprobation and surprise — then, finally, of terror, of horror, and of disgust[85].

In an assembly of phantasms such as I have painted, it may well be supposed that no ordinary appearance could have excited such sensation. In truth the masquerade license[86] of the night was nearly unlimited; but the figure in question had out-Heroded Herod, and gone beyond the bounds of even the prince's indefinite decorum[87]. There are chords in the hearts of the most reckless which cannot be touched without emotion. Even with the utterly lost, to whom life and death are equally jests, there are matters of which no jest can be made[88]. The whole company, indeed, seemed now deeply to feel that in the costume and bearing of the stranger neither wit nor propriety existed[89]. The figure was tall and gaunt, and shrouded from head to foot in the habiliments of the grave[90]. The mask which concealed the visage was made so nearly to resemble the countenance of a stiffened corpse[91] that the closest scrutiny[92] must have had difficulty in detecting the cheat. And yet all this might have been endured, if not approved, by the mad revellers around. But the mummer had gone so far as to assume the type of the Red Death[93]. His vesture was dabbled in blood[94] — and his broad brow, with all the features of the face, was besprinkled with[95] the scarlet horror.

When the eyes of Prince Prospero fell upon this spectral[96] image (which with a slow and solemn movement, as if more fully to sustain its role, stalked to and fro among the waltzers) he was seen to be convulsed, in the first moment with a strong shudder either of terror or distaste; but, in the next, his brow reddened with rage[97].

"Who dares?" he demanded hoarsely of the courtiers who stood near him—"who dares insult us with this blasphemous mockery[98]? Seize him and unmask him—that we may know whom we have to hang at sunrise, from the battlements[99]!"

It was in the eastern or blue chamber in which stood the Prince Prospero as he uttered these words. They rang throughout the seven rooms loudly and clearly—for the prince was a bold and robust man, and the music had become hushed at the waving of his hand.

It was in the blue room where stood the prince, with a group of pale courtiers by his side. At first, as he spoke, there was a slight rushing movement of this group in the direction of the intruder, who at the moment was also near at hand, and now, with deliberate and stately step[100], made closer approach to the speaker. But from a certain nameless awe with which the mad assumptions of the mummer had inspired the whole party, there were found none who put forth hand to seize him; so that, unimpeded, he passed within a yard of the prince's person; and, while the vast assembly, as if with one impulse, shrank from the centers of the rooms to the walls, he made his way uninterruptedly, but with the same solemn and measured step which had distinguished him from the first, through the blue chamber to the purple—through the purple to the green—through the green to the orange—through this again to the white—and even thence to the violet, ere a decided movement had been made to arrest him. It was then, however, that the Prince Prospero, maddening with rage and the shame of his own momentary cowardice[101], rushed hurriedly through the six chambers, while none followed him on account of a deadly terror that had seized upon all[102].

He bore aloft a drawn dagger[103], and had approached, in rapid impetuosity[104], to within three or four feet of the retreating figure, when the latter, having attained the extremity of the velvet apartment, turned suddenly and confronted his pursuer. There was a sharp cry — and the dagger dropped gleaming upon the sable carpet, upon which, instantly afterwards, fell prostrate in death the Prince Prospero[105]. Then, summoning the wild courage of despair, a throng of the revelers at once threw themselves into the black apartment, and, seizing the mummer, whose tall figure stood erect and motionless within the shadow of the ebony clock, gasped in unutterable horror at finding the grave-cerements[106] and corpse-like mask which they handled with so violent a rudeness, untenanted by any tangible form[107].

And now was acknowledged the presence of the Red Death. He had come like a thief in the night[108]. And one by one dropped the revelers in the blood-bedewed halls[109] of their revel, and died each in the despairing posture[110] of his fall. And the life of the ebony clock went out with that of the last of the gay. And the flames of the tripods expired. And Darkness and Decay and the Red Death held illimitable dominion over all[111].

Notes:

1. masque: 假面舞会（masquerade, a costume party at which masks are worn, a masked ball）

2. No pestilence had ever been so fatal, or so hideous: 从没有过如此致命或如此可怕的瘟疫。

3. Blood was its Avatar and its seal: 血液是它的象征，它的标志。Avatar: 象征, 化身（a sign of an invisible force; an embodiment or manifestation）

4. profuse bleeding at the pores, with dissolution: 全身毛孔大量的流血，随之便是死亡。profuse: plentiful; pore: 毛孔; dissolution: death

5. the whole seizure, progress and termination of the disease：从疾病的突然发作、发展到终止。seizure：（疾病的）突然发作（a sudden attack）

6. his dominions were half depopulated：他领地上的臣民（因为瘟疫）减少了一半。depopulate：使（某一地区）人口剧减（reduce greatly the population of），de-作为前缀，意思是"减少，降低"（make less；reduce）

7. hale and light-hearted：healthy and free from worry

8. dame：lady

9. seclusion：隐居（quietness and privateness）

10. castellated abbeys：构造如城堡的修道院。castellated：构造如城堡的（made to look like a castle）；abbey：修道院（a building in which monks or nuns live and work）

11. eccentric yet august taste：古怪却高贵的趣味。august：威严的；高贵的（marked by majestic dignity or grandeur）

12. girdle：surround or enclose

13. courtier：侍臣（in former times a noble who attended at the court of a king or other ruler）

14. massy：巨大的（massive）

15. welded the bolts：焊死所有的门闩

16. ingress or egress：进入或出去（the act of entering or going out, esp. from a building or enclosed place）

17. frenzy：疯狂（temporary madness）

18. provisioned：provided with food and supplies in large quantities for a long time

19. bid defiance to contagion：蔑视传染病

20. buffoon：clown

21. improvisatori：即兴演员 （actors who make up scenes at the suggestions of onlookers）

22. without：在（修道院）的外面（outside the abbey），与 within（在修道

院里)相对应

23. voluptuous：骄奢淫乐的（too much concerned with the enjoyment of physical pleasures）

24. There were seven—an imperial suite：有 7 间——这是个豪华的套间。imperial：豪华的（grand）。

25. vista：狭长的景色（a distant view to which the eye is directed between narrow limits）

26. bizarre：奇异的（odd；strange）

27. The apartments were so irregularly disposed that the vision embraced but little more than one at a time：房间布局如此不规则,以至于每一次只能看到一个地方。dispose：arrange

28. novel：new, unusual

29. windings：迂回曲折（twist）

30. stained glass：彩色玻璃

31. That at the eastern extremity was hung, for example, in blue：比如,最东边的房间里挂着的(挂毯)就是蓝色的。

32. tapestry：挂毯

33. pane：窗格玻璃（a sheet of glass, esp. in a window）

34. casement：又作 casement window,门式窗（a window that opens like a door）

35. candelabrum：枝状大烛台（a decorative holder for several candles or lamps）

36. profusion：丰富（abundance）

37. to and fro：from one side to the other

38. depend：垂下（hang down）

39. emanating from：coming from

40. tripod：三脚架（a three-legged support）

41. brazier：火盆（a container for burning coals）

42. a multitude of gaudy and fantastic appearances：许多光怪陆离、奇妙

46

诡异的现象。gaudy：色彩过于明亮（too bright in color）；fantastic：奇异的（strange）

43. ghastly in the extreme：极其可怕（extremely terrible）。ghastly：可怕的（causing very great fear or dislike）

44. precincts：区域；界限（bounds；limits）

45. gigantic clock of ebony：巨大的乌木钟

46. Its pendulum swung to and fro：它的钟摆来回摆来摆去。

47. clang：叮当声

48. made the circuit of the face：沿着钟面绕了一圈。circuit：环行（movement along a curving path that forms a complete circle round an area）

49. brazen：黄铜制的

50. lapse：时间的间隔（interval）

51. constrained：forced

52. hearken：listen

53. the waltzers perforce ceased their evolutions：跳华尔兹的人不得不停止他们的舞步。perforce：不得已（because it is necessary）

54. there was a brief disconcert of the whole gay company：在狂欢的人群当中出现了短暂的慌乱。gay：cheerful

55. chime：（时钟的）报时声

56. the giddiest：最轻浮的人。giddy：not serious

57. sedate：稳重的（quiet and dignified in behavior）

58. in confused reverie or meditation：陷入了混乱的幻想或沉思

59. pervade：弥漫（spread through every part of）

60. made whispering vows：低声发誓

61. tremulousness：颤抖（trembling because of nervousness）

62. revel：狂欢（a wild party or celebration）

63. He disregarded the decora of mere fashion：他漠视时尚的规定。decora：拉丁语，意思是"要求，规定"（Latin for "dictates"）

64. bold and fiery：大胆又热烈

65. his conceptions glowed with barbaric luster：他的构思闪烁着狂野的光辉。barbaric：野蛮的，狂野的（barbarian；wild）；luster：光泽（brightness）

66. in great part：在很大程度上，大部分地（in great degree）

67. embellishments：decorations

68. fete：节日（festival）

69. grotesque：怪诞的（strange and unnatural so as to cause fear, disbelief, or amusement）

70. There were much glare and glitter and piquancy and phantasm：有许多炫目的光和闪光装饰物，非常刺激，如梦如幻。piquancy：刺激；phantasm：幻象，幻觉（an illusion）

71. *Hernani*：法国作家雨果（1802—1885）的剧作《欧那尼》（a romantic stage tragedy of 1830 by the French writer Victor Hugo）

72. arabesque figures with unsuited limbs and appointments：四肢和装配不相称的奇特形象。arabesque：构思奇巧的

73. delirious：发狂的，精神错乱的（in an excited dreamy state, esp. caused by illness）

74. fashion：产生，形成（produce, contrive）

75. wanton：淫荡的（sexually improper）

76. there stalked, in fact, a multitude of dreams：事实上在那里游走的是一群幻影。stalk：高视阔步；大踏步走（walk stiffly, proudly, or with long steps）

77. writhe：扭动身体（twist and turn this way and that）

78. anon：soon

79. save：except

80. waning away：消逝（drawing near an end）

81. ruddy：red

82. the blackness of the sable drapery appalls：帏帐的乌黑使人惊骇。

sable：black；drapery：(供装饰用的)针织物,帷帐(dry goods)

83. a muffled peal more solemnly emphatic ... gaieties of the other apartments：一个闷雷般低沉的声音,听上去比其他更远的房间里纵情声色的人听到的都更庄严和有力。gaiety：happiness and excitement

84. there was an uneasy cessation of all things as before：像以前一样一切又陷入了不安的静止中。cessation：a short pause or a stop

85. expressive of disapprobation and surprise — then, finally, of terror, of horror, and of disgust：表达不满和惊奇——继而最终变成了惊骇、恐惧和厌恶。expressive of：showing, demonstrating

86. license：允许,许可(permission or freedom to behave as one wishes)

87. but the figure in question had out-Heroded Herod, and gone ... indefinite decorum：但是大家正在议论的那个人物比希律王还希律王,已经远远超出了亲王那几乎没有限制的限度。in question：被谈论着的(being talked about)；out-Herod Herod：比希律王更残暴,残暴超过任何人(be more cruel, violent, etc., than anyone else)；Herod：希律王,《圣经》中以残暴著称的犹太国王,为要杀死圣婴耶稣,命令杀死伯利恒城所有 2 岁以下的男婴(King of Judea who, according to the Bible, attempted to kill the infant Jesus by ordering the death of all male children under the age of 2 in Bethlehem)；decorum：礼貌,礼节(politeness, propriety)

88. Even with the utterly lost, to whom life and death ... no jest can be made：甚至对那些视生死为玩笑的完全堕落的人来说,也有些事是不能开玩笑的。

89. in the costume and bearing of the stranger neither wit nor propriety existed：这个陌生人的服饰和举止既没有情趣,也不合乎礼节。bearing：举止(the manner of carrying oneself)

90. The figure was tall and gaunt, and shrouded from head to foot in the habiliments of the grave：这个人又高又瘦,从头到脚包裹在裹尸布

里。gaunt：骨瘦如柴（thin, as if ill or hungry）；habiliments：服装（dress characteristic of an occupation or occasion）

91. the countenance of a stiffened corpse：一具僵尸的脸

92. scrutiny：细看（a close study or look）

93. But the mummer had gone so far as to assume the type of the Red Death：但是这个戏子走得太远了,他竟然假扮红死魔。mummer：伶人,戏子（masked figure）；assume：假扮（pretend to have or be）,名词是 assumption

94. His vesture was dabbled in blood：他（裹着）的尸布血迹斑斑。vesture：衣服（clothing）；dabble：弄湿（wet by splashing）

95. was besprinkled with：洒满,布满（was full of）

96. spectral：鬼怪（似）的（of or like a ghost）

97. he was seen to be convulsed, in the first moment ... his brow reddened with rage：人们见他大为震动,起初或出于恐惧或出于厌恶身体剧烈颤抖,但是接下来由于愤怒他的前额涨红。convulse：使剧烈震动（cause to shake violently with sudden uncontrolled movements）；shudder：tremble

98. this blasphemous mockery：这种亵渎的嘲弄

99. battlements：城垛（a wall around the top of a castle with regular spaces in it through which the people inside the castle can shoot）

100. with deliberate and stately step：迈着从容而堂皇的步子。deliberate：从容不迫的（unhurried）；stately：堂皇的（grand）

101. maddening with rage and the shame of his own momentary cowardice：因愤怒以及为自己瞬间的怯懦感到羞愧而恼羞成怒

102. on account of a deadly terror that had seized upon all：由于大家感到非常害怕。on account of：由于（because of）；seize upon：占有,抓住（possess; control）

103. He bore aloft a drawn dagger：他高举出鞘的短剑

104. in rapid impetuosity：心急火燎地。impetuosity：冲动,性急

（reckless）

105. fell prostrate in death the Prince Prospero：Prospero 亲王倒地身亡。prostrate：俯卧的（lying flat with face on the ground）

106. the grave-cerements：裹尸布,尸衣

107. untenanted by any tangible form：（裹尸布和面具）里面空洞无物。untenanted：没被占用的（not occupied）；tangible：可触摸到的,有形的（that can be felt by touch）

108. He had come like a thief in the night：他像夜间的贼一样来到。"a thief in the night"意思是"fast and unexpected death",指《圣经》的《帖撒罗尼迦前书》的第 5 章 2 ~ 3 节："因为你们自己明明晓得,主的日子来到,好像夜间的贼一样。人正说平安稳妥的时候,火灾忽然临到他们,如同产难临到怀胎的妇人一样,他们绝不能逃脱。"（"For yourselves know perfectly that the day of the Lord so cometh as a thief in the night. For when they shall say, peace and safety; then sudden destruction cometh upon them, as travail upon a woman with child; they shall not escape."—Thessalonians 5：2 ~ 3, the Bible）

109. the blood-bedewed halls：鲜血浸湿地板的大厅。bedewed：被沾湿的（made wet as with drops of water）

110. the despairing posture：绝望的姿势

111. Darkness and Decay and the Red Death held illimitable dominion over all：黑暗、腐朽和红死魔开始了无限的统治。illimitable：无限的（boundless）；dominion：power or right to rule

Questions：

1. How does Prince Prospero plan to keep away the Red Death? How are we to regard his seeking safety by shutting out the world? Is there anything to suggest that creating this "security" also creates a prison?

2. At first reading, the seven rooms seem equally vivid and bizarre. But

the dancers tend to avoid the seventh or farthest room. Why should this be so? How does that room differ from the other chambers? What fears does that room seem to arouse?

3. How do the revelers react to the sound of the ebony clock? Does the clock have any symbolic meaning?

4. What do the revelers find when they seize the stranger in the velvet apartment?

Nathaniel Hawthorne

(1804-1864)

Nathaniel Hawthorne (1804—1864) was born in Salem, Massachusetts. His clear, musical style made him one of America's most imitated authors. He was regarded as a guilt-ridden moralist. All his life, Hawthorne seemed to be haunted by his sense of sin and evil in life. His old New England family was involved in the Salem Witch Trials and Quaker persecutions. His reflections on his family's past became the theme of many of his works. Most of his works, set in colonial New England, deal with evil one way or another and have been read as moral allegories influenced by his Puritan background. It is believed that Hawthorne wrote some of his books like *The Scarlet Letter* and *The House of the Seven Gables* as an attempt at paying for the sin of his ancestors.

Hawthorne attended Bowdoin College in Maine from 1821—1824, making friends with his classmates Henry Wadsworth Longfellow, who would later become America's leading poet, and Franklin Pierce, who would become President of the United States. After his graduation in 1825 Hawthorne returned to his mother's house and lived in isolation for 12 years to practice his writing. In 1837 he published *Twice-Told Tales*, in which "The Minister's Black Veil" was collected. Before publishing this collection of short stories, he wrote scores of short stories and sketches, publishing them anonymously or pseudonymously. Only after 1837 did Hawthorne begin to attach his name to his works.

Hawthorne is best-known today for his many short stories (he called

53

them "tales") and his four major romances: *The Scarlet Letter* (1850),
The House of the Seven Gables (1851), *The Blithedale Romance*
(1852), and *The Marble Faun* (1860). Among his most brilliant stories
are "The Minister's Black Veil", "Roger Minister's Burial", "Young
Goodman Brown", "Rappaccini's Daughter", "The Great Stone Face",
and "Ethan Brand", *The Scarlet Letter* was Hawthorne's masterpiece.
Set in 17th-century Puritan New England, the novel explores deeply into
the human heart, presenting the problems of moral evil and guilt through
allegory and symbolism. It is often considered the first American
psychological novel.

"The Minister's Black Veil" is one of Hawthorne's best known and
most ambiguous short stories. It tells the story of a minister so
preoccupied with human sin and dishonesty that he puts on a black veil to
hide his face and manifest the spiritual veils that all humans wear. As in
such works as "Young Goodman Brown" (1835) and *The Scarlet Letter*,
Hawthorne employed the settings and themes that are characteristic of his
fiction: a Puritan New England setting, a fascination with the secret sins
of humanity, the transformation of an object into a symbol, a dark,
somber tone, and a reliance on ambiguity. On a Sunday Mr. Hooper
comes to the meeting-house with a black veil on his face, which
produces a shocking effect on his congregation. Despite many efforts to
persuade him to give up the veil, Mr. Hooper wears it not only in his
lifetime but also after his death. There are some rumors going about in
the village of Milford concerning why he puts on such a veil. The reasons
for the minister's actions and their implications are never fully explained,
leaving readers to ponder over Hawthorne's meaning. But Mr. Hooper's
remarks on his deathbed are thought-provoking and enlightening: "Why
do you tremble at me alone? Tremble also at each other! ... I look
around me, and, lo! on every visage a Black Veil!"

The Minister[1]'s Black Veil

Nathaniel Hawthorne

A Parable[2]

Hawthorne wrote the following footnote to the title of this story: "An other clergyman in New England[3], Mr. Joseph Moody, of York, Maine, who died about eighty years since[4], made himself remarkable by the same eccentricity[5] that is here related to the Reverend[6] Mr. Hooper. In his case, however, the symbol had a different import[7]. In early life he had accidentally killed a beloved friend; and from that day till the hour of his own death, he hid his face from men. "

The sexton[8] stood in the porch of Milford meeting-house, pulling busily at the bell rope. The old people of the village came stooping along the street. Children with bright faces tripped merrily beside their parents, or mimicked a graver gait[9], in the conscious dignity of their Sunday clothes. Spruce[10] bachelors looked sidelong at the pretty maidens and fancied that the Sabbath sunshine made them prettier than on weekdays. When the throng had mostly streamed into the porch, the sexton began to toll the bell, keeping his eye on the Reverend Mr. Hooper's door. The first glimpse of the clergy man's figure was the signal for the bell to cease its summons.

"But what has good Parson Hooper got upon his face?" cried the sexton in astonishment.

All within hearing immediately turned about, and beheld the semblance of Mr. Hooper, pacing slowly his meditative way towards the meeting-house. With one accord they started, expressing more wonder than

55

if some strange minister were coming to dust the cushions of Mr. Hooper's pulpit[11].

"Are you sure it is our parson?" inquired Goodman Gray[12] of the sexton.

"Of a certainty it is good Mr. Hooper," replied the sexton. "He was to have exchanged pulpits with Parson Shute, of Westbury; but Parson Shute sent to excuse himself yesterday, being to preach a funeral sermon[13]."

The cause of so much amazement may appear sufficiently slight. Mr. Hooper, a gentlemanly person, of about thirty, though still a bachelor, was dressed with due clerical neatness, as if a careful wife had starched his band, and brushed the weekly dust from his Sunday's garb. There was but one thing remarkable in his appearance. Swathed[14] about his forehead, and hanging down over his face, so low as to be shaken by his breath, Mr. Hooper had on a black veil. On a nearer view, it seemed to consist of two folds of crape[15], which entirely concealed his features, except the mouth and chin, but probably did not intercept his sight[16], farther than to give a darkened aspect to all living and inanimate things[17]. With this gloomy shade before him, good Mr. Hooper walked onward, at a slow and quiet pace, stooping somewhat and looking on the ground, as is customary with abstracted men, yet nodding kindly to those of his parishioners[18] who still waited on the meeting-house steps. But so wonder-struck were they, that his greeting hardly met with a return.

"I can't really feel as if good Mr. Hooper's face was behind that piece of crape," said the sexton.

"I don't like it," muttered an old woman, as she hobbled into the meeting-house. "He has changed himself into something awful, only by hiding his face."

"Our parson has gone mad!" cried Goodman Gray, following him across the threshold.

A rumor of some unaccountable phenomenon had preceded Mr. Hooper into the meeting-house and set all the congregation astir[19]. Few could refrain from twisting their heads towards the door; many stood upright, and turned directly about; while several little boys clambered upon[20] the seats and came down again with a terrible racket[21]. There was a general bustle, a rustling of the women's gowns and shuffling of the men's feet, greatly at variance with that hushed repose which should attend the entrance of the minister[22]. But Mr. Hooper appeared not to notice the perturbation[23] of his people. He entered with an almost noiseless step, bent his head mildly to the pews[24] on each side, and bowed as he passed his oldest parishioner, a white-haired great-grandsire, who occupied an armchair in the center of the aisle. It was strange to observe, how slowly this venerable man became conscious of something singular[25] in the appearance of his pastor. He seemed not fully to partake of the prevailing wonder[26], till Mr. Hooper had ascended the stairs and showed himself in the pulpit, face to face with his congregation, except for the black veil. That mysterious emblem was never once withdrawn. It shook with his measured breath, as he gave out the psalm[27]; it threw its obscurity between him and the holy page, as he read the Scriptures[28]; and while he prayed, the veil lay heavily on his uplifted countenance. Did he seek to hide it from the dread Being[29] whom he was addressing?

Such was the effect of this simple piece of crape, that more than one woman of delicate nerves was forced to leave the meeting-house. Yet perhaps the pale-faced congregation was almost as fearful a sight to the minister as his black veil to them[30].

Mr. Hooper had the reputation of a good preacher, but not an energetic one: he strove to win his people heavenward by mild, persuasive influences, rather than to drive them thither by the thunders of the Word[31].

The sermon which he now delivered was marked by the same characteristics of style and manner as the general series of his pulpit oratory[32]. But there was something, either in the sentiment of the discourse itself, or in the imagination of the auditors[33], which made it greatly the most powerful effort that they had ever heard from their pastor's lips. It was tinged, rather more darkly than usual, with the gentle gloom of Mr. Hooper's temperament[34]. The subject had reference to secret sin, and those sad mysteries which we hide from our nearest and dearest, and would fain[35] conceal from our own consciousness, even forgetting that the Omniscient[36] can detect them. A subtle power was breathed into his words. Each member of the congregation, the most innocent girl, and the man of hardened breast, felt as if the preacher had crept upon them, behind his awful veil, and discovered their hoarded iniquity of deed or thought[37]. Many spread their clasped hands on their bosoms. There was nothing terrible in what Mr. Hooper said, at least, no violence; and yet, with every tremor of his melancholy voice[38], the hearers quaked. An unsought pathos came hand in hand with awe. So sensible were the audience of some unwonted attribute in their minister that they longed for[39] a breath of wind to blow aside the veil, almost believing that a stranger's visage would be discovered, though the form, gesture, and voice were those of Mr. Hooper.

At the close of the services[40], the people hurried out with indecorous[41] confusion, eager to communicate their pent-up[42] amazement, and conscious of lighter spirits, the moment they lost sight of the black veil. Some gathered in little circles, huddled closely together, with their mouths all whispering in the center; some went homeward alone, wrapt in silent meditation[43]; some talked loudly and profaned the Sabbath day with ostentatious laughter[44]. A few shook their sagacious[45] heads, intimating that they could penetrate the mystery[46]; while one or two affirmed that there was no mystery at all, but only that Mr. Hooper's eyes were so weakened by the midnight lamp as to require a shade. After a brief interval, forth came good Mr. Hooper also, in the rear of his flock[47]. Turning his veiled face from one group to another, he paid due reverence to the hoary heads[48], saluted the middle-aged with kind dignity as their friend and spiritual guide, greeted the young with mingled authority and love, and laid his hands on the little children's heads to bless them. Such was always his custom on the Sabbath day. Strange and bewildered looks repaid him for his courtesy. None, as on former occasions, aspired to[49] the honor of walking by their pastor's side. Old Squire Saunders, doubtless by an accidental lapse of memory[50], neglected to invite Mr. Hooper to his table, where the good clergyman had been wont to bless the food, almost every Sunday since his settlement. He returned, therefore, to the parsonage[51], and, at the moment of closing the door, was observed to look back upon the people, all of whom had their eyes fixed upon the minister. A sad smile gleamed faintly from beneath the black veil and flickered about his mouth, glimmering as he disappeared[52].

"How strange," said a lady, "that a simple black veil such as any woman might wear on her bonnet, should become such a terrible thing on Mr. Hooper's face!"

"Something must surely be amiss with Mr. Hooper's intellects," observed her husband, the physician of the village. "But the strangest part of the affair is the effect of this vagary even on a sober-minded man like myself. The black veil, though it covers only our pastor's face, throws its influence over his whole person, and makes him ghostlike from head to foot. Do you not feel it so?"

"Truly do I," replied the lady, "and I would not be alone with him for the world[53]. I wonder he is not afraid to be alone with himself!"

"Men sometimes are so," said her husband.

59

The afternoon service was attended with similar circumstances. At its conclusion, the bell tolled for the funeral of a young lady. The relatives and friends were assembled in the house, and the more distant acquaintances stood about the door, speaking of the good qualities of the deceased, when their talk was interrupted by the appearance of Mr. Hooper, still covered with his black veil. It was now an appropriate emblem. The clergyman stepped into the room where the corpse was laid, and bent over the coffin to take a last farewell of his deceased parishioner[54]. As he stooped, the veil hung straight down from his forehead, so that, if her eyelids had not been closed forever, the dead maiden might have seen his face. Could Mr. Hooper be fearful of her glance, that he so hastily caught back the black veil? A person, who watched the interview between the dead and living, scrupled not to affirm, that, at the instant when the clergy man's features were disclosed, the corpse had slightly shuddered, rustling the shroud and muslin cap, though the countenance retained the composure of death[55]. A superstitious old woman was the only witness of this prodigy. From the coffin Mr. Hooper passed into the chamber of the mourners, and thence to the head of the staircase, to make the funeral prayer. It was a tender and heart-dissolving prayer, full of sorrow,`yet so imbued with celestial hopes[56], that the music of a heavenly harp, swept by the fingers of the dead, seemed faintly to be heard among the saddest accents of the minister. The people trembled, though they but darkly understood him when he prayed that they, and himself, and all of mortal[57] race, might be ready, as he trusted this young maiden had been, for the dreadful hour that should snatch the veil from their faces. The bearers went heavily forth, and the mourners followed, saddening all the street, with the dead before them, and Mr. Hooper in his black veil behind.

"Why do you look back?" said one in the procession to his partner.

60

"I had a fancy," replied she, "that the minister and the maiden's spirit were walking hand in hand."

"And so had I, at the same moment," said the other.

That night, the handsomest couple in Milford village were to be joined in wedlock[58]. Though reckoned a melancholy man, Mr. Hooper had a placid cheerfulness for such occasions[59], which often excited a sympathetic smile, where livelier merriment would have been thrown away. There was no quality of his disposition which made him more beloved than this. The company at the wedding awaited his arrival with impatience, trusting that the strange awe, which had gathered over him throughout the day, would now be dispelled. But such was not the result. When Mr. Hooper came, the first thing that their eyes rested on was the same horrible black veil, which had added deeper gloom to the funeral, and could portend nothing but evil to the wedding[60]. Such was its immediate effect on the guests, that a cloud seemed to have rolled duskily from beneath the black crepe and dimmed the light of the candles. The bridal pair stood up before the minister. But the bride's cold fingers quivered in the tremulous hand of the bridegroom, and her deathlike paleness caused a whisper, that the maiden who had been buried a few hours before was come[61] from her grave to be married. If ever another wedding were so dismal, it was that famous one, where they tolled the wedding knell[62]. After performing the ceremony, Mr. Hooper raised a glass of wine to his lips, wishing happiness to the new-married couple in a strain of mild pleasantry[63] that ought to have brightened the features of the guests, like a cheerful gleam from the hearth. At that instant, catching a glimpse of his figure in the looking glass, the black veil involved his own spirit in the horror with which it overwhelmed all others[64]. His frame shuddered, his lips grew white, he spilt the untasted wine upon the carpet, and rushed forth into the darkness. For the Earth, too, had on her Black Veil.

The next day, the whole village of Milford talked of little else than[65] Parson Hooper's black veil. That, and the mystery concealed behind it, supplied a topic for discussion between acquaintances meeting in the street and good women gossiping at their open windows. It was the first item of news that the tavern keeper told to his guests. The children babbled of it on their way to school. One imitative little imp covered his face with an old black handkerchief, thereby so affrighting his playmates that the panic seized himself, and he well-nigh lost his wits by his own waggery[66].

It was remarkable that of all the busybodies and impertinent people[67] in the parish, not one ventured to put the plain question to Mr. Hooper, wherefore[68] he did this thing. Hitherto[69], whenever there appeared the slightest call for such interference, he had never lacked advisers, nor shown himself averse to[70] be guided by their judgment. If he erred at all, it was by so painful a degree of self-distrust, that even the mildest censure would lead him to consider an indifferent action as a crime[71]. Yet, though so well acquainted with this amiable weakness, no individual among his parishioners chose to make the black veil a subject of friendly remonstrance[72]. There was a feeling of dread, neither plainly confessed nor carefully concealed, which caused each to shift the responsibility upon another, till at length it was found expedient to send a deputation of the church[73], in order to deal with Mr. Hooper about the mystery, before it should grow into a scandal. Never did an embassy so ill discharge its duties[74]. The minister received them with friendly courtesy but became silent after they were seated, leaving to his visitors the whole burden of introducing their important business. The topic, it might be supposed, was obvious enough. There was the black veil, swathed round Mr. Hooper's forehead, and concealing every feature above his placid mouth, on which, at times, they could perceive the glimmering of a melancholy smile. But that piece of crape, to their imagination, seemed to hang down before his

62

heart, the symbol of a fearful secret between him and them. Were the veil but cast aside, they might speak freely of it, but not till then[75]. Thus they sat a considerable time, speechless, confused, and shrinking uneasily from Mr. Hooper's eye, which they felt to be fixed upon them with an invisible glance. Finally, the deputies returned abashed to their constituents[76], pronouncing the matter too weighty to be handled, except by a council of the churches, if, indeed, it might not require a general synod[77].

But there was one person in the village, unappalled by the awe with which the black veil had impressed all beside herself. When the deputies returned without an explanation, or even venturing to demand one, she, with the calm energy of her character, determined to chase away the strange cloud that appeared to be settling round Mr. Hooper, every moment more darkly than before. As his plighted wife[78], it should be her privilege to know what the black veil concealed. At the minister's first visit, therefore, she entered upon the subject with a direct simplicity, which made the task easier both for him and her. After he had seated himself, she fixed her eyes steadfastly upon the veil, but could discern nothing of the dreadful gloom that had so overawed the multitude: it was but a double fold of crape, hanging down from his forehead to his mouth, and slightly stirring with his breath.

"No," said she aloud, and smiling, "there is nothing terrible in this piece of crape, except that it hides a face which I am always glad to look upon. Come, good sir, let the sun shine from behind the cloud. First lay aside your black veil; then tell me why you put it on. "

Mr. Hooper's smile glimmered faintly.

"There is an hour to come, " said he, "when all of us shall cast aside our veils. Take it not amiss[79], beloved friend, if I wear this piece of crape till then. "

"Your words are a mystery, too, " returned the young lady. "Take away the veil from them, at least. "

"Elizabeth, I will," said he, "so far as my vow may suffer me[80]. Know, then, this veil is a type and a symbol, and I am bound to wear it ever, both in light and darkness, in solitude and before the gaze of multitudes, and as with strangers, so with my familiar friends. No mortal eye will see it withdrawn. This dismal shade must separate me from the world: even you, Elizabeth, can never come behind it. "

"What grievous affliction hath befallen you[81]," she earnestly inquired, "that you should thus darken your eyes forever?"

"If it be a sign of mourning," replied Mr. Hooper, "I, perhaps, like most other mortals, have sorrows dark enough to be typified by a black veil. "

"But what if the world will not believe that it is the type of an innocent sorrow?" urged Elizabeth. "Beloved and respected as you are, there may be whispers that you hide your face under the consciousness of secret sin. For the sake of your holy office, do away this scandal!"

The color rose into her cheeks, as she intimated the nature of the rumors that were already abroad in the village. But Mr. Hooper's mildness did not forsake him. He even smiled again—that same sad smile, which always appeared like a faint glimmering of light, proceeding from the obscurity beneath the veil.

"If I hide my face for sorrow, there is cause enough," he merely replied, "and if I cover it for secret sin, what mortal might not do the same?"

And with this gentle, but unconquerable obstinacy did he resist all entreaties[82]. At length Elizabeth sat silent. For a few moments she appeared lost in thought, considering probably, what new methods might be tried, to withdraw her lover from so dark a fantasy, which, if it had no other meaning, was perhaps a symptom of mental disease. Though of a firmer character than his own[83], the tears rolled down her cheeks. But in an instant, as it were, a new feeling took the place of sorrow: her eyes were fixed insensibly on the black veil, when, like a sudden twilight in the air, its terrors fell around her. She arose and stood trembling before him.

"And do you feel it then at last?" said he mournfully.

She made no reply, but covered her eyes with her hand, and turned to leave the room. He rushed forward and caught her arm.

"Have patience with me, Elizabeth!" cried he passionately. "Do not desert me, though this veil must be between us here on earth. Be mine; and hereafter there shall be no veil over my face, no darkness between our souls! It is but a mortal veil—it is not for eternity! Oh! You know not how lonely I am, and how frightened, to be alone behind my black veil. Do not leave me in this miserable obscurity for ever!"

"Lift the veil but once, and look me in the face," said she.

"Never! It cannot be!" replied Mr. Hooper.

"Then farewell!" said Elizabeth.

She withdrew her arm from his grasp and slowly departed, pausing at the door, to give one long, shuddering gaze that seemed almost to penetrate the mystery of the black veil. But, even amid his grief, Mr. Hooper smiled to think that only a material emblem had separated him from happiness, though the horrors which it shadowed forth must be drawn darkly between the fondest of lovers.

From that time no attempts were made to remove Mr. Hooper's black veil or, by a direct appeal, to discover the secret which it was supposed to hide. By persons who claimed a superiority to popular prejudice, it was reckoned merely an eccentric whim, such as often mingles with the sober actions of men otherwise rational, and tinges them all with its own semblance of insanity[84]. But with the multitude, good Mr. Hooper was irreparably a bugbear[85]. He could not walk the street with any peace of mind, so conscious was he that the gentle and timid would turn aside to avoid him, and that others would make it a point of hardihood[86] to throw themselves in his way. The impertinence of the latter class[87] compelled him to give up his customary walk, at sunset, to the burial ground; for when he leaned pensively over the gate, there would always be faces behind the grave-stones, peeping at his black veil. A fable went the rounds, that the stare of the dead people drove him thence. It grieved him, to the very depth of his kind heart, to observe how the children fled from his approach, breaking up their merriest sports, while his melancholy figure was yet afar off. Their instinctive dread caused him to feel, more strongly than aught else[88], that a preternatural[89] horror was interwoven with the threads of the black crape. In truth, his own antipathy[90] to the veil was known to be so great that he never willingly passed before a mirror, nor stooped to drink at a still fountain, lest, in its peaceful bosom, he should be affrighted by himself. This was what gave plausibility to the whispers, that Mr. Hooper's conscience tortured him for some great crime too horrible to be entirely concealed, or otherwise than so obscurely intimated[91]. Thus, from beneath the black veil, there rolled a cloud into the sunshine, an ambiguity of sin or sorrow which enveloped the poor minister, so that love or sympathy could never reach him. It was said that ghost and fiend consorted with him there[92]. With self-shudderings and outward terrors, he walked continually in its shadow, groping darkly within his own soul or gazing through a medium[93] that saddened the whole world. Even the lawless wind, it was believed, respected his dreadful secret and never blew aside the veil. But still good Mr. Hooper sadly smiled at the pale visages of the worldly throng[94] as he passed by.

Among all its bad influences, the black veil had the one desirable effect of making its wearer a very efficient clergyman. By the aid of his mysterious emblem—for there was no other apparent cause—he became a

66

man of awful power, over souls that were in agony for sin[95]. His converts always regarded him with a dread peculiar to themselves, affirming, though but figuratively, that, before he brought them to celestial light, they had been with him behind the black veil[96]. Its gloom, indeed, enabled him to sympathize with all dark affections. Dying sinners cried aloud for Mr. Hooper, and would not yield their breath till he appeared; though ever, as he stooped to whisper consolation, they shuddered at the veiled face so near their own. Such were the terrors of the black veil, even when Death had bared his visage! Strangers came long distances to attend service at his church, with the mere idle purpose of gazing at his figure, because it was forbidden them to behold his face. But many were made to quake ere[97] they departed! Once, during Governor Belcher's administration, Mr. Hooper was appointed to preach the election sermon[98]. Covered with his black veil, he stood before the chief magistrate, the council, and the representatives, and wrought so deep an impression, that the legislative measures of that year were characterized by all the gloom and piety of our earliest ancestral sway[99].

In this manner Mr. Hooper spent a long life irreproachable in outward act, yet shrouded in dismal suspicions[100]; kind and loving, though unloved and dimly feared; a man apart from men, shunned in their health and joy, but ever summoned to their aid in mortal anguish[101]. As years wore on, shedding their snows above his sable veil[102], he acquired a name throughout the New England churches, and they called him Father Hooper. Nearly all his parishioners, who were of mature age when he was settled, had been borne away by many a funeral[103]: he had one congregation in the church, and a more crowded one in the churchyard; and having wrought so late into the evening, and done his work so well, it was now good Father Hooper's turn to rest.

Several persons were visible by the shaded candlelight, in the death chamber of the old clergyman. Natural connections he had none[104]. But there was the decorously grave, though unmoved physician, seeking only to mitigate the last pangs of the patient[105] whom he could not save. There were the deacons, and other eminently pious members of his church[106]. There, also, was the Reverend Mr. Clark, of Westbury, a young and zealous divine, who had ridden in haste to pray by the bedside of the expiring minister. There was the nurse, no hired handmaiden of death[107], but one whose calm affection had endured thus long in secrecy, in solitude, amid the chill of age, and would not perish, even at the dying hour. Who but Elizabeth! And there lay the hoary head of good Father Hooper upon the death-pillow, with the black veil still swathed about his brow and reaching down over his face, so that each more difficult gasp of his faint breath caused it to stir. All through life that piece of crape had hung between him and the world: it had separated him from cheerful brotherhood and woman's love, and kept him in that saddest of all prison, his own heart; and still it lay upon his face, as if to deepen the gloom of his darksome chamber, and shade him from the sunshine of eternity[108].

For some time previous, his mind had been confused, wavering doubtfully between the past and the present, and hovering forward, as it were, at intervals, into the indistinctness of the world to come. There had been feverish turns, which tossed him from side to side, and wore away what little strength he had. But in his most convulsive struggles, and in the wildest vagaries of his intellect, when no other thought retained its sober influence, he still showed an awful solicitude lest the black veil should slip aside[109]. Even if his bewildered soul could have forgotten, there was a faithful woman at his pillow, who, with averted eyes, would have covered that aged face, which she had last beheld in the comeliness of manhood. At length the death-stricken old man lay quietly in the torpor of mental and bodily exhaustion, with an imperceptible pulse[110], and breath that grew

68

fainter and fainter, except when a long, deep, and irregular inspiration seemed to prelude the flight of his spirit.

The minister of Westbury approached the bedside.

"Venerable Father Hooper," said he, "the moment of your release is at hand. Are you ready for the lifting of the veil that shuts in time from eternity?"

Father Hooper at first replied merely by a feeble motion of his head; then, apprehensive, perhaps, that his meaning might be doubtful, he exerted himself to speak.

"Yea," said he, in faint accents, "my soul hath a patient weariness until that veil be lifted."

"And is it fitting," resumed the Reverend Mr. Clark, "that a man so given to prayer, of such a blameless example, holy in deed and thought, so far as mortal judgment may pronounce; is it fitting that a father in the church should leave a shadow on his memory that may seem to blacken a life so pure? I pray you, my venerable brother, let not this thing be! Suffer us to be gladdened by your triumphant aspect, as you go to your reward[111]. Before the veil of eternity be lifted, let me cast aside this black veil from your face!"

And thus speaking, the Reverend Mr. Clark bent forward to reveal the mystery of so many years. But, exerting a sudden energy that made all the beholders stand aghast[112], Father Hooper snatched both his hands from beneath the bedclothes and pressed them strongly on the black veil, resolute to struggle, if the minister of Westbury would contend with a dying man.

"Never!" cried the veiled clergyman. "On earth, never!"

"Dark old man!" exclaimed the affrighted minister, "with what horrible crime upon your soul are you now passing to the judgment[113]?"

Father Hooper's breath heaved; it rattled in his throat[114]; but, with a mighty effort, grasping forward with his hands, he caught hold of life and held it back till he should speak. He even raised himself in bed; and there he sat, shivering with the arms of death around him, while the black veil hung down, awful, at that last moment, in the gathered terrors of a lifetime. And yet the faint, sad smile, so often there, now seemed to glimmer from its obscurity and linger on Father Hooper's lips.

"Why do you tremble at me alone?" cried he, turning his veiled face round the circle of pale spectators. "Tremble also at each other! Have men avoided me, and women shown no pity, and children screamed and fled, only for my black veil? What, but the mystery which it obscurely typifies, has made this piece of crape so awful? When the friend shows his inmost heart to his friend; the lover to his best beloved; when man does not vainly shrink from the eye of his Creator, loathsomely treasuring up the secret of his sin; then deem me a monster, for the symbol beneath which I have lived, and die!^{115} I look around me, and, lo! on every visage a Black Veil^{116}."

While his auditors shrank from one another, in mutual affright, Father Hooper fell back upon his pillow, a veiled corpse, with a faint smile lingering on the lips. Still veiled, they laid him in his coffin, and a veiled corpse they bore him to the grave. The grass of many years has sprung up and withered on that grave, the burial stone is moss-grown, and good Mr. Hooper's face is dust; but awful is still the thought that it moldered beneath the Black Veil^{117}!

Notes:

1. minister: (基督教新教)牧师(a clergyman especially of a Protestant communion)。在小说中,表示牧师的词还有 clergyman, parson, pastor 和 divine。

2. parable: 寓言(a short narrative that draws a moral lesson or illustrates a

religious truth)

3. New England：新英格兰(a region of the United States located in the northeastern corner of the country, consisting of the modern states of Maine, Vermont, New Hampshire, Massachusetts, Rhode Island and Connecticut)

4. since：ago

5. eccentricity：古怪(the quality of being eccentric)

6. Reverend：可尊敬的(用作对许多基督教堂中某些神职人员的称号及敬称形式,在正式用法中,前面加 the)

7. In his case, however, the symbol had a different import：As far as Mr. Joseph Moody is concerned, the black veil had a different meaning.

8. sexton：教堂司事(an employee or officer of a church who is responsible for the care and upkeep of church property and sometimes for ringing bells and digging graves)

9. mimicked a graver gait：模仿更稳重的步态(注意这一段动词的使用,它们生动地描写了村里的男女老少在去教堂的路上展现的各种神态。)

10. spruce：整洁漂亮的(neat, trim, and smart in appearance)

11. All within hearing ... to dust the cushions of Mr. Hooper's pulpit：听到这话的所有人立刻转身,看到 Mr. Hooper 正若有所思慢慢地朝教堂走来。他们全都吃了一惊,比看到某个陌生的牧师来接替 Mr. Hooper 牧师的位置还惊奇。within hearing：在可以听见的距离内; behold：see; semblance：appearance;with one accord：一致;dust the cushion of Mr. Hooper's pulpit：掸掉 Mr. Hooper 讲道坛垫子上的灰尘,意思是接替 Mr. Hooper 牧师的位置

12. Goodman Gray：Gray 先生。Goodman：先生,以前用于姓氏前作为尊称(a title of address similar to "Mr.")

13. but Parson Shute sent to excuse ... a funeral sermon：但是 Shute 牧师昨天派人来说,他不能来了,因为他要做一个葬礼布道。

14. swathe：绑（bind）

15. crape：黑绉纱

16. intercept his sight：挡住了他的视线

17. farther than to give a darkened aspect to all living and inanimate things：不过使世间万物染上了一层昏暗的色调。inanimate：没有生命的（animate, lifeless）

18. parishioner：教区的居民（a member of a parish）

19. A rumor of some unaccountable phenomenon ... and set all the congregation astir：关于某个无法解释的现象的谣言在 Mr. Hooper 进入教堂前就传开了，使全体教徒们骚动起来。precede：先于（come or go in front of）；astir：骚动的（being active）

20. clambered upon：climbed onto

21. racket：吵闹声（a loud, distressing noise）

22. There was a general bustle ... attend the entrance of the minister：（教堂里）一片乱哄哄的，女人的衣裙沙沙作响，男人的脚在地板上滑来滑去，和往常牧师走进教堂时鸦雀无声的气氛大不相同。at variance with：与……不符（not in agreement with）；repose：安静（calmness）；attend：伴随（accompany）

23. perturbation：骚乱不安（agitation）

24. pew：教堂内的靠背长凳

25. singular：异常的（odd, strange）

26. to partake of the prevailing wonder：感受到充满教堂的惊诧情绪。partake of：参与，分享（take part in or experience something along with others）

27. It shook with his measured breath, as he gave out the psalm：在他领唱圣歌时，它随着他均匀的呼吸而起伏。measured：均匀的（regular）； psalm：圣歌,赞美诗;《圣经》中《诗篇》中的任何一篇（a song or poem in praise of God, esp. one of those in the Bible）

28. the Scriptures：the Bible

72

29. the dread Being：the God

30. Such was the effect ... as his black veil to them：这一段要注意 2 个结构：such ... that ... 和 as ... as ...

31. rather than to drive them thither by the thunders of the Word：而不是借助雷霆震撼般的圣言把他们赶向天国。thither：to that place（小说中指"到天国"）

32. oratory：雄辩的演说（public speaking that employs the art of speaking in public eloquently or effectively）

33. auditor：听者（a person who listens）

34. It was tinged ... Mr. Hooper's temperament：它比平日的布道更带有 Mr. Hooper 气质中所具有的那种淡淡的忧郁色调。tinge：微染（color slightly）

35. fain：乐意地（with pleasure）

36. the Omniscient：the God

37. discovered their hoarded iniquity of deed or thought：发现他们行为或思想中所隐藏的罪孽。hoarded：隐藏的（hidden）；iniquity：罪，罪孽（sin）

38. with every tremor of his melancholy voice：随着他忧郁声音的每次颤动。tremor：颤抖，震颤（a shaking or trembling movement caused by fear, nervousness, illness, weakness, etc.）

39. So sensible were the audience of some unwonted attribute in their minister that they longed for：The audience were so sensible of some unusual quality in their minister that they longed for ... 听众们如此强烈地感觉到他们的牧师有些反常以至于他们渴望……

40. the service：礼拜；（宗教）仪式（a fixed form of public worship; a religious ceremony）

41. indecorous：不合礼节的（conflicting with accepted standards of good conduct or good taste）

42. pent-up：被压抑的（suppressed）

43. wrapt in silent meditation：埋头于沉思默想中

44. profaned the Sabbath day with ostentatious laughter：故意放声大笑来亵渎安息日。ostentatious：夸张的,卖弄的(showy)

45. sagacious：wise

46. intimating that they could penetrate the mystery：暗示他们能看穿这个秘密。intimate：暗示(imply)

47. his flock：他的教民(the church congregation under his guidance)

48. he paid due reverence to the hoary heads：他对白发长者表示应有的敬意。hoary：(因年迈而)头发灰白的(gray or white with age)

49. aspired to：热望(longed for)

50. doubtless by an accidental lapse of memory：无疑是由于记忆的偶然出错。lapse：过失,失误(a minor error)

51. parsonage：牧师住宅(the house provided by a church for its pastor)

52. 注意这一句出现了 3 个与发光有关的动词:gleam 发微光(give out a gentle light)；flicker 闪烁(shine with an unsteady light)；glimmer 发出闪烁的微光(give a very faint unsteady light)

53. not ... for the world：无论如何不,肯定不会(certainly not)

54. bent over the coffin to take a last farewell of his deceased parishioner：俯身在棺材上,向自己去世的教民作最后的告别

55. scrupled not to affirm ... though the countenance retained the composure of death：毫不迟疑地断言,就在牧师露出面容的那一瞬间,尸体曾微微地战栗起来,尸衣和薄纱女帽都沙沙作响,虽然死者的面容仍然保持着死亡的宁静。

56. imbued with celestial hopes：充满天国的希望。imbue with：充满,浸透(fill with)(一般用于被动语态)

57. mortal：人(类)的(human)；死的,临死的(of death)。mortal 在小说中出现多次,如 mortal eye 人眼；mortal veil 现世的面纱；mortal race 人类；mortal anguish 临死的痛苦；mortal judgment 人的判断。mortal 还可以用作名词,意思是"人","凡人"(a human being as

74

compared with a god, a spirit, etc.)

58. were to be joined in wedlock：were to get married. wedlock：已婚状态(the state of being married)

59. Though reckoned a melancholy man, Mr. Hooper had a placid cheerfulness for such occasions：虽然 Mr. Hooper 被认为是个性格忧郁的人,但他在这种场合也会有一种平静的快乐。reckon：认为(regard as)； placid：平静的,镇静的(calm)

60. could portend nothing but evil to the wedding：给婚礼带来的只是凶兆。portend：预示(不详之事) (predict)

61. was come：had come

62. If ever another wedding were so dismal, it was that famous one, where they tolled the wedding knell：如果说世上还有像这么阴沉的婚礼,那只能是那场响起丧钟的著名婚礼了。这里指的是霍桑在 1836 年发表的一个短篇《婚礼上的丧钟》(The Wedding Knell),小说叙事者讲述了自己奶奶最喜欢的一个故事:有一对老人在纽约的一个教堂里举行婚礼,可在婚礼上却敲响了刺耳的丧钟。knell：(丧) 钟声 (the sound of a bell rung slowly, esp. for a death or funeral)

63. in a strain of mild pleasantry：以温和而幽默的语调。strain：语调 (the general tone)；pleasantry：幽默,开玩笑(a humorous remark)

64. the black veil involved his own spirit ... with which it overwhelmed all others：黑面纱也将他的心灵卷进了震慑众人的恐惧之中。overwhelm：使不知所措(upset)

65. than：except

66. One imitative little imp covered his face ... by his own waggery：一个爱模仿的小顽童,用一块旧的黑手巾把自己的脸也遮了起来,结果恶作剧不但把同伴们吓得要命,他自己也差点吓得神志失常。affright：惊吓(frighten)；well-nigh：almost；lose one's wits：神志失常；waggery：开玩笑,恶作剧(mischievous merriment)

67. the busybodies and impertinent people：爱管闲事、莽撞冒失的人

68. wherefore：why

69. hitherto：在此之前（up to this or that time）

70. averse to：对……讨厌的（not liking to）

71. If he erred at all, it was ... to consider an indifferent action as a crime：如果说他曾有什么过错，那是因为过分缺乏自信，哪怕最温和的批评都会使他把无关紧要的举动当作罪孽。

72. remonstrance：抗议（complaint）

73. till at length it was found expedient to send a deputation of the church：直到最后只好想出一条权宜之计，选派一个教会代表。expedient：权宜之计的（useful or helpful for a purpose, esp. one's own purpose or advantage, although not necessarily morally correct）

74. Never did an embassy so ill discharge its duties：从来没有一个使团会这么糟糕地履行自己的职责。

75. Were the veil but cast aside, they might speak freely of it, but not till then：只要拉开面纱，他们就能自在地对此事发表议论，但不拉开它就无法启齿。"Were the veil but cast aside"是虚拟语气，等于"If the veil were cast aside"，"but"用于加强语气。

76. the deputies returned abashed to their constituents：代表们羞愧地回去见他们的推举人。abashed：羞愧的（embarrassed, ashamed）；constituent：推举人（voter）

77. a general synod：宗教会议（在一个国家或一个大的地理区域内一教派所有教堂共同设立的机构）

78. As his plighted wife：作为他的未婚妻。plight：订婚（engage）

79. Take it not amiss：请别见怪。take sth. amiss：对某事生气（be angry about sth., esp. because of a misunderstanding）

80. so far as my vow may suffer me：只要在我的誓言所允许的范围内。suffer：allow

81. What grievous affliction hath befallen you：是什么沉重的苦难降临到了你的头上。befall：（常指不幸的事）发生于（happen to）

82. And with this gentle, but unconquerable obstinacy did he resist all entreaties：他就这样温和却又非常固执地拒绝了她的一切恳求。

83. Though of a firmer character than his own：尽管她性格比他更坚强

84. By persons who claimed a superiority ... tinges them all with its own semblance of insanity：那些自以为比世俗偏见高明的人,将此事仅仅看作一时的古怪念头,说这种古怪念头经常会与正常人的理智行为混在一起,结果使他们的所有行为都显得疯疯癫癫。otherwise：在其他方面（in other respects）；semblance：样子（appearance）

85. irreparably a bugbear：一个无可挽救的怪物。irreparably：无可挽救地,不可挽回地

86. make it a point of hardihood：显示胆量

87. The impertinence of the latter class：后者的无礼

88. aught else：anything else

89. preternatural：异常的（beyond what is usual）。preter-：前缀,表示"超","过","多于"

90. antipathy：反感,厌恶（a strong dislike or opposition）

91. to be entirely concealed, or otherwise than so obscurely intimated：既不能完全掩盖起来,又不能和盘托出,只能这样模模糊糊地暗示一下。otherwise：in a different way or manner（from the way of being "entirely concealed"）,即全部说出来

92. ghost and fiend consorted with him there：鬼魂和魔鬼在黑面纱后面与他做伴。consort with：与……做伴（keep company with）

93. medium：媒介,这里指 black veil

94. the pale visages of the worldly throng：熙熙攘攘的人群的苍白的面孔。throng：crowd

95. souls that were in agony for sin：由于罪恶而处于极度痛苦中的灵魂

96. His converts always regarded him ... they had been with him behind the black veil：那些经他说教开导而皈依的教徒总是怀着独特的恐

惧心理看待他,并断言,虽然只是比喻,在他们见到天国的光明之前,一直和他一起隐藏在黑面纱的后面(即他们都是 Mr. Hooper 一样的罪人)。

97. ere：before

98. election sermon：选举布道。It was a great honor for a minister to be chosen to make this formal address.

99. wrought so deep an impression ... our earliest ancestral sway：给众人留下深刻印象,连那年通过的法案都具有早期统治的黑暗与虔诚。wrought：work 的一种过去式和过去分词；ancestral：祖先的(belonging to one's ancestors)；sway：统治(rule)

100. irreproachable in outward act, yet shrouded in dismal suspicions：他的行为无可指责,但却笼罩在阴沉的疑云之中。shroud：(一般用于被动语态)覆盖,遮蔽(cover and hide)

101. a man apart from men ... but ever summoned to their aid in mortal anguish：一个与世人隔绝的人,他们健康和快乐时躲避他,面临死亡痛苦时却召唤他去帮忙。"a man"指的是 Mr. Hooper,"their"指世人的(men's),"shunned""summoned"是过去分词,修饰"a man"

102. shedding their snows above his sable veil：使他的头发变成了白发。shed：洒落(scatter, spill)；sable：black

103. had been borne away by many a funeral：had died

104. Natural connections he had none：他无亲无故。connection：(一般用复数)亲属(a person connected to others by a family relationship)

105. mitigate the last pangs of the patient：减轻病人最后的痛苦。mitigate：reduce.

106. There were the deacons, and other eminently pious members of his church：有教堂执事和其他非常虔诚的教会人士。deacon：(基督教)教堂执事(a religious official in various Christian churches who is directly below a priest in rank)；eminently：very

107. no hired handmaiden of death：不是受雇专门来侍候临死病人的女侍

108. shade him from the sunshine of eternity：使他受不到天国阳光的照耀

109. But in his most convulsive struggles … lest the black veil should slip aside：但即使在他周身抽搐，大脑失去控制，没有任何其他清醒的神智时，他还表现出极度的担心，唯恐黑面纱会滑落一边。convulsive：抽搐的；vagary：奇特行为，奇想（an eccentric idea or action）；solicitude：担心（anxiety, concern）

110. At length the death-stricken old man … with an imperceptible pulse：最后，濒临死亡的老人静静地躺着，因精神和肉体的衰竭而陷于麻木之中，脉搏也感觉不到了。torpor：麻木（the state of being lifeless or inactive）；imperceptible：觉察不到的（too slight to be perceived）

111. Suffer us to be gladdened by your triumphant aspect, as you go to your reward：当您到天国去时，让我们能一睹您喜乐的面容而高兴高兴吧。triumphant：喜气洋洋的（joyful）；reward：酬劳，奖赏，这里指进天国，那是上帝对 Mr. Hooper 虔诚服务一生的最大奖赏

112. exerting a sudden energy that made all the beholders stand aghast：突然一用力，把所有旁观者吓得目瞪口呆。aghast：大为震惊的，吓呆的（struck with amazement or horror）

113. passing to the judgment：到上帝面前去接受最后的审判

114. it rattled in his throat：一丝气息在喉咙里呼噜呼噜作响。rattle：（人死前）喉咙发出呼噜呼噜响声

115. When the friend shows his inmost heart … which I have lived, and die!：如果有一天，朋友之间，情人之间，可以吐露真情，坦诚相见；如果有一天，人们不再徒劳地躲避上帝的目光，令人厌恶地藏匿自己罪恶的秘密，那时就可以因为我生时戴着、死时也不离的这个黑面纱把我看成怪物吧！"symbol"一词指的是 black veil，在小说中指黑面纱的词还有 crape, emblem, crepe, shade 和 sable

veil; deem: consider

116. lo! on every visage a Black Veil: 瞧！（你们）每个人的脸上都有一块黑面纱。lo: look

117. awful is still the thought that it moldered beneath the Black Veil: 但是一想到它在那块黑面纱下面慢慢地腐烂，人们仍然觉得可怕。molder: 腐朽（decay slowly）

Questions:

1. What is the subject of Parson Hooper's sermon on the first Sunday he appears wearing the black veil?

2. What influence does the veil have on Reverend Hooper's effectiveness as a clergyman?

3. The first paragraph presents the congregation before the appearance of the Reverend Mr. Hooper. What is the mood of the scene before the arrival of the minister? How does the mood change after Hooper appears in the black veil?

4. Why might one woman imagine, during the procession to the graveyard, that the minister walks "hand in hand" with the dead girl's spirit? In what sense does he now seem "dead" to others?

5. At first Elizabeth refuses to see anything evil in the veil. Then, suddenly, "in an instant, as it were," a new emotion replaces sorrow. As she stares at the black veil, she begins to comprehend its terrible significance. What revelation does Elizabeth experience? Why is she suddenly terrified?

6. Over the years rumors are spread about the reason for the minister's actions. As there are no explicit clues toward a "crime" in the ordinary sense, in what larger sense does Hooper feel he is guilty of a crime? As this short story is subtitled "A Parable", what moral lesson can be drawn from it?

Mark Twain

(1835-1910)

Mark Twain (1835—1910), pen name of Samuel Langhorne Clemens, was an American humorist, satirist, lecturer and writer. He was born in Florida, Missouri. His father was a country merchant. When Twain was four, his family moved to Hannibal, a port town on the Mississippi River that would serve as the inspiration for the fictional town of St. Petersburg in *The Adventures of Tom Sawyer* (1876) and *Adventures of Huckleberry Finn* (1885), the two novels for which Twain is most noted. Twain enjoyed immense public popularity. He introduced colloquial speech into American fiction and changed American literature forever. His colloquial style, keen wit and sharp satire earned him praise from both critics and peers. He described uniquely American subjects in a humorous and colloquial, yet poetic, language. William Faulkner called Twain "the father of American literature". Hemingway remarked, "All modern American literature comes from one book by Mark Twain called *Huckleberry Finn.*"

Twain did not receive much formal education. He was 12 when his father died a bankrupt man. He was forced to leave school and was apprenticed to a printer. This trade gave him a useful education because his work required him to travel a lot and that he could have access to many good books printed in the print shop. At the age of 21, he apprenticed himself as a steamboat pilot on the Mississippi. He may have taken his pen name from the cry of the steamboat leadsmen, "by the

81

mark, twain", which means that the water was a safe depth of two fathoms. He worked on the steamboat for 4 years. Everyday he met assorted people, hence a wide acquaintance with human nature. In order to try his luck, he went west to Nevada to join in the gold rush. He was not successful in mining, so he was happy to accept a job as a reporter on a newspaper, where he started using the name Mark Twain.

Besides *The Adventures of Tom Sawyer* and *Adventures of Huckleberry Finn*, Twain's major works include The *Innocents Abroad* (1869), *Roughing It* (1872), *A Tramp Abroad* (1880), *The Prince and the Pauper* (1882), *Life on the Mississippi* (1883), *A Connecticut Yankee in King Arthur's Court* (1889), *Autobiography* (1924), and short stories like "The Man That Corrupted Hadleyburg" (1899) and "The War Prayer" (1905). Twain is a great realist writer. Most of his works draw upon the scenes and experiences of his boyhood and youth in the South and the West and present social life through portraits of the local characters and local places Twain knew best, including the landscapes, the customs, dialects, costumes and so on. Another fact that made Twain unique is his use of vernacular English, the colloquial speech of uneducated Americans. His words are colloquial, concrete and direct in effect, and his sentence structures are simple, even ungrammatical, which is typical of the spoken language. His characters, confined to a particular region and to a particular historical moment, speak with a strong accent, which is true of his local colorism. Indeed, with his great mastery and effective use of vernacular, Twain has made colloquial speech an accepted, respectable literary medium in the literary history of the United States. His style of language was later taken up by his descendants, Sherwood Anderson and Ernest Hemingway, and has influenced generations of American authors.

"The Celebrated Jumping Frog of Calaveras County" is one of Twain's best-loved stories. It was first published in 1865 and became an instant success. It helped establish Twain's reputation as a fiction writer and a humorist. It is a frame tale in which one story appears in — that is, it is framed by — another story. The story is set in a gold-mining camp in Calaveras County, California, and has its origins in the folklore of the Gold Rush era. The narrator of the outer tale, Twain, at the request of a friend in the East, goes to Angel's ming camp in California to visit an old miner named Simon Wheeler to inquire after his friend's friend. Wheeler tells him a funny tale about another miner, Jim Smiley, an addicted gambler who loved to make bets on nearly anything. What makes the story successful is Twain's impressive use of dialect, his comic description of the animals and the structure of the story. Wheeler is an uneducated man from the West. He tells his tale in the vernacular of the American West. He ignores many grammatical rules, and speaks with an accent. He says "feller" instead of "fellow", and "Dan'l" for "Daniel". Through the use of dialect, humor and exaggeration, Twain vividly depicts life in the American West in the days of the Gold Rush and satires American society and human nature.

The Celebrated Jumping Frog of Calaveras County

Mark Twain

In compliance with[1] the request of a friend of mine, who wrote me from the East, I called on good-natured, garrulous[2] old Simon Wheeler, and inquired after my friend's friend, Leonidas W. Smiley, as requested to do, and I hereunto append the result[3]. I have a lurking[4] suspicion that *Leonidas W.* Smiley is a myth; that my friend never knew such a personage; and that he only conjectured[5] that if I asked old Wheeler about him, it would remind him of his infamous[6] *Jim* Smiley, and he would go to work and bore me to death with some exasperating reminiscence[7] of him as long and as tedious as it should be useless to me. If that was the design, it succeeded.

I found Simon Wheeler dozing comfortably by the bar-room stove of the dilapidated[8] tavern in the decayed mining camp of Angel's[9], and I noticed that he was fat and bald-headed, and had an expression of winning gentleness and simplicity upon his tranquil countenance[10]. He roused up, and gave me good day. I told him that a friend of mine had commissioned me to make some inquiries about a cherished companion of his boyhood named *Leonidas W*. Smi-ley—*Rev. Leonidas W.* Smiley, a young minister of the Gospel[11], who he had heard was at one time a resident of Angel's Camp. I added that if Mr. Wheeler could tell me anything about this Rev. Leonidas W. Smiley, I would feel under many obligations to him[12].

Simon Wheeler backed me into a corner and blockaded me there with his chair[13], and then sat down and reeled off the monotonous narrative which follows this paragraph[14]. He never smiled, he never frowned, he never changed his voice from the gentle-flowing key to which he tuned his initial sentence[15], he never betrayed the slightest suspicion of enthusiasm; but all through the interminable narrative there ran a vein[16] of impressive earnestness and sincerity, which showed me plainly that, so far from his imagining that there was anything ridiculous or funny about his story, he regarded it as a really important matter, and admired its two heroes as men of transcendent genius in finesse[17]. I let him go on in his own way, and never interrupted him once.

"Rev. Leonidas W. H'm, Reverend Le—well, there was a feller[18] here once by the name of *Jim* Smiley, in the winter of '49—or maybe it was the spring of '50—I don't recollect exactly, somehow, though what makes me think it was one or the other is because I remember the big flume warn't finished[19] when he first came to the camp; but anyway, he was the curiousest man about always betting on anything that turned up you ever see[20], if he could get anybody to bet on the other side; and if he couldn't

84

he'd change sides. Any way that suited the other man would suit *him*—any way just so's he got a bet, he was satisfied. But still he was lucky, uncommon lucky; he most always come out winner. He was always ready and laying for a chance[21]; there couldn't be no solit'ry thing mentioned but that feller'd offer bet on it[22], and take any side you please, as I was any just telling you. If there was a horse race, you'd find him flush or you'd find him busted[23] at the end of it; if there was a dog-fight, he'd bet on it; if there was a cat-fight, he'd bet on it; if there was a chicken-fight, he'd bet on it; why, if there was two birds setting on a fence, he would bet you which one would fly first; or if there was a camp meeting[24], he would be there reg'lar[25] to bet on Parson Walker, which he judged to be the best exhorter[26] about here, and so he was too, and a good man. If he even see a straddle-bug start to go anywheres, he would bet you how long it would take him to get to—to wherever he was going to, and if you took him up, he would foller that straddle-bug to Mexico but what he would find out where he was bound for[27] and how long he was on the road. Lots of the boys here has[28] seen that Smiley, and can tell you about him. Why, it never made no difference to *him*—he'd bet on *any* thing—the dangest feller[29]. Parson Walker's wife laid very sick once, for a good while; and it seemed as if they warn't going to save her; but one morning he come[30] in, and Smiley up[31] and asked him how she was, and he said she was considerable better—thank the Lord for his inf'nit'[32] mercy—and coming on so smart[33] that with the blessing of Prov'dence[34] She'd get well yet; and Smiley, before he thought, say[35]: "Well, I'll risk two-and-a-half she don't[36], anyway."

"Thish-yer[37] Smiley had a mare—the boys called her the fifteen-minute nag[38], but that was only in fun, you know, because of course she was faster than that—and he used to win money on that horse, for all she was so slow and always had the asthma, or the distemper, or the

85

consumption[39], or something of that kind. They used to give her two or three hundred yards' start, and then pass her under way; but always at the fag-end of the race[40] She'd get excited and desperate-like, and come cavorting and straddling up, and scattering her legs around limber[41], sometimes in the air, and sometimes out to one side among the fences, and kicking up m-o-r-e dust and raising m-o-r-e racket with her coughing and sneezing and blowing her nose—and always fetch up at the stand just about a neck ahead[42], as near as you could cipher it down[43].

"And he had a little small bull-pup[44], that to look at him you'd think he warn't worth a cent but to set around and look ornery[45] and lay for a chance to steal something. But as soon as money was up on him[46] he was a different dog; his under-jaw'd begin to stick out like the fo'castle[47] of a steamboat, and his teeth would uncover and shine like the furnaces. And a dog might tackle him and bully-rag him[48], and bite him, and throw him over his shoulder two or three times, and Andrew Jackson—which was the name of the pup—Andrew Jackson would never let on but what he was satisfied[49], and hadn't expected nothing else—and the bets[50] being doubled and doubled on the other side all the time, till the money was all up; and then all of a sudden he would grab that other dog jest by the j'int of his hind leg and freeze to it[51]—not chaw[52], you understand, but only just grip and hang on till they throwed up the sponge[53], if it was a year. Smiley always come out winner on that pup, till he harnessed a dog once that didn't have no hind legs, because they'd been sawed off in a circular saw[54], and when the thing had gone along far enough, and the money was all up, and he come to make a snatch for his pet holt[55], he see in a minute how he'd been imposed on, and how the other dog had him in the door, so to speak, and he 'peared[56] surprised, and then he looked sorter[57] discouraged-like, and didn't try no more to win the fight, and so he got shucked out bad[58]. He give Smiley a look, as much as to say his heart was

86

broke, and it was his fault, for putting up a dog that hadn't no hind legs for him to take holt of, which was his main dependence in a fight, and then he limped off a piece[59] and laid down and died. It was a good pup, was that Andrew Jackson, and would have made a name for hisself[60] if he'd lived, for the stuff was in him and he had genius—I know it, because he hadn't no opportunities to speak of, and it don't stand to reason[61] that a dog could make such a fight as he could under the circumstances if he hadn't no talent. It always makes me feel sorry when I think of that last fight of hisn[62], and the way it turned out.

"Well, thish-yer Smiley had rat tarriers[63], and chicken cocks, and tomcats and all them kind of things, till you couldn't rest, and you couldn't fetch nothing for him to bet on but he'd match you. He ketched[64] a frog one day, and took him home, and said he cal'lated[65] to educate him; and so he never done nothing for three months but set in his backyard and learn[66] that frog to jump. And you bet he did learn him, too. He'd give him a little punch behind, and the next minute you'd see that frog whirling in the air like a doughnut[67]—see him turn one summerset, or maybe a couple, if he got a good start, and come down flat-footed and all right[68], like a cat. He got him up so in the matter of ketching flies, and kep' him in practice so constant, that he'd nail[69] a fly every time as fur as[70] he could see him. Smiley said all a frog wanted was education, and he could do 'most[71] anything—and I believe him. Why, I've seen him set Dan'l Webster[72] down here on this floor—Dan'l Webster was the name of the frog—and sing out, "Flies, Dan'l, flies!" and quicker'n[73] you could wink he'd spring straight up and snake a fly off'n[74] the counter there, and flop down on the floor ag'in as solid as a gob of mud[75], and fall to[76] scratching the side of his head with his hind foot as indifferent as if he hadn't no idea he'd been doin' any more'n any frog might do. You never see a frog so modest and straightfor'ard[77] as he was, for all he was so gifted. And when it come to fair and square jumping on a dead level, he could get over more ground at one straddle than any animal of his breed you ever see[78]. Jumping on a dead level was his strong suit[79] you understand; and when it come to that, Smiley would ante up money on him as long as he had a red[80]. Smiley was monstrous[81] proud of his frog, and well he might be, for fellers that had traveled and been everywheres all said he laid over[82] any frog that ever they see.

"Well, Smiley kep' the beast in a little lattice box, and he used to fetch him downtown sometimes and lay for a bet. One day a feller—a stranger in the camp, he was—come acrost him with his box, and says:

"What might it be that you've got in the box?"

"And Smiley says, sorter indifferent-like, 'It might be a parrot, or it might be a canary, maybe, but it ain't—it's only just a frog.'

"And the feller took it, and looked at it care-ful, and turned it round this way and that, and says, 'H'm—so 'tis. Well, what's he good for?'

"Well, Smiley says, easy and careless, 'he's good enough for one thing, I should judge—he can outjump any frog in Calaveras County.'

"The feller took the box again, and took another long, particular look, and give it back to Smiley, and says, very deliberate, 'Well,' he says, 'I don't see no p'ints[83] about that frog that's any better'n any other frog.'

" 'Maybe you don't,' Smiley says. 'Maybe you understand frogs and maybe you don't understand 'em; maybe you've had experience, and maybe you ain't only a amature[84], as it were. Anyways, I've got *my* opinion, and I'll resk[85] forty dollars that he can outjump any frog in Calaveras County.'

"And the feller studied a minute, and then says, kinder sad-like, 'Well, I'm only a stranger here, and I ain't got no frog; but if I had a frog, I'd bet you.'

88

"And then Smiley says, 'that's all right—that's all right—if you'll hold my box a minute, I'll go and get you a frog. And so the feller took the box, and put up his forty dollars along with Smiley's, and set down to wait.

"So he set there a good while thinking and thinking to himself, and then he got the frog out and prized his mouth open[86] and took a teaspoon and filled him full of quail shot[87]—filled him pretty near up to his chin—and set him on the floor. Smiley he went to the swamp and slopped around in the mud for a long time, and finally he ketched a frog, and fetched him in, and give him to this feller, and says:

" ' Now, if You're ready, set him alongside of Dan'l, with his forepaws just even with Dan'l's[88]; and I'll give the word.' Then he says, 'One-two-three git!' and him and the feller touched up the frogs from behind; and the new frog hopped off lively, but Dan'l give a heave, and hysted up his shoulders[89]—so—like a Frenchman, but it warn't no use—he couldn't budge[90]; he was planted as solid as a church, and he couldn't no more stir than if he was anchored out[91]. Smiley was a good deal surprised, and he was disgusted too, but he didn't have no idea what the matter was, of course.

"The feller took the money and started away; and when he was going out at the door, he sorter jerked his thumb over his shoulder—so—at Dan'l, and says again, very deliberate, 'Well,' he says, 'I don't see no p'ints about that frog that's any better'n any other frog.'

"Smiley he stood scratching his head and looking down at Dan'l a long time, and at last he says, 'I do wonder what in the nation that frog throw'd off for[92]—I wonder if there ain't something the matter with him—he 'pears to look mighty baggy[93], somehow.' And he ketched Dan'l by the nap of the neck, and hefted him[94], and says, 'Why blame my cats if he don't weigh five pound[95]!' and turned him upside down and he belched out[96] a double handful of shot. And then he see how it was, and he was the maddest man—he set the frog down and took out after[97] that feller, but he never ketched him. And—"

[Here Simon Wheeler heard his name called from the front yard, and got up to see what was wanted.] And turning to me as he moved away, he said: "Just set where you are, stranger, and rest easy—I ain't going to be gone a second."

But, by your leave[98], I did not think that a continuation of the history of the enterprising vagabond[99] *Jim* Smiley would be likely to afford me much information concerning the Rev. *Leonidas W.* Smiley, and so I started away.

At the door I met the sociable Wheeler returning, and he buttonholed me and recommenced[100]:

"Well, thish-yer Smiley had a yaller[101] one-eyed cow that didn't have no tail, only just a short stump like a bannanner[102], and—

However, lacking both time and inclination, I did not wait to hear about the afflicted cow, but took my leave.

Notes:

1. in compliance with: 遵照

2. garrulous: 喋喋不休的(habitually talking too much)

3. I hereunto append the result: 我在此加上结果。hereunto: 于此(to this point of time); append: 增加(add)

4. lurk: 暗藏(exist unseen)

5. conjecture: 猜测(guess)

6. infamous: 臭名昭著的(well-known for being bad, esp. morally wicked)

7. exasperating reminiscence: 恼人的回忆

8. dilapidated: 破旧的(in bad condition because of age, or lack of care)

9. Angel's: Angel's Camp, a gold mining settlement

10. had an expression of winning gentleness and simplicity upon his tranquil countenance: 他安详的脸上带着讨人喜欢的温和与质朴的表情。winning: 迷人的, 讨人喜欢的(attractive)

11. a young minister of the Gospel: 一个年轻的福音牧师

12. I would feel under many obligations to him: 我对他将不胜感激。

13. Simon Wheeler backed me into a corner and blockaded me there with his chair: Simon Wheeler 使我退到一个角落, 然后用椅子把我挡在那里。

14. reeled off the monotonous narrative which follows this paragraph: 滔滔不绝地讲述那个从下一段开始的单调故事。reel off: 滔滔不绝地讲(repeat sth. quickly and easily from memory)

15. he never changed his voice from the gentle-flowing key to which he tuned his initial sentence: 他的语气一直没变, 还是他讲第一句话时所用的那种轻缓的语调。

16. vein: 几分, 相当程度(a noticeable amount)

17. admired its two heroes as men of transcendent genius in finesse: 把故事中的两个主人公看成是技巧超常的天才。finesse: 手段, 技巧(skill, cleverness)

18. feller: fellow

19. the big flume warn't finished: 大水渠还没完工。flume: 水渠, 水槽(an artificial channel for conducting water, such as one used to transport logs); warn't: wasn't, weren't

20. he was the curiousest man about always betting on anything that turned up you ever see: 他是你见过的最古怪的人, 遇到的任何事情总是要拿来打赌。

21. laying for a chance: 等待机会

22. there couldn't be no solit'ry thing mentioned but that feller'd offer bet on it: that fellow would offer a bet on anything mentioned

23. you'd find him flush or you'd find him busted：你会发现他发了财或输得精光。flush：having plenty of money；busted：broke, penniless

24. camp meeting：野外的布道会（outdoor religious meeting）

25. reg'lar = regularly.

26. exhorter：规劝者，说教者（the person who gives warnings or advice），这里应该是"宣讲人，传道士（preacher）"的意思

27. if you took him up, he would foller that straddle-bug ... where he was bound for：要是你答应和他打赌，他就会跟那只屎壳郎到墨西哥，仅仅是为了弄清楚它要到什么地方去。

28. has = have

29. the dangest feller：最该死的家伙（the most damned fellow）

30. come = came

31. Smiley up：Smiley went up

32. inf'nit' = infinite 无限的

33. coming on so smart：大有好转。come on：（健康）好转（improve in health）

34. the blessing of Prov'dence：上帝保佑。Prov'dence = Providence：上帝

35. say = said

36. don't = doesn't

37. Thish-yer = This

38. the fifteen-minute nag：只能跑15分钟的老爷马

39. for all she was so slow and always had the asthma, or the distemper, or the consumption：尽管它这么慢，又总是得哮喘病，瘟热病，或痨病。distemper：动物瘟热病（an infectious disease of animals, causing fever, disordered breathing, and general weakness）；consumption：痨病，肺结核（tuberculosis）

40. at the fag-end of the race：在接近比赛终点的时候。fag end：末端

92

(last part of something)

41. come cavorting and straddling up, and scattering her legs around
limber：欢腾着迈步过来,灵活地撒开四腿。cavort：乱跳乱蹦
(jump or dance about noisily); straddle：跨立,大迈步; limber：易
弯曲的(moving and bending easily)

42. fetch up at the stand just about a neck ahead：以一颈只差领先到达
看台。fetch up：arrive

43. cipher it down：calculate it

44. bull-pup：小斗牛犬

45. ornery：脾气坏的(bad-tempered)

46. as soon as money was up on him：一旦给它押上赌注

47. fo'castle = forecastle：轮船前部的水手舵

48. a dog might tackle him and bully-rag him：别的狗可能会把它拽倒,
欺负它。

49. Andrew Jackson would never let on but what he was satisfied：Andrew
Jackson 在心满意足之前从来就不露声色。Andrew Jackson：美国
第 7 任总统,在小说中是只小狗。let on：reveal

50. bet：赌注,赌金

51. grab that other dog jest by the j'int of his hind leg and freeze to it：刚
好咬住另外那只小狗的后腿弯,并且紧咬不放。jest = just; j'int
= joint.

52. chaw = chew：咀嚼,啃(keep biting with the teeth)

53. throwed up the sponge = threw up the sponge 认输。throw up the
sponge：认输(admit the defeat)

54. sawed off in a circular saw：被一把圆形锯锯掉了

55. make a snatch for his pet holt：向它一贯爱咬的地方咬去。holt =
hold

56. 'peared = appeared

57. sorter = sort of：有点

58. so he got shucked out bad：因此它吃了大亏。

59. a piece：（时间、路程等）一小段

60. would have made a name for hisself：本来可以出名。make a name for oneself：成名，出名（become famous）; hisself = himself

61. it don't stand to reason = it doesn't stand to reason：这不合乎情理。stand to reason：合乎情理（be logical or reasonable）

62. hisn = his

63. rat tarriers = rat terriers：dogs used for catching rats

64. ketched = caught

65. cal'lated = calculated, planned

66. learn：teach

67. like a doughnut：very quickly. doughnut：油炸面圈饼

68. come down flat-footed and all right：四脚着地落下来，好好地

69. nail：catch or trap

70. as fur as = as far as

71. 'most = almost

72. Dan'l Webster：Daniel Webster（1782 — 1852），美国政治家、众议员、参议员、著名演说家（congressman, U. S. senator, statesman, and the most famous orator of his time），在小说中是一只青蛙的名字

73. quicker'n：quicker than

74. off'n = off on

75. flop down on the floor ag'in as solid as a gob of mud：又像一团烂泥一样噗的一声扎扎实实地落在地板上。ag'in = again

76. fall to：begin

77. straightfor'ard = straightforward：honest

78. And when it come to fair and square jumping … you ever see：讲到规规矩矩立定起跳的话，它能使劲一跳，比你看到过的它的同类中的任何一个都远。when it comes to sth.：说到……; fair and square：honestly; straddle：jump

79. strong suit：特长（a quality, activity, or skill in which a person excels）

80. Smiley would ante up money on him as long as he had a red：Smiley 只要有一分钱，就会给它加大赌注。a red：a cent

81. monstrous = monstrously：非常, 极其

82. laid over：defeated

83. p'ints = points

84. you ain't only a amature：you are only an amateur, 你只是客串

85. resk = risk

86. prized his mouth open：撬开它的嘴。prize = pry：撬

87. quail shot：打鹌鹑的铅弹

88. with his forepaws just even with Dan'l's：让它的前爪跟丹尼尔的并齐。even：齐的（on the same level）

89. hysted up his shoulders：耸起它的肩膀。hysted = hoisted：提起, 升起

90. budge：move a little

91. and he couldn't no more stir than if he was anchored out：它再也不能动弹了, 像只船抛了锚一样。

92. what in the nation that frog throw'd off for：究竟为什么这只青蛙这回不争气。

93. baggy：膨胀如袋

94. hefted him：掂量掂量它的重量

95. Why blame my cats if he don't weigh five pound：嗨, 它要是没五磅重才怪呢。why blame my cats：口头禅, 表示感叹

96. belch out：猛烈喷出（send forth violently）

97. took out after：追赶（pursued）

98. by your leave：请原谅（a request for permission）

99. the enterprising vagabond：胆大妄为的流氓

100. and he buttonholed me and recommenced：他把我留住, 又开始了

（他的故事）。

101. yaller: yellow

102 . only just a short stump like a bannanner: 仅仅只是一段短短的残肢, 像根香蕉一样。bannanner: banana

Questions:

1. How does the stranger outsmart Jim Smiley?

2. What is the effect of Twain's personification of the race horse, the dog Andrew Jackson, and the frog Dan'l Webster?

3. What is the story beneath the story of "The Celebrated Jumping Frog of Calaveras County" which Twain wishes to tell? What does he want the reader to understand about Western communities as a result of having read this story?

4. Why is the use of dialect and slang so important to the humor of this story?

5. The tall tale was a popular form of the American Frontier story, primarily an oral form. Tall tales are humorous, exaggerated stories that feature an adventurous hero who is generally superhuman in some way. How does "The Celebrated Jumping Frog of Calaveras County" fit the definition of a tall tale? In what ways does the story go against conventions of the tall-tale genre?

O. Henry

(1862-1910)

O. **Henry** (1862—1910), pen name for William Sydney Porter, was a prolific short-story writer, who mostly wrote about the life of ordinary people in New York City. His stories are famous for wit, wordplay, warm characterization and clever twist endings. A twist ending or surprise ending is an unexpected conclusion or climax to a work of fiction, and which often contains irony or causes the audience to reevaluate the narrative or characters. This kind of ending is often seen in O. Henry's short stories, hence often referred to as an "O. Henry ending".

O. Henry was born in Greensboro, North Carolina. His father was a physician. His mother died when he was three. At the age of 15, he dropped out of school to work in his uncle's drugstore. During his 20s he moved to Texas, where he worked for more than ten years as a clerk and a bank teller. In 1897 he was convicted of embezzling money, although there has been much debate over his actual guilt. In 1898 he entered a prison at Columbus, Ohio.

While in prison, O. Henry started to write short stories. His first work, "Whistling Dick's Christmas Stocking" was published in 1899. After serving three years of the five years' sentence, Porter emerged from the prison in 1901 and changed his name to O. Henry. In 1902 he moved to New York City. His first collection, *Cabbages And Kings*, appeared in 1904. The second, *The Four Million*, was published two years later and included his well-known stories "The Gift of the Magi" and

97

"The Furnished Room". *The Trimmed Lamp* (1907) included the famous "The Last Leaf". His best known work is perhaps the much anthologized "The Ransom of Red Chief", included in the collection *Whirligigs* (1910). *The Heart Of The West* (1907) presents tales of the Texas range. *The Voice of the City* (1908) shows sympathy for poor people. During his lifetime O. Henry published 10 collections and over 600 short stories.

O. Henry's last years were shadowed by alcoholism, ill health, and financial problems. He died of cirrhosis of the liver at the age of 48 in New York. Three more collections, *Sixes And Sevens* (1911), *Rolling Stones* (1912) and *Waifs And Strays* (1917), were published posthumously.

"The Gift of the Magi" (1905) is one of Henry's most famous short stories. It concerns a young couple, Della and Jim, who are short of money but desperately want to buy each other Christmas gifts. It features O. Henry's characteristic humorous tone, characters, twist ending, realistic detail and coincidence. A major reason for its enduring appeal is its affirmation of unselfish love. Such love, as the story and its title suggest, is like the gifts to the newborn Jesus given by the wise men, called magi in the Bible.

The Gift of the Magi[1]

O. Henry

One dollar and eighty-seven cents. That was all. And sixty cents of it was in pennies. Pennies saved one and two at a time by bulldozing[2] the grocer and the vegetable man and the butcher until one's cheeks burned with the silent imputation[3] of parsimony[4] that such close dealing[5] implied. Three times Della counted it. One dollar and eighty-seven cents. And the next day would be Christmas.

There was clearly nothing to do but flop[6] down on the shabby little couch and howl. So Della did it. Which instigates the moral reflection that life is made up of sobs, sniffles, and smiles, with sniffles predominating[7].

While the mistress of the home is gradually subsiding from the first stage to the second, take a look at the home. A furnished flat at $8 per week. It did not exactly beggar description[8], but it certainly had that word on the lookout for the mendicancy squad[9].

In the vestibule[10] below was a letter-box into which no letter would go, and an electric button from which no mortal finger could coax a ring[11]. Also appertaining thereunto[12] was a card bearing the name "Mr. James Dillingham Young".

The "Dillingham" had been flung to the breeze during a former period of prosperity when its possessor was being paid $30 per week. Now, when the income was shrunk to $20, the letters of "Dillingham" looked blurred, as though they were thinking seriously of contracting to a modest and unassuming[13] D. But whenever Mr. James Dillingham Young came home and reached his flat above he was called "Jim" and greatly hugged by Mrs. James Dillingham Young, already introduced to you as Della. Which is all very good.

Della finished her cry and attended to her cheeks with the powder rag[14]. She stood by the window and looked out dully at a gray cat walking a gray fence in a gray backyard. Tomorrow would be Christmas Day, and she had only $1.87 with which to buy Jim a present. She had been saving every penny she could for months, with this result. Twenty dollars a week doesn't go far. Expenses had been greater than she had calculated. They always are. Only $1.87 to buy a present for Jim. Her Jim. Many a happy hour she had spent planning for something nice for him. Something fine and rare and sterling[15]—something just a little bit near to being worthy of the honor of being owned by Jim.

There was a pier-glass[16] between the windows of the room. Perhaps you have seen a pier-glass in an $8 flat. A very thin and very agile person may, by observing his reflection in a rapid sequence of longitudinal strips[17], obtain a fairly accurate conception of his looks. Della, being slender, had mastered the art.

Suddenly she whirled from the window and stood before the glass. Her eyes were shining brilliantly, but her face had lost its color within twenty seconds. Rapidly she pulled down her hair and let it fall to its full length.

Now, there were two possessions of the James Dillingham Youngs in which they both took a mighty pride. One was Jim's gold watch that had been his father's and his grand father's. The other was Della's hair. Had the queen of Sheba[18] lived in the flat across the airshaft[19], Della would have let her hair hang out the window some day to dry just to depreciate[20] Her Majesty's jewels and gifts. Had King Solomon been the janitor[21], with all his treasures piled up in the basement, Jim would have pulled out his watch every time he passed, just to see him pluck at his beard from envy[22].

So now Della's beautiful hair fell about her rippling and shining like a cascade of brown waters[23]. It reached below her knee and made itself almost a garment for her. And then she did it up[24] again nervously and quickly. Once she faltered[25] for a minute and stood still while a tear or two splashed on the worn red carpet.

On went her old brown jacket; on went her old brown hat. With a whirl of skirts and with the brilliant sparkle still in her eyes[26], she fluttered out the door and down the stairs to the street.

Where she stopped the sign read: "Mme. Sofronie. Hair Goods of All Kinds." One flight up Della ran, and collected herself, panting[27]. Madame, large, too white, chilly, hardly looked the "Sofronie[28]".

"Will you buy my hair?" asked Della.

"I buy hair," said Madame. "Take yer hat off and Let's have a sight at the looks of it."

100

Down rippled the brown cascade.

"Twenty dollars," said Madame, lifting the mass with a practised hand.

"Give it to me quick," said Della.

Oh, and the next two hours tripped[29] by on rosy wings. Forget the hashed[30] metaphor. She was ransacking[31] the stores for Jim's present.

She found it at last. It surely had been made for Jim and no one else. There was no other like it in any of the stores, and she had turned all of them inside out[32]. It was a platinum fob chain simple and chaste in design[33], properly proclaiming its value by substance alone and not by meretricious ornamentation[34]—as all good things should do. It was even worthy of The Watch. As soon as she saw it she knew that it must be Jim's. It was like him. Quietness and value—the description applied to both. Twenty-one dollars they took from her for it, and she hurried home with the 87 cents. With that chain on his watch Jim might be properly anxious about the time in any company[35]. Grand as the watch was, he sometimes looked at it on the sly[36] on account of the old leather strap that he used in place of a chain[37].

When Della reached home her intoxication gave way a little to prudence and reason[38]. She got out her curling irons[39] and lighted the gas and went to work repairing the ravages[40] made by generosity added to love. Which is always a tremendous task, dear friends—a mammoth[41] task.

Within forty minutes her head was covered with tiny, close-lying curls that made her look wonderfully like a truant[42] schoolboy. She looked at her reflection in the mirror long, carefully, and critically.

"If Jim doesn't kill me," she said to herself, "before he takes a second look at me, he'll say I look like a Coney Island[43] chorus girl. But what could I do—oh! what could I do with a dollar and eighty-seven cents?"

101

At 7 o'clock the coffee was made and the frying-pan was on the back of the stove hot and ready to cook the chops[44].

Jim was never late. Della doubled the fob chain in her hand and sat on the corner of the table near the door that he always entered. Then she heard his step on the stair away down on the first flight, and she turned white for just a moment. She had a habit of saying little silent prayers about the simplest everyday things, and now she whispered: "Please God, make him think I am still pretty."

The door opened and Jim stepped in and closed it. He looked thin and very serious. Poor fellow, he was only twenty-two—and to be burdened with a family! He needed a new overcoat and he was without gloves.

Jim stopped inside the door, as immovable as a setter at the scent of quail[45]. His eyes were fixed upon Della, and there was an expression in them that she could not read, and it terrified her. It was not anger, nor surprise, nor disapproval, nor horror, nor any of the sentiments that she had been prepared for. He simply stared at her fixedly with that peculiar expression on his face.

Della wriggled off the table[46] and went for him.

"Jim, darling," she cried, "don't look at me that way. I had my hair cut off and sold it because I couldn't have lived through Christmas without giving you a present. It'll grow out again—you won't mind, will you? I just had to do it. My hair grows awfully fast. Say 'Merry Christmas!' Jim, and Let's be happy. You don't know what a nice—what a beautiful, nice gift I've got for you."

"You've cut off your hair?" asked Jim, laboriously, as if he had not arrived at that patent fact yet even after the hardest mental labor.

"Cut it off and sold it," said Della. "don't you like me just as well, anyhow? I'm me without my hair, ain't I?"

Jim looked about the room curiously.

"You say your hair is gone?" he said, with an air almost of idiocy[47].

"You needn't look for it," said Della. "It's sold, I tell you—sold and gone, too. It's Christmas Eve, boy. Be good to me, for it went for you. Maybe the hairs of my head were numbered," she went on with sudden serious sweetness, "but nobody could ever count my love for you. Shall I put the chops on, Jim?"

Out of his trance[48] Jim seemed quickly to wake. He enfolded[49] his Della. For ten seconds let us regard with discreet scrutiny some inconsequential object in the other direction[50]. Eight dollars a week or a million a year—what is the difference? A mathematician or a wit would give you the wrong answer. The magi brought valuable gifts, but that was not among them. This dark assertion will be illuminated later on[51].

Jim drew a package from his overcoat pocket and threw it upon the table.

"Don't make any mistake, Dell," he said, "about me. I don't think there's anything in the way of a haircut or a shave or a shampoo that could make me like my girl any less. But if you'll unwrap that package you may see why you had me going a while[52] at first. "

White fingers and nimble tore at the string and paper. And then an ecstatic scream of joy; and then, alas! a quick feminine change to hysterical tears and wails, necessitating the immediate employment of all the comforting powers of the lord of the flat[53].

For there lay The Combs—the set of combs, side and back[54], that Della had worshipped long in a Broadway window. Beautiful combs, pure tortoise shell, with jewelled rims—just the shade to wear in the beautiful vanished hair[55]. They were expensive combs, she knew, and her heart had simply craved and yearned over them without the least hope of possession. And now, they were hers, but the tresses that should have adorned the coveted adornments were gone[56].

But she hugged them to her bosom, and at length she was able to look up with dim eyes and a smile and say: "My hair grows so fast, Jim!"

And then Della leaped up like a little singed cat and cried, "Oh, oh!"

Jim had not yet seen his beautiful present. She held it out to him eagerly upon her open palm. The dull precious metal seemed to flash with a reflection of her bright and ardent spirit.

"Isn't it a dandy, Jim? I hunted all over town to find it. You'll have to look at the time a hundred times a day now. Give me your watch. I want to see how it looks on it."

Instead of obeying, Jim tumbled down on the couch and put his hands under the back of his head and smiled.

"Dell," said he, "Let's put our Christmas presents away and keep 'em a while. They're too nice to use just at present. I sold the watch to get the money to buy your combs. And now suppose you put the chops on."

The magi, as you know, were wise men—wonderfully wise men—who brought gifts to the Babe in the manger[57]. They invented the art of giving Christmas presents. Being wise, their gifts were no doubt wise ones, possibly bearing the privilege of exchange in case of duplication[58]. And here I have lamely related to you the uneventful chronicle[59] of two foolish children in a flat who most unwisely sacrificed for each other the greatest treasures of their house. But in a last word to the wise of these days let it be said that of all who give gifts these two were the wisest. Of all who give and receive gifts, such as they are wisest. Everywhere they are wisest. They are the magi.

Notes:

1. the Magi: 耶稣降生时携带礼物(黄金、乳香、没药)前来朝见祝贺的东方三博士(Wise Men),载于圣经马太福音第二章。(After Jesus was born in Bethlehem in Judea, during the time of King Herod, Magi from the east came to Jerusalem and asked, "Where is the one who has been born king of the Jews? We saw his star in the east and have come to worship him." ... When they saw the star, they were overjoyed. On coming to the house, they saw the child with his mother Mary, and they bowed down and worshiped him. Then they opened their treasures and presented him with gifts of gold and of incense and of myrrh. —Matthew 2 : 1 ~ 2, 10 ~ 11, the Bible)

2. bulldoze:强行,胁迫(force sb. to do sth. by bullying)

3. imputation:罪名,污名(a criminal charge or suggestion of sth. bad)

4. parsimony:吝啬(stinginess, great or extreme unwillingness to spend money)

5. close dealing:吝啬的交易

6. flop:猛然坐下(fall in a loose, heavy or awkward way)

7. Which instigates the moral reflection that life is made up of sobs, sniffles, and smiles, with sniffles predominating:这使她感慨万千,让她认识到生活是由啜泣、抽噎和微笑组成的,其中抽噎占主导地位。(意思是人生有苦也有甜,但痛苦占多数)。instigate:促使(provoke);moral:(事件、故事等的)教育意义,寓意(a piece of guidance on how to live one's life, how to act more effectively, etc., that can be learnt from a story or event)

8. beggar description:非语言所能描述(be beyond the powers of language to describe)

9. the mendicancy squad:乞丐帮,乞讨队

10. vestibule:门厅,前厅(entrance hall)

11. from which no mortal finger could coax a ring:没有凡人的手指按响门铃

12. appertaining thereunto:与那有关的(appertaining to that)。appertain

to：属于(belong to sth. by right)

13. unassuming：不摆架子的,谦虚的(modest)

14. attended to her cheeks with the powder rag：用旧碎布在脸颊上扑了粉

15. sterling：excellent

16. pier-glass：窗间镜

17. by observing his reflection in a rapid sequence of longitudinal strips：通过观察一连串纵向的、细长条的镜像

18. the queen of Sheba:《圣经》中朝觐所罗门王,以难题测其智慧的示巴女王,她以美貌和财富著称。据《圣经·旧约·列王纪上》记载：示巴女王听说所罗门贤明,就亲自前来用难题考他。她带了一大队随从,用骆驼驮上大批香料和金银珠宝来到耶路撒冷……示巴女王看到了所罗门的智慧……于是她赠给国王大批的金子、香料和珠宝。

19. airshaft：天井

20. depreciate：降低……的价值(reduce or lower the value of)

21. Had King Solomon been the janitor：假如所罗门王是看门人。King Solomon：所罗门王,据《圣经》记载,他是大卫之子,公元前10世纪以色列国王,以智慧、财富和权利著称。

22. pluck at his beard from envy：出于嫉妒拽自己的胡须

23. Della's beautiful hair fell about her rippling and shining like a cascade of brown waters：德拉美丽的头发披散下来,像一道褐色的小瀑布,微波起伏,闪闪发亮。

24. she did it up：她把头发扎起来。do up：扎起来(tie up)

25. falter：hesitate

26. with the brilliant sparkle still in her eyes：眼睛里仍然含着晶莹的泪花

27. One flight up Della ran, and collected herself, panting：德拉跑上了一段楼梯,气喘吁吁,定了定神。collect：get control of

28. Sofronie：索夫罗妮，是十六世纪意大利诗人塔索（Tasso，1544—1595）的作品《被解放的耶路撒冷》的主人公。为了拯救耶路撒冷全城的基督徒，索夫罗妮承认了自己并未犯过的罪行，是舍己救人的典型。看来商店女老板索夫罗妮是意大利人，她说的英语不大合乎标准。

29. trip：轻快地移动（move with light quick steps）

30. hashed：糟糕的，乱七八糟的

31. ransack：search or examine thoroughly

32. and she had turned all of them inside out：因为她把所有商店都翻了个底朝天。

33. It was a platinum fob chain simple and chaste in design：这是一条白金表链，款式简单朴素。chaste：简洁的，朴素的（simple, not highly decorated）

34. meretricious ornamentation：华而不实的装饰。meretricious：华而不实的（attractive on the surface, but of no real value）

35. in any company：在任何同伴面前

36. on the sly：secretly

37. on account of the old leather strap that he used in place of a chain：由于他用一条旧的皮带子代替表链

38. her intoxication gave way a little to prudence and reason：她的极度兴奋稍稍让位于慎重与理智。

39. curling irons：卷发用的铁卷子

40. ravages：造成的破坏（great damage）

41. mammoth：huge.

42. truant：逃学的学生（a student who stays out of school without permission）

43. Coney Island：科尼岛，是位于美国纽约市布鲁克林区的半岛，原本为一座海岛，其面向大西洋的海滩是美国知名的休闲娱乐区域。（a peninsula, formerly an island, with a beach on the Atlantic Ocean,

New York City's most famous amusement park, located in the borough of Brooklyn.)

44. chop: 排骨

45. as immovable as a setter at the scent of quail: 像一条猎犬嗅到了鹌鹑的气味,一动不动。

46. Della wriggled off the table: 德拉一扭身,离开桌子。

47. with an air almost of idiocy: 几乎带着白痴的神情。idiocy: 白痴状态(the state of being an idiot)

48. trance: 恍惚(a sleeplike condition of the mind in which one does not notice the things around one)

49. enfold: 拥抱(hug, embrace)

50. For ten seconds let us regard with discreet scrutiny some inconsequential object in the other direction: 现在让我们用十秒钟从另外的角度慎重考虑一个无关紧要的东西。inconsequential: unimportant

51. This dark assertion will be illuminated later on: 这令人费解的话将在后面得到解释。assertion: 主张,断言(a forceful statement or claim)

52. why you had me going a while: 为什么你一下子把我弄得晕头转向

53. a quick feminine change to hysterical tears and . . . comforting powers of the lord of the flat: 突然变成了女性不可抑制的眼泪和号啕大哭,需要公寓的男主人用一切力量来安慰她。hysterical: 歇斯底里的,不可抑制的; necessitate: make necessary

54. the set of combs, side and back: 整套梳子,有两鬓用的,有后面用的

55. with jewelled rims—just the shade to wear in the beautiful vanished hair: 边上镶着宝石,那颜色正好与那失去的秀发相配

56. but the tresses that should have adorned the coveted adornments were gone: 但是那头本应该为这套渴望已久的装饰品增色的秀发已经没有了。tresses: 披肩长发; adorn: make more beautiful, attractive,

or interesting; covet: 垂涎,贪求(desire eagerly)

57. the Babe in the manger: 马槽里的婴孩耶稣,根据《圣经》记载,耶稣是降生在伯利恒城的一个马槽里的。

58. in case of duplication: 在同样情况下。duplication: 复制,重复

59. And here I have lamely related to you the uneventful chronicle: 我这里笨拙地给你们叙述了这个平凡的故事。uneventful: 平淡无奇的,平凡的; chronicle: 编年史,纪事(a record of events in the order in which they occurred)

Questions:

1. Why does the writer call Jim and Della the magis of the modern world?

2. Why does the writer call Jim and Della foolish and wise at the same time?

3. What is the true "gift" in the story? Why? Explain.

4. What is the theme of the story?

5. Compare the time period of the story to the period in which you live today. What are some of the differences? What are some of the similarities? Explain.

Sherwood Anderson

(1876-1941)

Sherwood Anderson (1876—1941) was born in Ohio into a harness-maker's family of seven children. After the father's business failed, the family ran into financial difficulties. Young Anderson had to leave school at the age of 14 and did various odd jobs to help his family, which earned him the nickname "Jobby". He enlisted in the United States Army and went to the Spanish-American War (1898). After the war, in 1900, he enrolled at Wittenberg University, Ohio. He became a successful businessman and managed a mail-order business and paint manufacturing firms. After he suffered a mental breakdown, he left his job and his family for Chicago to become a writer. But it was not until at the age of 40 that his first novel, *Windy McPherson's Son*, was published. In 1917 he published his second novel, *Marching Men*. Both novels contain the psychological themes of inner lives of Midwestern villages, the pursuit of success and disillusionment.

The novel that established Anderson as an important writer was *Winesburg, Ohio* (1919). It consists of twenty-three thematically related stories and depicts small-town, Midwestern American life from late 1800s to early 1900s, the period from a rural to an industrial society. The narrative is united by the appearance of George Willard, a young reporter who has ambitions to become a famous writer. George observes keenly and listens attentively to the grotesques, the inhabitants of Winesburg, about their dreams, frustration, loneliness, and sadness. The themes

110

that are explored in the novel are comparable to those of T. S. Eliot and other modernist writers. *Winesburg, Ohio* is now regarded as one of the finest American novels of the 20th century. In addition to the books mentioned, Anderson wrote a number of fine short stories collected in *The Triumph of the Egg* (1921), *Horses and Men* (1923), and *Death in the Woods, and other Stories* (1933) and novels *Poor White* (1920), *Many Marriages* (1923), and *Dark Laughter* (1925), a bestseller.

Anderson was called a "writer's writer". His best works influenced almost every important American writer of the next generation. His style, derived from everyday speech, influenced American short story writing between World Wars I and II. He was probably the first writer since Mark Twain to write in the colloquial style. He regarded the vernacular as an honest medium and developed a style the major features of which included clarity, directness and a deceptive simplicity. He was one of the earliest American writers who responded to Freud's theories. He encouraged William Faulkner and Ernest Hemingway in their writing aspirations, although they eventually turned against him. Anderson died of peritonitis from having swallowed a toothpick while visiting Panama, at the age of 64. After his death, Anderson's reputation soon declined, but in the 1970s, scholars and critics found a new interest in his work.

"Sophistication" is a short story in *Winesburg, Ohio*. It is about two people: George Willard and Helen White, who are caught between adolescence and maturity. George is leaving Winesburg for better prospects and a brighter future in a big city. He is longing to become a great man and be different from other men. But he often feels lonely and helpless, feelings which often accompany a person's sophistication. He needs someone to know what he is going through, and understand how he feels. Helen White is the right girl he longs for. George and Helen have their farewell meeting at the fair in the evening, and they embrace and kiss, which makes them feel embarrassed. To relive their embarrassment they drop into the animation of youth. In

" Sophistication ", the psychological process of a boy from the adolescence to maturity is vividly depicted and easily recognized by adult readers. The style is typical of Anderson's writing: colloquial, realistic and simple.

Sophistication

Sherwood Anderson

It was early evening of a day in the late fall and the Winesburg County Fair had brought crowds of country people to town. The day had been clear and the night came on warm and pleasant. On the Trunion Pike, where the road after it left town stretched away between berry fields now covered with dry brown leaves; the dust from passing wagons arose in clouds. Children, curled into little balls, slept on the straw scattered on wagon beds. Their hair was full of dust and their fingers black and sticky. The dust rolled away over the fields and the departing sun set it ablaze[1] with colors.

In the main street of Winesburg crowds filled the stores and the sidewalks. Night came on, horses whinnied[2], the clerks in the stores ran madly about, children became lost and cried lustily[3], an American town worked terribly at the task of amusing itself.

Pushing his way through the crowds in Main Street, young George Willard concealed himself in the stairway leading to Doctor Reefy's office and looked at the people. With feverish eyes he watched the faces drifting past under the store lights. Thoughts kept coming into his head and he did not want to think. He stamped impatiently on the wooden steps and looked sharply about. "Well, is she going to stay with him all day? Have I done all this waiting for nothing?" he muttered.

George Willard, the Ohio village boy, was fast growing into manhood and new thoughts had been coming into his mind. All that day, amid the jam of people at the Fair, he had gone about feeling lonely. He was about to leave Winesburg to go away to some city where he hoped to get work on a city newspaper and he felt grown-up. The mood that had taken possession of him was a thing known to men and unknown to boys. He felt old and a little tired. Memories awoke in him. To his mind his new sense of maturity set him apart, made of him a half-tragic figure. He wanted someone to understand the feeling that had taken possession of him after his mother's death.

There is a time in the life of every boy when he for the first time takes the backward view of life. Perhaps that is the moment when he crosses the line into manhood. The boy is walking through the street of his town. He is thinking of the future and of the figure he will cut in the world. Ambitions and regrets awake within him. Suddenly something happens; he stops under a tree and waits as for a voice calling his name. Ghosts of old things creep into his consciousness; the voices outside of himself whisper a message concerning the limitations of life. From being quite sure of himself and his future he becomes not at all sure. If he be an imaginative boy a door is torn open and for the first time he looks out upon the world, seeing, as though they marched in procession before him, the countless figures of men who before his time have come out of nothingness into the world, lived their lives and again disappeared into nothingness. The sadness of sophistication has come to the boy. With a little gasp he sees himself as merely a leaf blown by the wind through the streets of his village. He knows that in spite of all the stout talk of his fellows he must live and die in uncertainty, a thing blown by the winds, a thing destined like corn to wilt in the sun[4]. He shivers and looks eagerly about. The eighteen years he has lived seem but a moment, a breathing space in the long march of humanity. Already he hears death calling. With all his heart he wants to come close to some other human, touch someone with his hands, be touched by the hand of another. If he prefers that the other be a woman, that is because he believes that a woman will be gentle, that she will understand. He wants, most of all, understanding.

When the moment of sophistication came to George Willard his mind turned to Helen White, the Winesburg banker's daughter. Always he had been conscious of the girl growing into womanhood as he grew into manhood. Once on a summer night when he was eighteen, he had walked with her on a country road and in her presence had given way to an impulse to boast, to make himself appear big and significant in her eyes. Now he wanted to see her for another purpose. He wanted to tell her of the new impulses that had come to him. He had tried to make her think of him as a man when he knew nothing of manhood and now he wanted to be with her and to try to make her feel the change he believed had taken place in his nature.

As for Helen White, she also had come to a period of change. What George felt, she in her young woman's way felt also. She was no longer a girl and hungered to reach into the grace and beauty of womanhood. She had come home from Cleveland, where she was attending college, to spend a day at the Fair. She also had begun to have memories. During the day she sat in the grandstand[5] with a young man, one of the instructors from the college, who was a guest of her mother's. The young man was of a pedantic turn of mind[6] and she felt at once he would not do for her purpose[7]. At the Fair she was glad to be seen in his company as he was well dressed and a stranger. She knew that the fact of his presence would create an impression. During the day she was happy, but when night came on she began to grow restless. She wanted to drive the instructor away, to get out of his presence. While they sat together in the grandstand and while the eyes of former schoolmates were upon them, she paid so much attention

114

to her escort[8] that he grew interested. "A scholar needs money. I should marry a woman with money," he mused[9].

Helen White was thinking of George Willard even as he wandered gloomily through the crowds thinking of her. She remembered the summer evening when they had walked together and wanted to walk with him again. She thought that the months she had spent in the city, the going to theaters and the seeing of great crowds wandering in lighted thoroughfares[10], had changed her profoundly. She wanted him to feel and be conscious of the change in her nature.

The summer evening together that had left its mark on the memory of both the young man and the woman had, when looked at quite sensibly, been rather stupidly spent. They had walked out of town along a country road. Then they had stopped by a fence near a field of young corn and George had taken off his coat and let it hang on his arm. "Well, I've stayed here in Winesburg—yes—I've not yet gone away but I'm growing up," he had said. "I've been reading books and I've been thinking. I'm going to try to amount to something in life."

"Well," he explained, "that isn't the point. Perhaps I'd better quit talking."

The confused boy put his hand on the girl's arm. His voice trembled. The two started to walk back along the road toward town. In his desperation George boasted, "I'm going to be a big man, the biggest that ever lived here in Winesburg," he declared. "I want you to do something, I don't know what. Perhaps it is none of my business. I want you to try to be different from other women. You see the point. It's none of my business, I tell you. I want you to be a beautiful woman. You see what I want."

The boy's voice failed and in silence the two came back into town and went along the street to Helen White's house. At the gate he tried to say something impressive. Speeches he had thought out came into his head, but they seemed utterly pointless. "I thought—I used to think—I had in my mind you would marry Seth Richmond. Now I know you won't," was all he could find to say as she went through the gate and toward the door of her house.

On the warm fall evening as he stood in the stairway and looked at the crowd drifting through Main Street, George thought of the talk beside the field of young corn and was ashamed of the figure he had made of himself. In the street the people surged[11] up and down like cattle confined in a pen[12]. Buggies[13] and wagons almost filled the narrow thoroughfare. A band played and small boys raced along the sidewalk, diving between the legs of men. Young men with shining red faces walked awkwardly about with girls on their arms. In a room above one of the stores, where a dance was to be held, the fiddlers tuned their instruments. The broken sounds floated down through an open window and out across the murmur of voices and the loud blare of the horns of the band[14]. The medley of songs got on young Willard's nerves[15]. Everywhere, on all sides, the sense of crowding, moving life closed in about[16] him. He wanted to run away by himself and think. "If she wants to stay with that fellow she may. Why should I care? What difference does it make to me?" he growled and went along Main Street and through Hern's Grocery into a side street.

George felt so utterly lonely and dejected[17] that he wanted to weep but pride made him walk rapidly along, swinging his arms. He came to Wesley Moyer's livery barn[18] and stopped in the shadows to listen to a group of men who talked of a race Wesley's stallion[19], Tony Tip, had won at the Fair during the afternoon. A crowd had gathered in front of the barn and before the crowd walked Wesley, prancing up and down and boasting. He held a whip in his hand and kept tapping the ground. Little puffs of dust arose in the lamplight. "Quit your talking," Wesley exclaimed. "I wasn't afraid, I knew I had 'em beat all the time. I wasn't afraid."

Ordinarily George Willard would have been intensely interested in the boasting of Moyer, the horseman. Now it made him angry. He turned and hurried away along the street. "Old windbag," he sputtered[20]. "Why does he want to be bragging[21]? Why don't he shut up?"

George went into a vacant lot[22], and as he hurried along, fell over a pile of rubbish. A nail protruding from an empty barrel[23] tore his trousers. He sat down on the ground and swore. With a pin he mended the torn place and then arose and went on. "I'll go to Helen White's house, that's what I'll do. I'll walk right in. I'll say that I want to see her. I'll walk right in and sit down, that's what I'll do," he declared, climbing over a fence and beginning to run.

On the veranda of Banker White's house Helen was restless and distraught[24]. The instructor sat between the mother and daughter. His talk wearied the girl. Although he had also been raised in an Ohio town, the instructor began to put on the airs of the city[25]. He wanted to appear cosmopolitan[26]. "I like the chance you have given me to study the background out of which most of our girls come," he declared. "It was good of you, Mrs. White, to have me down for the day." He turned to Helen and laughed. "Your life is still bound up with the life of this town?" he asked. "There are people here in whom you are interested?" To the girl his voice sounded pompous and heavy.

Helen arose and went into the house. At the door leading to a garden at the back she stopped and stood listening. Her mother began to talk. "There is no one here fit to associate with a girl of Helen's breeding," she said.

Helen ran down a flight of stairs at the back of the house and into the garden. In the darkness she stopped and stood trembling. It seemed to her that the world was full of meaningless people saying words. Afire with eagerness[27] she ran through the garden gate and, turning a corner by the banker's barn, went into a little side street. "George! Where are you, George?" she cried, filled with nervous excitement. She stopped running, and leaned against a tree to laugh hysterically. Along the dark little street came George Willard, still saying words. "I'm going to walk right into her house. I'll go right in and sit down," he declared as he came up to her. He stopped and stared stupidly. "Come on," he said and took hold of her hand. With hanging heads they walked away along the street under the trees. Dry leaves rustled underfoot. Now that he had found her George wondered what he had better do and say.

At the upper end of the Fair Ground, in Winesburg, there is a half-decayed old grandstand. It has never been painted and the boards are all warped out of shape. The Fair Ground stands on top of a low hill rising out of the valley of Wine Creek and from the grandstand one can see at night, over a cornfield, the lights of the town reflected against the sky.

George and Helen climbed the hill to the Fair Ground, coming by the path past Water-works Pond. The feeling of loneliness and isolation that had come to the young man in the crowded streets of his town was both broken and intensified by the presence of Helen. What he felt was reflected in her.

In youth there are always two forces fighting in people. The warm unthinking little animal struggles against the thing that reflects and remembers, and the older, the more sophisticated thing had possession of George Willard. Sensing his mood, Helen walked beside him filled with respect. When they got to the grandstand they climbed up under the roof and sat down on one of the long benchlike seats.

There is something memorable in the experience to be had by going into a fairground that stands at the edge of a Middle Western town on a night after the annual fair has been held. The sensation is one never to be forgotten. On all sides are ghosts, not of the dead, but of living people.

118

Here, during the day just passed, have come the people pouring in from the town and the country around. Farmers with their wives and children and all the people from the hundreds of little frame houses have gathered within these board walls. Young girls have laughed and men with beards have talked of the affairs of their lives. The place has been filled to overflowing with life. It has itched and squirmed with life[28] and now it is night and the life has all gone away. The silence is almost terrifying. One conceals oneself standing silently beside the trunk of a tree and what there is of a reflective tendency in his nature is intensified. One shudders at the thought of the meaninglessness of life while at the same instant, and if the people of the town are his people, one lives life so intensely that tears come into the eyes.

In the darkness under the roof of the grandstand, George Willard sat beside Helen White and felt very keenly his own insignificance in the scheme of existence. Now that he had come out of town where the presence of the people stirring about, busy with a multitude of affairs, had been so irritating, the irritation was all gone. The presence of Helen renewed and refreshed him. It was as though her woman's hand was assisting him to make some minute readjustment of the machinery of his life[29]. He began to think of the people in the town where he had always lived with something like reverence. He had reverence for Helen. He wanted to love and to be loved by her, but he did not want at the moment to be confused by her womanhood. In the darkness he took hold of her hand and when she crept close put a hand on her shoulder. A wind began to blow and he shivered. With all his strength he tried to hold and to understand the mood that had come upon him. In that high place in the darkness the two oddly sensitive human atoms held each other tightly and waited. In the mind of each was the same thought. "I have come to this lonely place and here is this other," was the substance of the thing felt.

In Winesburg the crowded day had run itself out into the long night of the late fall. Farm horses jogged away along lonely country roads pulling their portion of weary people. Clerks began to bring samples of goods in off the sidewalks and lock the doors of stores. In the Opera House a crowd had gathered to see a show and further down Main Street the fiddlers, their instruments tuned, sweated and worked to keep the feet of youth flying over a dance floor.

In the darkness in the grandstand Helen White and George Willard remained silent. Now and then the spell that held them was broken and they turned and tried in the dim light to see into each other's eyes. They kissed but that impulse did not last. At the upper end of the Fair Ground a half-dozen men worked over horses that had raced during the afternoon. The men had built a fire and were heating kettles of water. Only their legs could be seen as they passed back and forth in the light. When the wind blew, the little flames of the fire danced crazily about.

George and Helen arose and walked away into the darkness. They went along a path past a field of corn that had not yet been cut. The wind whispered among the dry corn blades. For a moment during the walk back into town the spell that held them was broken. When they had come to the crest of Waterworks Hill they stopped by a tree and George again put his hands on the girl's shoulders. She embraced him eagerly and then again they drew quickly back from that impulse. They stopped kissing and stood a little apart. Mutual respect grew big in them. They were both embarrassed and to relieve their embarrassment dropped into the animalism of youth. They laughed and began to pull and haul at each other. In some way chastened and purified by the mood they had been in, they became, not man and woman, not boy and girl, but excited little animals.

It was so they went down the hill. In the darkness they played like two splendid young things in a young world. Once, running swiftly forward,

Helen tripped George and he fell. He squirmed and shouted. Shaking with laughter, he rolled down the hill. Helen ran after him. For just a moment she stopped in the darkness. There is no way of knowing what woman's thoughts went through her mind but, when the bottom of the hill was reached and she came up to the boy, she took his arm and walked beside him in dignified silence. For some reason they could not have explained they had both got from their silent evening together the thing needed. Man or boy, woman or girl, they had for a moment taken hold of the thing that makes the mature life of men and women in the modern world possible.

Notes:

1. ablaze：光辉明亮的（shining brightly）

2. whinny：轻声地嘶鸣

3. lustily：洪亮地（full of strength）

4. a thing destined like corn to wilt in the sun：注定像玉米一样要在太阳底下枯萎的东西

5. grandstand：（比赛场地的）正面看台

6. The young man was of a pedantic turn of mind：这个年轻人性格迂腐。

7. he would not do for her purpose：他并不适合她。

8. escort：社交陪伴者（a social companion, esp. a man who takes a woman out for the evening）

9. muse：沉思（think deeply, forgetting about the world around one）

10. thoroughfares：大街，大道（a public road or street）

11. surge：涌现（rise and fall actively）

12. like cattle confined in a pen：像被关在牛栏里的牛一样。confine：监禁（shut or keep in a small or enclosed space）; pen：（家畜的）栏，圈,棚

13. buggy：轻型马车（a light carriage pulled by one horse）

14. the loud blare of the horns of the band：乐队喇叭的刺耳的大声吹

奏。blare：刺耳的大声鸣响

15. The medley of songs got on young Willard's nerves：那个组合曲令年轻的 Willard 心烦。get on sb.'s nerves：使人心烦不安或发脾气（make sb. annoyed or bad-tempered）

16. close in about：包围

17. George felt so utterly lonely and dejected：George 感到非常孤独和沮丧。dejected：沮丧的（low in spirits）

18. livery barn：（代客养马、喂马的）代养马房

19. stallion：种马（a male horse）

20. sputter：慌乱地说，语无伦次地说（speak or say in confusion）

21. brag：自夸，吹嘘（boast）

22. vacant lot：空地。lot：（有特定用途的）一块地（an area of land, esp. one for a particular purpose such as for building or parking cars on）

23. protruding from an empty barrel：从一个空桶里突出的

24. distraught：几乎发狂的（very anxious and troubled almost to the point of madness）

25. put on the airs of the city：摆出城里人的样子

26. cosmopolitan：见多识广的（showing wide experience of different people and places）

27. Afire with eagerness：怀着非常热切的心情。afire with：burning with.

28. It has itched and squirmed with life：这个地方人太多,让人很不舒服。squirm：扭曲身体（twist the body about like a worm, esp. from discomfort, shame, or nervousness）

29. make some minute readjustment of the machinery of his life：对他自己人生的这部机器作某种极小的重新调整

30. animalism：动物特性,活力充沛（enjoyment of vigorous health and physical drives）

Questions:

1. Why does George want to see Helen when the moment of sophistication came to him?

2. At the end of the story, what do George and Helen gain from the silent evening together that "makes the mature life of men and women in the modern world possible"?

3. What are the conflicts in the story?

4. Discuss symbolism in the story.

Katherine Anne Porter

(1890-1980)

Katherine Anne Porter (1890—1980) was born in Indian Creek, Texas. She was only two years old when her mother died. She was primarily brought up by her paternal grandmother and received her education in convent schools in the South. At the age of 16 she married. Under the influence of her husband's family, she converted to Catholicism, which would become an important influence on her works. She married 4 times, but remained childless. Before she became a serious fiction writer, she worked as an actress, a singer, a secretary and a society columnist. Between 1920 and 1930, she traveled back and forth between Mexico and New York City. During the 1930s, she spent several years in Europe. Her travels and life in the South, Mexico, Eastern cities, the Rocky Mountain, and Europe provided inspiration for her stories and are reflected in many of the themes expressed in her fiction. Between 1948 and 1958, Porter taught at Stanford University, the University of Michigan and the University of Texas.

Porter's works are mainly concerned with the themes of justice, betrayal, and the unforgiving nature of the human race. In 1930 her first book, *Flowering Judas*, was published. It is such a masterly collection of short stories that it alone virtually assured her place in American literature. Her second book, *Pale Horse, Pale Rider*, is a collection of three short novels. She followed this in 1944 with *The Leaning Tower and Other Stories*. In 1962 Porter published her first and only novel, the allegorical epic *Ship of Fools*, which became an instant success. After 1962, Porter did very little writing, though four years later she won both the Pulitzer Prize and the National Book Award for *The Collected Stories of Katherine Anne Porter* (1965) and was appointed to the American Academy of Arts and Letters.

At the age of 90 Porter died, leaving behind a thin but insightful body of work. As a master of short stories, she has been praised for the technical accomplishments of her stories in matters of style, form, and language. Her works have been compared to that of Faulkner and Hemingway in their stylistic beauty. Her perfect pen and harsh criticism of not only her times, but of human society, made Porter a major voice in twentieth century American literature.

"The Jilting of Granny Weatherall" (1930) is one of Porter's famous short stories. This is a story about a woman who is jilted twice, first by her lover, second by her God. It is an exploration of the human mind as it struggles to come to terms with loss and death. Granny Weatherall, 80 years old, is lying on her deathbed with the doctor, her children and the priest surrounding her. She recalls events throughout her life, from being left at the altar on her wedding day to losing a child, and ponders her own death. The story is not told in strict chronological order, which is quite confusing at first. There is a constant shiftying from the present to the past. Porter employs an important modernist technique, the stream of consciousness, the flow of thoughts and feelings within a character. This technique is especially well-suited to the story because it reveals Grannys alternating confused and clear thoughts during her final moments as she moves from lucid consciousness to confused semiconsciousness. With this technique Porter effectively gives a sense of immediacy to Granny's thoughts, feelings, memories, and judgements. By following Granny's confused, fading memories, the reader can understand her and sympathize with her in a way that could be achieved by no other means.

125

The Jilting[1] of Granny Weatherall

Katherine Anne Porter

She flicked her wrist neatly out of Doctor Harry's pudgy careful fingers[2] and pulled the sheet up to her chin. The brat ought to be in knee breeches[3]. Doctoring[4] around the country with spectacles on his nose! "Get along now, take your schoolbooks and go. There's nothing wrong with me."

Doctor Harry spread a warm paw like a cushion on her forehead where the forked[5] green vein danced and made her eyelids twitch[6]. "Now, now, be a good girl, and we'll have you up in no time."

"That's no way to speak to a woman nearly eighty years old just because she's down. I'd have you respect your elders, young man."

"Well, Missy, excuse me." Doctor Harry patted her cheek. "But I've got to warn you, haven't I? You're a marvel, but you must be careful or you're going to be good and sorry[7]."

"Don't tell me what I'm going to be. I'm on my feet now, morally speaking. It's Cornelia. I had to go to bed to get rid of her."

Her bones felt loose, and floated around in her skin, and Doctor Harry floated like a balloon around the foot of the bed. He floated and pulled down his waistcoat and swung his glasses on a cord. "Well, stay where you are, it certainly can't hurt you."

"Get along and doctor your sick," said Granny Weatherall. "Leave a well woman alone. I'll call for you when I want you... Where were you forty years ago when I pulled through milk leg and double pneumonia[8]? You weren't even born. Don't let Cornelia lead you on," she shouted, because Doctor Harry appeared to float up to the ceiling and out. "I pay

126

my own bills, and I don't throw my money away on nonsense!"

She meant to wave goodbye, but it was too much trouble. Her eyes closed of themselves, it was like a dark curtain drawn around the bed. The pillow rose and floated under her, pleasant as a hammock in a light wind. She listened to the leaves rustling outside the window. No, somebody was swishing[9] newspapers: no, Cornelia and Doctor Harry were whispering together. She leaped broad awake[10], thinking they whispered in her ear.

"She was never like this, *never* like this!" "Well, what can we expect?" "Yes, eighty years old..."

Well, and what if she was? She still had ears. It was like Cornelia to whisper around doors. She always kept things secret in such a public way. She was always being tactful and kind. Cornelia was dutiful; that was the trouble with her. Dutiful and good: "So good and dutiful," said Granny, "that I'd like to spank her." She saw herself spanking Cornelia and making a fine job of it[11].

"What'd you say, Mother?"

Granny felt her face tying up in hard knots.

"Can't a body[12] think, I'd like to know?"

"I thought you might want something."

"I do. I want a lot of things. First off, go away and don't whisper."

She lay and drowsed, hoping in her sleep that the children would keep out and let her rest a minute. It had been a long day. Not that she was tired. It was always pleasant to snatch a minute now and then. There was always so much to be done, let me see: tomorrow.

Tomorrow was far away and there was nothing to trouble about. Things were finished somehow when the time came; thank God there was always a little margin over for peace[13]: then a person could spread out the plan of life and tuck in the edges orderly[14]. It was good to have everything clean and folded away, with the hair brushes and tonic[15] bottles sitting straight on

127

the white embroidered linen; the day started without fuss and the pantry shelves laid out with rows of jelly glasses and brown jugs and white stone-china jars with blue whirligigs and words painted on them[16]: coffee, tea, sugar, ginger, cinnamon[17], allspice[18]; and the bronze clock with the lion on top nicely dusted off. The dust that lion could collect in twenty-four hours! The box in the attic with all those letters tied up, well She'd have to go through that tomorrow. All those letters— George's letters and John's letters and her letters to them both—lying around for the children to find afterwards made her uneasy. Yes, that would be tomorrow's business. No use to let them know how silly she had been once.

While she was rummaging around[19] she found death in her mind and it felt clammy[20] and unfamiliar. She had spent so much time preparing for death there was no need for bringing it up again. Let it take care of itself now. When she was sixty she had felt very old, finished, and went around making farewell trips to see her children and grandchildren! Then she made her will and came down with a long fever. That was all just a notion like a lot of other things, but it was lucky too, for she had once for all got over the idea of dying for a long time. Now she couldn't be worried. She hoped she had better sense now. Her father had lived to be one hundred and two years old and had drunk a noggin of strong hot toddy[21] on his last birthday. He told the reporters it was his daily habit, and he owed his long life to that. He had made quite a scandal and was very pleased about it. She believed she'd just plague Cornelia a little.

"Cornelia! Cornelia!" No footsteps, but a sudden hand on her cheek. "Bless you, where have you been?"

"Here, mother."

"Well, Cornelia, I want a noggin of hot toddy."

"Are you cold, darling?"

"I'm chilly, Cornelia. Lying in bed stops the circulation. I must

128

have told you that a thousand times. "

Well, she could just hear Cornelia telling her husband that Mother was getting childish and they'd have to humor her. The thing that most annoyed her was that Cornelia thought she was deaf, dumb, and blind. Little hasty glances and tiny gestures tossed around her and over her head saying, "don't cross her, let her have her way, she's eighty years old," and sitting there as if she lived in a thin glass cage. Sometimes Granny almost made up her mind to pack up and move back to her own house where nobody could remind her every minute that she was old. Wait, wait, Cornelia, till your own children whisper behind your back!

In her day she had kept a better house and had got more work done. She wasn't too old yet for Lydia to be driving eighty miles for advice when one of the children jumped the track[22], and Jimmy still dropped in and talked things over: "Now, Mammy, you've a good business head, I want to know what you think of this?..." Old Cornelia couldn't change the furniture around without asking. Little things, little things! They had been so sweet when they were little. Granny wished the old days were back again with the children young and everything to be done over[23]. It had been a hard pull, but not too much for her. When she thought of all the food she had cooked, and all the clothes she had cut and sewed, and all the gardens she had made — well, the children showed it. There they were, made out of her, and they couldn't get away from that. Sometimes she wanted to see John again and point to them and say, Well, I didn't do so badly, did I? But that would have to wait. That was for tomorrow. She used to think of him as a man, but now all the children were older than their father, and he would be a child beside her if she saw him now. It seemed strange and there was something wrong in the idea. Why, he couldn't possibly recognize her. She had fenced in a hundred acres once, digging the post holes herself and clamping the wires with just a Negro boy to help. That

129

changed a woman. John would be looking for a young woman with the peaked Spanish comb in her hair and the painted fan. Digging post holes changed a woman. Riding country roads in the winter when women had their babies was another thing: sitting up nights with sick horses and sick Negroes and sick children and hardly ever losing one. John, I hardly ever lost one of them! John would see that in a minute, that would be something he could understand, she wouldn't have to explain anything!

It made her feel like rolling up her sleeves and putting the whole place to rights[24] again. No matter if Cornelia was determined to be everywhere at once, there were a great many things left undone on this place. She would start tomorrow and do them. It was good to be strong enough for everything, even if all you made melted and changed and slipped under your hands, so that by the time you finished you almost forgot what you were working for. What was it I set out to do? She asked herself intently, but she could not remember. A fog rose over the valley, she saw it marching across the creek swallowing the trees and moving up the hill like an army of ghosts. Soon it would be at the near edge of the orchard, and then it was time to go in and light the lamps. Come in, children, don't stay out in the night air.

Lighting the lamps had been beautiful. The children huddled up to her and breathed like little calves waiting at the bars in the twilight[25]. Their eyes followed the match and watched the flame rise and settle in a blue curve, then they moved away from her. The lamp was lit, they didn't have to be scared and hang on to mother any more. Never, never, never more. God, for all my life I thank Thee. Without Thee, my God, I could never have done it. Hail, Mary, full of grace[26].

I want you to pick all the fruit this year and see that nothing is wasted. There's always someone who can use it. Don't let good things rot for want of using. You waste life when you waste good food. Don't let things get lost. It's bitter to lose things. Now, don't let me get to thinking, not when I am tired and taking a little nap before supper...

The pillow rose about her shoulders and pressed against her heart and the memory was being squeezed out of it: oh, push down the pillow, somebody: it would smother her if she tried to hold it. Such a fresh breeze blowing and such a green day with no threats in it. But he had not come, just the same. What does a woman do when she has put on the white veil and set out the white cake for a man and he doesn't come? She tried to remember. No, I swear he never harmed me but in that. He never harmed me but in that... and what if he did? There was the day, the day, but a whirl of dark smoke rose and covered it, crept up and over into the bright field where everything was planted so carefully in orderly rows. That was hell, she knew hell when she saw it. For sixty years she had prayed against remembering him and against losing her soul in the deep pit of hell[27], and now the two things were mingled in one and the thought of him was a smoking cloud from hell that moved and crept in her head when she had just got rid of Doctor Harry and was trying to rest a minute: Wounded vanity, Ellen, said a sharp voice in the top of her mind. Don't let your wounded vanity get the upper hand of you[28]. Plenty of girls get jilted. You were jilted, weren't you? Then stand up to it. Her eyelids wavered and let in streamers of blue-gray light like tissue paper over her eyes. She must get up and pull the shades down or she'd never sleep. She was in bed again and the shades were not down. How could that happen? Better turn over, hide from the light, sleeping in the light gave you nightmares. "Mother, how do you feel now?" and a stinging wetness on her forehead[29]. But I don't like having my face washed in cold water!

Hapsy? George? Lydia? Jimmy? No, Cornelia, and her features were swollen and full of little puddles[30]. "They're coming, darling, they'll all be here soon." Go wash your face, child, you look funny.

131

Instead of obeying, Cornelia knelt down and put her head on the pillow. She seemed to be talking but there was no sound. "Well, are you tongue-tied[31]? Whose birthday is it? Are you going to give a party?"

Cornelia's mouth moved urgently in strange shapes. "Don't do that, you bother me, daughter."

"Oh, no, Mother, Oh, no..."

Nonsense. It was strange about children. They disputed your every word. "No what, Cornelia?"

"Here's Doctor Harry."

"I won't see that boy again. He just left five minutes ago."

"That was this morning, Mother. It's night now. Here's the nurse."

"This is Doctor Harry, Mrs. Weatherall. I never saw you look so young and happy!"

"Ah, I'll never be young again—but I'd be happy if they'd let me be in peace and get rested."

She thought she spoke up loudly, but no one answered. A warm weight on her forehead, a warm bracelet on her wrist, and a breeze went on whispering, trying to tell her something[32]. A shuffle of leaves[33] in the everlasting hand of God. He blew on them and they danced and rattled[34]. "Mother, don't mind, we're going to give you a little hypodermic[35]." "Look here, daughter, how do ants get in this bed? I saw sugar ants yesterday." Did you send for Hapsy too?

It was Hapsy she really wanted. She had to go a long way back through a great many rooms to find Hapsy standing with a baby on her arm. She seemed to herself to be Hapsy also, and the baby on Hapsy's arm was Hapsy and himself and herself, all at once, and there was no surprise in the meeting. Then Hapsy melted from within and turned flimsy as gray gauze[36] and the baby was a gauzy shadow, and Hapsy came up close and said, "I thought you'd never come," and looked at her very searchingly

132

and said, "You haven't changed a bit!" They leaned forward to kiss, when Cornelia began whispering from a long way off, "Oh, is there anything you want to tell me? Is there anything I can do for you?"

Yes, she had changed her mind after sixty years and she would like to see George. I want you to find George. Find him and be sure to tell him I forgot him. I want him to know I had my husband just the same and my children and my house like any other woman. A good house too and a good husband that I loved and fine children out of him. Better than I hoped for even. Tell him I was given back everything he took away and more. Oh, no, oh, God, no, there was something else besides the house and the man and the children. Oh, surely they were not all? What was it? Something not given back. . . Her breath crowded down under her ribs and grew into a monstrous frightening shape with cutting edges; it bored up into her head[37], and the agony was unbelievable: Yes, John, get the doctor now, no more talk, my time has come[38].

When this one was born it should be the last. The last. It should have been born first, for it was the one she had truly wanted. Everything came in good time. Nothing left out, left over. She was strong, in three days she would be as well as ever. Better. A woman needed milk in her to have her full health.

"Mother, do you hear me?"

"I've been telling you—"

"Mother, Father Connolly's here[39]."

"I went to Holy Communion[40] only last week. Tell him I'm not so sinful as all that."

"Father just wants to speak to you."

He could speak as much as he pleased. It was like him to drop in and inquire about her soul as if it were a teething baby[41], and then stay on for a cup of tea and a round of cards and gossip. He always had a funny story of some sort, usually about an Irishman who made his little mistakes and confessed them, and the point lay in some absurd thing he would blurt out in the confessional showing his struggles between native piety and original sin[42]. Granny felt easy about her soul. Cornelia, where are your manners? Give Father Connolly a chair. She had her secret, comfortable understanding with a few favorite saints who cleared a straight road to God for her. All as surely signed and sealed as the papers for the new Forty Acres[43]. Forever... heirs and assigns forever. Since the day the wedding cake was not cut, but thrown out and wasted. The whole bottom dropped out of the world, and there she was blind and sweating with nothing under her feet and the walls falling away. His hand caught her under the breast, she had not fallen, there was the freshly polished floor with the green rug on it, just as before. He had cursed like a sailor's parrot and said, "I'll kill him for you." Don't lay a hand on him, for my sake leave something to God[44]. "Now, Ellen, you must believe what I tell you..."

So there was nothing, nothing to worry about any more, except sometimes in the night one of the children screamed in a nightmare, and they both hustled out shaking[45] and hunting for the matches and calling, "There, wait a minute, here we are!" John, get the doctor now. Hapsy's time has come. But there was Hapsy standing by the bed in a white cap. "Cornelia, tell Hapsy to take off her cap. I can't see her plain."

Her eyes opened very wide and the room stood out like a picture she had seen somewhere. Dark colors with the shadows rising towards the ceiling in long angles. The tall black dresser gleamed with nothing on it but John's picture, enlarged from a little one, with John's eyes very black when they should have been blue. You never saw him, so how do you know how he looked? But the man insisted the copy was perfect, it was very rich and handsome. For a picture, yes, but it's not my husband. The table by the bed had a linen cover and a candle and a crucifix[46]. The light

134

was blue from Cornelia's silk lampshades. No sort of light at all, just frippery[47]. You had to live forty years with kerosene lamps to appreciate honest electricity. She felt very strong and she saw Doctor Harry with a rosy nimbus[48] around him.

"You look like a saint, Doctor Harry, and I vow that's as near as you'll ever come to it. "

"She's saying something. "

"I heard you, Cornelia. What's all this carrying-on[49]?"

"Father Connolly's saying —"

Cornelia's voice staggered and bumped like a cart in a bad road. It rounded corners and turned back again and arrived nowhere. Granny stepped up in the cart very lightly and reached for the reins, but a man sat beside her and she knew him by his hands, driving the cart. She did not look in his face, for she knew without seeing, but looked instead down the road where the trees leaned over and bowed to each other and a thousand birds were singing a Mass[50]. She felt like singing too, but she put her hand in the bosom of her dress and pulled out a rosary[51], and Father Connolly murmured Latin in a very solemn voice and tickled her feet[52]. My God, will you stop that nonsense? I'm a married woman. What if he did run away and leave me to face the priest by myself? I found another a whole world better[53]. I wouldn't have exchanged my husband for anybody except St. Michael[54] himself, and you may tell him that for me with a thank you in the bargain[55].

Light flashed on her closed eyelids, and a deep roaring shook her. Cornelia, is that lightning? I hear thunder. There's going to be a storm. Close all the windows. Call the children in... "Mother, here we are, all of us. " "Is that you, Hapsy?" "Oh, no, I'm Lydia. We drove as fast as we could. " Their faces drifted above her, drifted away. The rosary fell out of her hands and Lydia put it back. Jimmy tried to help, their hands fumbled together, and Granny closed two fingers around Jimmy's thumb. Beads wouldn't do it, it must be something alive. She was so amazed her thoughts ran round and round. So, my dear Lord, this is my death and I wasn't even thinking about it. My children have come to see me die. But I can't, it's not time. Oh, I always hated surprises. I wanted to give Cornelia the amethyst set[56]—Cornelia, you're to have the amethyst set, but Hapsy's to wear it when she wants, and, Doctor Harry, do shut up. Nobody sent for you. Oh, my dear Lord, do wait a minute. I meant to do something about the Forty Acres, Jimmy doesn't need it and Lydia will later on, with that worthless husband of hers. I meant to finish the altar cloth and send six bottles of wine to Sister Borgia for her dyspepsia[57]. I want to send six bottles of wine to Sister Borgia, Father Connolly, now don't let me forget.

Cornelia's voice made short turns and tilted over and crashed. "Oh, Mother, oh, Mother, oh, Mother..."

"I'm not going, Cornelia. I'm taken by surprise. I can't go."

You'll see Hapsy again. What about her? "I thought you'd never come." Granny made a long journey outward, looking for Hapsy. What if I don't find her? What then? Her heart sank down and down, there was no bottom to death, she couldn't come to the end of it. The blue light from Cornelia's lampshade drew into a tiny point in the center of her brain, it flickered and winked like an eye, quietly it fluttered and dwindled. Granny lay curled down within herself, amazed and watchful, staring at the point of light that was herself; her body was now only a deeper mass of shadow in an endless darkness and this darkness would curl around the light and swallow it up. God, give me a sign!

For the second time there was no sign[58]. Again no bridegroom[59] and the priest in the house. She could not remember any other sorrow because this grief wiped them all away. Oh, no, there's nothing more cruel than this—I'll never forgive it. She stretched herself with a deep breath and blew out the light[60].

Notes:

1. jilt: unexpectedly refuse to marry (someone) after having promised to do so

2. She flicked her wrist neatly out of Doctor Harry's pudgy careful fingers: 她利落地把 Doctor Harry 小心握住自己手腕的短胖手指拂开。 pudgy: short and fat

3. The brat ought to be in knee breeches: 这小子应该穿上短腿马裤。 brat: 小坏蛋,淘气鬼(a child, esp. a bad-mannered one)

4. doctor: 行医;诊治(practice medicine; give medical treatment to)

5. forked: shaped like a fork

6. twitch: 颤动

7. good and sorry: very sorry

8. when I pulled through milk leg and double pneumonia: 当我战胜产后乳色腿病和双侧肺炎活下来的时候。pull through: 渡过逆境、危机等(come safely through an illness or a crisis, etc.);milk leg: 乳色腿,指妇女产后腿部出现的疼痛浮肿,由股静脉充血和发炎引起(a painful swelling of the leg occurring to a woman usually as a result of infection during childbirth)

9. swish: 带着嗖嗖声挥动

10. She leaped broad awake: 她猛然坐起身来,完全醒了。

11. She saw herself spanking Cornelia and making a fine job of it: 她看见自己打 Cornelia 的屁股,狠狠地打。make a fine job of sth.: 把某事做得好,处理得好(do sth. well)

12. a body: a person, usually a woman

13. there was always a little margin over for peace: 总是有点时间享受安宁

137

14. tuck in the edges orderly：把边往里塞得整整齐齐。这是一种比喻，意思是完善人生计划

15. tonic：奎宁苏打水（soda water with quinine）

16. the pantry shelves laid out with rows of jelly glasses and brown jugs and white stone-china jars with blue whirligigs and words painted on them：餐具架上摆着一排排的果酱玻璃杯、棕色壶和白色硬质陶罐，上面画着蓝色的陀螺并写着这些字。

17. cinnamon：桂皮香料（the sweet-smelling bark of a tropical Asian tree, used for giving a special taste to food）

18. allspice：多香果粉（a powder made from the berries of a tropical American tree, used for giving a special taste to food）

19. rummage around：到处翻寻（turn things over and look into all the corners while trying to find something）

20. clammy：湿冷的（unpleasantly sticky, slightly wet, and usu. cold）

21. a noggin of strong hot toddy：一小杯热的烈性甜酒。noggin：一小杯（a small mug）；toddy：热甜酒（a sweetened mixture of whisky and hot water）

22. jump the track：出轨，走入歧途

23. everything to be done over：everything to be done again

24. putting the whole place to rights：把整个屋子收拾好

25. like little calves waiting at the bars in the twilight：像黄昏时在牛栏边等待的小牛

26. Hail, Mary, full of grace：（天主教徒在祈祷开始时说）万福玛利亚，宽厚仁慈的圣母！

27. she had prayed against remembering him and against losing her soul in the deep pit of hell：她祈祷不要再想他，不要让自己的灵魂落在地狱的深渊。

28. Don't let your wounded vanity get the upper hand of you：不要让你受伤的虚荣心占了上风。

29. a stinging wetness on her forehead：她感觉前额上有什么东西湿湿的，(像虫子似的)叮了她一下。

30. her features were swollen and full of little puddles：她的脸都肿了，布满一个个的小水坑。

31. tongue-tied：舌头打结的（unable to speak, as from shyness, embarrassment, or surprise）

32. A warm weight on her forehead, ... went on whispering, trying to tell her something：有人用温暖的手按着她的额头，握着她的手腕，并轻声细语地跟她在讲什么。weight, bracelet, breeze 都是比喻。

33. A shuffle of leaves：叶子的晃动

34. rattle：摇得格格响

35. hypodermic：皮下注射

36. turned flimsy as gray gauze：变成像灰色薄纱那样轻而薄。flimsy：（of material）light and thin

37. Her breath crowded down under her ribs ... with cutting edges; it bored up into her head：她的呼吸往下挤，被挤到肋骨下面，变成了一个怪异可怕、边缘锋利的形状；它又向上钻入她的脑袋。

38. my time has come：我要生了。（Granny Weatherall 从被 George 抛弃的痛苦联想到后来分娩时的痛苦。）

39. Father Connolly's here：Connolly 神父在这里。（天主教信徒生病临终前，神父要为他们祝福，或由病人向神父忏悔，祈求上帝的宽恕。）

40. Holy Communion：圣餐仪式（the Christian ceremony in which bread and wine are shared as a sign of Christ's body and blood to remember him）

41. a teething baby：出乳牙的婴儿

42. the point lay in some absurd thing he would ... between native piety and original sin：关键点在于他在忏悔室冲口说出的某件荒唐事，展示了他与生俱来的虔诚和原罪间的争斗。original sin：人类始祖

亚当违背上帝(即天主教所称的天主)的命令,造成人类与上帝隔离,这就是"原罪"。"原罪"使人失去人生终向(即终点的方向,在天主教看来,人生的终向不是死亡,而是天国,是上帝),人类无法自身纠正,必须仰赖上帝主动的救赎,这也就是耶稣为何要降生赎世的原因。

43. Forty Acres：Granny Weatherall 新购买的农场

44. Don't lay a hand on him, for my sake leave something to God：不要动他,为了我,这事留给上帝去对付吧(指惩罚 George)。

45. they both hustled out shaking：他们俩发着抖赶紧起床出来。hustle：急速行进(move hurriedly)

46. crucifix：十字架

47. frippery：俗气无用的装饰(foolish, unnecessary, and useless decoration)

48. nimbus：光环,(神像头上的)光轮

49. carrying-on：foolish behavior

50. Mass：弥撒曲

51. rosary：(念玫瑰经用的)一串念珠

52. tickled her feet：Connolly 神父正在主持罗马天主教教会的最后仪式

53. I found another a whole world better：我找到一个更好的人。a whole world 是 better 的修饰语

54. St. Michael：《圣经》中的天使长,曾打败魔鬼撒旦,是天主教徒崇拜的一位圣人。在宗教绘画中他是个年轻、英俊的天使长。

55. in the bargain：in addition

56. the amethyst set：一套紫色水晶首饰

57. dyspepsia：消化不良

58. sign：sign Granny has been waiting for from Jesus Christ

59. bridegroom：the first bridegroom should be George who does not appear at the altar; this bridegroom refers to Jesus Christ who does not come to

get her.

60. blew out the light: died

Questions:

1. What are the names of Granny's children? How does she feel about Cornelia? Does Hapsy really exist?

2. In the story figurative language is often used to convey Granny's state of mind. For example, to Granny "Doctor Harry floated like a balloon around the foot of the bed." Find three other examples of figurative language used to convey a state of mind.

3. Why is the jilting so important to Granny? How is the jilting related to the last paragraph of the story?

4. Is Granny well prepared for death? Explain.

5. What are the outstanding traits of Granny Weatherall? Identify the passages that illustrate these traits.

6. What does Granny's name "Weatherall" symbolize? How is it a suitable name for her?

141

William Faulkner

(1897-1962)

William Faulkner (1897—1962) was a Nobel Prize-winning novelist, and a short story writer. In the realm of American literature, Faulkner is regarded as a giant and acclaimed throughout the world as one of the twentieth century's greatest writers, one who transformed his "postage stamp" of native soil into an apocryphal setting in which he explored, articulated, and challenged "the old verities and truths of the heart". He was a daring formal experimentalist. His works are noted for a master craftsmanship in employing the techniques of stream of consciounsness and multiple points of view.

Faulkner was born in New Albany, Mississippi, in a well-respected but no longer wealthy family. While he was still a child, the family settled in Oxford in north-central Mississippi. Faulkner lived most of his life in the town, which became the model for his fictional Jefferson, the seat of his fictional Yoknapatawpha county. After the fifth grade, he attended school only occassionaly and never graduated from any university. But he read widely from *The Bible* to the modern literary works as of the French symbolist poets, James Joyce and T. S. Eliot. In 1926, with the help of Sherwood Anderson, Faulkner published his first novel *Soldier's Pay*.

Faulkner wrote altogether 19 novels and 7 collections of short stories, most of which are set in Yoknapatawpha County. Thus his works are often called the Yoknaptawpha saga. Among his best novels are *The Sound and the Fury* (1929), *As I Lay Dying* (1930), *Light in August* (1932),

Absalom, Absalom! (1936), and *Go Down, Moses* (1942). In 1949 Faulkner was awarded the Nobel Prize for Literature for "his powerful and artistically unique contribution to the modern American novel". He won Pulitzer Prize in 1955 and 1963 respectively. He also won two National Book Awards, one in 1951 and the other in 1955.

Faulkner is considered as one of the most important "Southern writers". Most of his works deal with the subject of the decline of the South and frequently reflect the chaotic history of the South while developing perceptive explorations of human character. Faulkner paints a picture of a culture in ruins, populated by grotesques and living ghosts who refuse to recognize their alienation and defeat. His use of bizarre, grotesque, and violent imagery, melodrama, and sensationalism to depict the corruption and decay of the region make him one of the earliest practitioners of the subgenre known as Southern Gothic literature. Faulkner's works that are especially well known for their Gothic qualities include the novels *Sanctuary* (1931), *Light in August*, and *Absalom, Absalom!*, *As I Lay Dying*, and the short story "A Rose for Emily" (1930). They combine burlesque and dark humor with realism and elements of the horrific and macabre to caricature a society that is unable to break from its past and look to the future.

Faulkner was also a prolific writer of short stories. His most frequently anthologized stories include "A Rose for Emily", "Red Leaves" (1930), "That Evening Sun" (1931), "Dry September" (1931), "Barn Burning" (1939), and "The Bear" (1942). "A Rose for Emily" takes place in Faulkner's fictional city, Jefferson. It is about the conflict between the change of time and the inability of people to adjust to change. It recounts the tragic story of an eccentric lady, Emily Grierson, of an old aristocratic Southern family which has fallen into decay. The Griersons regard themselves as very important and superior to the townspeople. Emily's father dominates her life and chases away her potential suitors because none of them are "good enough" for his daughter. His death leaves

Emily a tragic, penniless spinster. Later she falls in love with Homer
Barron, a Yankee construction foreman. But she kills Barron with arsenic.
It is not until the very end of the story that the reader actually understands
what she has done to her lover.

A Rose for Emily

William Faulkner

I

When Miss Emily Grierson died, our whole town went to her funeral:
the men through a sort of respectful affection for a fallen monument, the
women mostly out of curiosity to see the inside of her house, which no one
save an old man-servant—a combined gardener and cook—had seen in at
least ten years.

It was a big, squarish frame house[1] that had once been white,
decorated with cupolas and spires and scrolled balconies in the heavily
lightsome style of the seventies[2], set on what had once been our most select
street. But garages and cotton gins had encroached and obliterated even the
august names of that neighborhood[3]; only Miss Emily's house was left,
lifting its stubborn and coquettish decay[4] above the cotton wagons and the
gasoline pumps—an eyesore among eyesores[5]. And now Miss Emily had
gone to join the representatives of those august names where they lay in the
cedar-bemused cemetery among the ranked and anonymous graves of Union
and Confederate soldiers[6] who fell at the battle of Jefferson.

Alive, Miss Emily had been a tradition, a duty, and a care; a sort of
hereditary obligation upon the town, dating from that day in 1894 when
Colonel Sartoris, the mayor—he who fathered the edict[7] that no Negro
woman should appear on the streets without an apron—remitted her taxes,

144

the dispensation[8] dating from the death of her father on into perpetuity[9]. Not that Miss Emily would have accepted charity. Colonel Sartoris invented an involved tale to the effect that[10] Miss Emily's father had loaned money to the town, which the town, as a matter of business, preferred this way of repaying. Only a man of Colonel Sartoris' generation and thought could have invented it, and only a woman could have believed it.

When the next generation, with its more modern ideas, became mayors and aldermen[11], this arrangement created some little dissatisfaction. On the first of the year they mailed her a tax notice. February came, and there was no reply. They wrote her a formal letter, asking her to call at the sheriff's office at her convenience[12]. A week later the mayor wrote her himself, offering to call or to send his car for her, and received in reply a note on paper of an archaic shape, in a thin, flowing calligraphy in faded ink, to the effect that she no longer went out at all. The tax notice was also enclosed, without comment.

They called a special meeting of the Board of Aldermen. A deputation waited upon her, knocked at the door through which no visitor had passed since she ceased giving china-painting lessons eight or ten years earlier. They were admitted by the old Negro into a dim hall from which a stairway mounted into still more shadow. It smelled of dust and disuse—a close, dank smell[13]. The Negro led them into the parlor. It was furnished in heavy, leather-covered furniture. When the Negro opened the blinds of one window, they could see that the leather was cracked; and when they sat down, a faint dust rose sluggishly[14] about their thighs, spinning with slow motes in the single sun-ray[15]. On a tarnished gilt easel[16] before the fireplace stood a crayon portrait of Miss Emily's father.

They rose when she entered—a small, fat woman in black, with a thin gold chain descending to her waist and vanishing into her belt, leaning on an ebony cane with a tarnished gold head. Her skeleton was small and

145

spare[17]; perhaps that was why what would have been merely plumpness in another was obesity[18] in her. She looked bloated[19], like a body long submerged in motionless water, and of that pallid hue[20]. Her eyes, lost in the fatty ridges of her face, looked like two small pieces of coal pressed into a lump of dough[21] as they moved from one face to another while the visitors stated their errand.

She did not ask them to sit. She just stood in the door and listened quietly until the spokesman came to a stumbling halt. Then they could hear the invisible watch ticking at the end of the gold chain.

Her voice was dry and cold. "I have no taxes in Jefferson. Colonel Sartoris explained it to me. Perhaps one of you can gain access to the city records and satisfy yourselves. "

"But we have. We are the city authorities, Miss Emily. Didn't you get a notice from the sheriff, signed by him?"

"I received a paper, yes, " Miss Emily said. "Perhaps he considers himself the sheriff . . . I have no taxes in Jefferson. "

"But there is nothing on the books to show that, you see. We must go by the—"

"See Colonel Sartoris. I have no taxes in Jefferson. "

"But, Miss Emily—"

"See Colonel Sartoris. " (Colonel Sartoris had been dead almost ten years.) "I have no taxes in Jefferson. Tobe! " The Negro appeared. "Show these gentlemen out. "

II

So she vanquished them, horse and foot[22], just as she had vanquished their fathers thirty years before about the smell.

That was two years after her father's death and a short time after her sweetheart—the one we believed would marry her—had deserted her. After her father's death she went out very little; after her sweetheart went away,

146

people hardly saw her at all. A few of the ladies had the temerity[23] to call, but were not received, and the only sign of life about the place was the Negro man—a young man then—going in and out with a market basket.

"Just as if a man—any man—could keep a kitchen properly," the ladies said; so they were not surprised when the smell developed. It was another link between the gross, teeming world and the high and mighty Griersons[24].

A neighbor, a woman, complained to the mayor, Judge Stevens, eighty years old.

"But what will you have me do about it, madam?" he said.

"Why, send her word to stop it," the woman said. "Isn't there a law?"

"I'm sure that won't be necessary," Judge Stevens said. "It's probably just a snake or a rat that nigger of hers killed in the yard. I'll speak to him about it."

The next day he received two more complaints, one from a man who came in diffident deprecation[25]. "We really must do something about it, Judge. I'd be the last one in the world to bother Miss Emily, but we've got to do something." That night the Board of Aldermen met—three graybeards[26] and one younger man, a member of the rising generation.

"It's simple enough," he said. "Send her word to have her place cleaned up. Give her a certain time to do it in, and if she don't ..."

"Dammit, sir," Judge Stevens said, "will you accuse a lady to her face of smelling bad?"

So the next night, after midnight, four men crossed Miss Emily's lawn and slunk about the house like burglars, sniffing along the base of the brickwork and at the cellar openings while one of them performed a regular sowing motion with his hand out of a sack slung from his shoulder. They broke open the cellar door and sprinkled lime there, and in all the

147

outbuildings. As they recrossed the lawn, a window that had been dark was lighted and Miss Emily sat in it, the light behind her, and her upright torso[27] motionless as that of an idol. They crept quietly across the lawn and into the shadow of the locusts[28] that lined the street. After a week or two the smell went away.

That was when people had begun to feel really sorry for her. People in our town, remembering how old lady Wyatt, her great-aunt, had gone completely crazy at last, believed that the Griersons held themselves a little too high for what they really were[29]. None of the young men were quite good enough for Miss Emily and such[30]. We had long thought of them as a tableau[31], Miss Emily a slender figure in white in the background, her father a spraddled silhouette[32] in the foreground, his back to her and clutching a horsewhip, the two of them framed by the back-flung front door[33]. So when she got to be thirty and was still single, we were not pleased exactly, but vindicated[34]; even with insanity in the family she wouldn't have turned down all of her chances if they had really materialized[35].

When her father died, it got about that[36] the house was all that was left to her; and in a way, people were glad. At last they could pity Miss Emily. Being left alone, and a pauper[37], she had become humanized. Now she too would know the old thrill and the old despair of a penny more or less.

The day after his death all the ladies prepared to call at the house and offer condolence and aid, as is our custom. Miss Emily met them at the door, dressed as usual and with no trace of grief on her face. She told them that her father was not dead. She did that for three days, with the ministers calling on her, and the doctors, trying to persuade her to let them dispose of the body. Just as they were about to resort to[38] law and force, she broke down, and they buried her father quickly.

We did not say she was crazy then. We believed she had to do that. We remembered all the young men her father had driven away, and we knew that with nothing left, she would have to cling to that which had robbed her[39], as people will.

Ⅲ

She was sick for a long time. When we saw her again, her hair was cut short, making her look like a girl, with a vague resemblance to those angels in colored church windows—sort of tragic and serene.

The town had just let the contracts[40] for paving the sidewalks, and in the summer after her father's death they began the work. The construction company came with niggers[41] and mules and machinery, and a foreman named Homer Barron, a Yankee—a big, dark, ready[42] man, with a big voice and eyes lighter than his face. The little boys would follow in groups to hear him cuss[43] the niggers, and the niggers singing in time to the rise and fall of picks. Pretty soon he knew everybody in town. Whenever you heard a lot of laughing anywhere about the square, Homer Barron would be in the center of the group. Presently we began to see him and Miss Emily on Sunday afternoons driving in the yellow-wheeled buggy and the matched team of bays from the livery stable[44].

At first we were glad that Miss Emily would have an interest, because the ladies all said, "Of course a Grierson would not think seriously of a Northerner, a day laborer." But there were still others, older people, who said that even grief could not cause a real lady to forget *noblesse oblige*[45]— without calling it *noblesse oblige*. They just said, "Poor Emily. Her kinsfolk should come to her." She had some kin in Alabama; but years ago her father had fallen out[46] with them over the estate of old lady Wyatt, the crazy woman, and there was no communication between the two families. They had not even been represented at the funeral.

And as soon as the old people said, "Poor Emily," the whispering began. "Do you suppose it's really so?" they said to one another. "Of course it is. What else could ..." This behind their hands[47]; rustling of craned silk and satin behind jalousies[48] closed upon the sun of Sunday afternoon as the thin, swift clop-clop-clop of the matched team passed: "Poor Emily."

She carried her head high enough—even when we believed that she was fallen. It was as if she demanded more than ever the recognition of her dignity as the last Grierson; as if it had wanted that touch of earthiness to reaffirm her imperviousness[49]. Like when she bought the rat poison, the arsenic[50]. That was over a year after they had begun to say "Poor Emily", and while the two female cousins were visiting her.

"I want some poison," she said to the druggist. She was over thirty then, still a slight woman, though thinner than usual, with cold, haughty black eyes in a face the flesh of which was strained across the temples and about the eyesockets as you imagine a lighthouse-keeper's face ought to look[51]. "I want some poison," she said.

"Yes, Miss Emily. What kind? For rats and such? I'd recom—"

"I want the best you have. I don't care what kind."

The druggist named several. "They'll kill anything up to an elephant. But what you want is—"

"Arsenic," Miss Emily said. "Is that a good one?"

"Is ... arsenic? Yes, ma'am. But what you want—"

"I want arsenic."

The druggist looked down at her. She looked back at him, erect, her face like a strained flag. "Why, of course," the druggist said. "If that's what you want. But the law requires you to tell what you are going to use it for."

Miss Emily just stared at him, her head tilted back in order to look him eye for eye, until he looked away and went and got the arsenic and wrapped it up. The Negro delivery boy brought her the package; the druggist didn't come back. When she opened the package at home there was written on the box, under the skull and bones: "For rats."

IV

So the next day we all said, "She will kill herself"; and we said it would be the best thing. When she had first begun to be seen with Homer Barron, we had said, "She will marry him." Then we said, "She will persuade him yet," because Homer himself had remarked—he liked men, and it was known that he drank with the younger men in the Elks' Club— that he was not a marrying man. Later we said, "Poor Emily" behind the jalousies as they passed on Sunday afternoon in the glittering buggy, Miss Emily with her head high and Homer Barron with his hat cocked and a cigar in his teeth, reins and whip in a yellow glove.

Then some of the ladies began to say that it was a disgrace to the town and a bad example to the young people. The men did not want to interfere, but at last the ladies forced the Baptist minister—Miss Emily's people were Episcopal[52]— to call upon her. He would never divulge[53] what happened during that interview, but he refused to go back again. The next Sunday they again drove about the streets, and the following day the minister's wife wrote to Miss Emily's relations in Alabama.

So she had blood-kin under her roof again and we sat back to watch developments. At first nothing happened. Then we were sure that they were to be married. We learned that Miss Emily had been to the jeweler's and ordered a man's toilet set in silver, with the letters H. B. on each piece. Two days later we learned that she had bought a complete outfit of men's clothing, including a nightshirt, and we said, "They are married." We were really glad. We were glad because the two female cousins were even more Grierson than Miss Emily had ever been.

So we were not surprised when Homer Barron—the streets had been

151

finished some time since—was gone. We were a little disappointed that there was not a public blowing-off[54], but we believed that he had gone on to prepare for Miss Emily's coming, or to give her a chance to get rid of the cousins. (By that time it was a cabal[55], and we were all Miss Emily's allies to help circumvent[56] the cousins.) Sure enough, after another week they departed. And, as we had expected all along, within three days Homer Barron was back in town. A neighbor saw the Negro man admit him at the kitchen door at dusk one evening.

And that was the last we saw of Homer Barron. And of Miss Emily for some time. The Negro man went in and out with the market basket, but the front door remained closed. Now and then we would see her at a window for a moment, as the men did that night when they sprinkled the lime, but for almost six months she did not appear on the streets. Then we knew that this was to be expected too; as if that quality of her father which had thwarted[57] her woman's life so many times had been too virulent[58] and too furious to die.

When we next saw Miss Emily, she had grown fat and her hair was turning gray. During the next few years it grew grayer and grayer until it attained an even pepper-and-salt iron-gray, when it ceased turning. Up to the day of her death at seventy-four it was still that vigorous iron-gray, like the hair of an active man.

From that time on her front door remained closed, save for a period of six or seven years, when she was about forty, during which she gave lessons in china-painting. She fitted up a studio in one of the downstairs rooms, where the daughters and granddaughters of Colonel Sartoris' contemporaries were sent to her with the same regularity and in the same spirit that they were sent to church on Sundays with a twenty-five-cent piece for the collection plate[59]. Meanwhile her taxes had been remitted.

Then the newer generation became the backbone and the spirit of the town, and the painting pupils grew up and fell away and did not send their children to her with boxes of color and tedious brushes and pictures cut from the ladies' magazines. The front door closed upon the last one and remained closed for good[60]. When the town got free postal delivery, Miss Emily alone refused to let them fasten the metal numbers above her door and attach a mailbox to it. She would not listen to them.

Daily, monthly, yearly we watched the Negro grow grayer and more stooped, going in and out with the market basket. Each December we sent her a tax notice, which would be returned by the post office a week later, unclaimed. Now and then we would see her in one of the downstairs windows—she had evidently shut up the top floor of the house—like the carven torso of an idol in a niche[61], looking or not looking at us, we could never tell which. Thus she passed from generation to generation—dear, inescapable, impervious, tranquil, and perverse.

And so she died. Fell ill in the house filled with dust and shadows, with only a doddering[62] Negro man to wait on her. We did not even know she was sick; we had long since given up trying to get any information from the Negro

He talked to no one, probably not even to her, for his voice had grown harsh and rusty, as if from disuse.

She died in one of the downstairs rooms, in a heavy walnut bed with a curtain, her gray head propped on a pillow yellow and moldy with age and lack of sunlight.

V

The Negro met the first of the ladies at the front door and let them in, with their hushed, sibilant[63] voices and their quick, curious glances, and then he disappeared. He walked right through the house and out the back and was not seen again.

The two female cousins came at once. They held the funeral on the

153

second day, with the town coming to look at Miss Emily beneath a mass of bought flowers, with the crayon face of her father musing profoundly above the bier[64] and the ladies sibilant and macabre[65]; and the very old men — some in their brushed Confederate uniforms—on the porch and the lawn, talking of Miss Emily as if she had been a contemporary of theirs, believing that they had danced with her and courted her perhaps, confusing time with its mathematical progression, as the old do, to whom all the past is not a diminishing road but, instead, a huge meadow which no winter ever quite touches, divided from them now by the narrow bottle-neck of the most recent decade of years.

Already we knew that there was one room in that region above stairs which no one had seen in forty years, and which would have to be forced. They waited until Miss Emily was decently in the ground before they opened it.

The violence of breaking down the door seemed to fill this room with pervading dust. A thin, acrid pall[66] as of the tomb seemed to lie everywhere upon this room decked[67] and furnished as for a bridal: upon the valance curtains[68] of faded rose color, upon the rose-shaded lights, upon the dressing table, upon the delicate array of crystal and the man's toilet things backed with tarnished silver, silver so tarnished that the monogram[69] was obscured. Among them lay a collar and tie, as if they had just been removed, which, lifted, left upon the surface a pale crescent in the dust. Upon a chair hung the suit, carefully folded; beneath it the two mute shoes and the discarded socks.

The man himself lay in the bed.

For a long while we just stood there, looking down at the profound and fleshless grin. The body had apparently once lain in the attitude of an embrace, but now the long sleep that outlasts love, that conquers even the grimace[70] of love, had cuckolded[71] him. What was left of him, rotted beneath what was left of the nightshirt, had become inextricable[72] from the bed in which he lay; and upon him and upon the pillow beside him lay that even coating of the patient and biding dust.

Then we noticed that in the second pillow was the indentation[73] of a head. One of us lifted something from it, and leaning forward, that faint and invisible dust dry and acrid in the nostrils, we saw a long strand of iron-gray hair.

Notes:

1. squarish frame house：方形木板房

2. decorated with cupolas and spires and scrolled balconies in the heavily lightsome style of the seventies：还装点着圆形屋顶、尖塔和涡形花纹的阳台,具有 19 世纪 70 年代那种既沉重又轻盈的风格

3. But garages and cotton gins had encroached and obliterated even the august names of that neighborhood：可是汽车间和轧棉机逐渐侵占、湮没了甚至是那一带高贵的名字。cotton gins：轧棉机

4. coquettish decay：卖弄风情的破败

5. an eyesore among eyesores：难看极了（the most unpleasant thing to look at）

6. they lay in the cedar-bemused cemetery among the ranked and anonymous graves of Union and Confederate soldiers：他们躺在沉思的雪松环绕的墓园中,那里尽是一排排南北战争时期的南方和北方的无名军人墓。bemused：沉思的（meditative）; Union：the United States of America,即北方联邦; Confederate：the Confederate States of America,即南部邦联,其中 11 个州曾宣布退出联邦

7. fathered the edict：制定了法规

8. dispensation：豁免,特许（an exemption or release from an obligation or rule, granted by or as if by an authority）

9. perpetuity：永远（eternity）

10. Colonel Sartoris invented an involved tale to the effect that：沙多里斯上校编造了一个复杂的故事，大意是……to the effect that：大意是，意思是（with a purport or meaning that）。

11. aldermen：市参议员

12. asking her to call at the sheriff's office at her convenience：请她在方便的时候到司法长官办公室去一趟

13. a close, dank smell：一种不透气又阴冷潮湿的气味。close：不透气的（stuffy）；dank：阴冷潮湿的（unpleasant wet and usually cold）

14. sluggishly：slowly

15. spinning with slow motes in the single sun-ray：尘粒在那一缕阳光中缓缓旋转。mote：微尘，微粒（a small particle）

16. a tarnished gilt easel：失去金色光泽的镀金画架

17. Her skeleton was small and spare：她的骨架细小。spare：rather thin

18. obesity：the state of being excessively fat

19. bloated：发胀的，臃肿的（unpleasantly swollen）

20. of that pallid hue：肤色苍白。pallid：（of the face, skin, etc.）unusually or unhealthy pale.

21. a lump of dough：一团生面

22. she vanquished them, horse and foot：她把他们全部打败了。vanquish：defeat；horse and foot：全体（one and all）

23. temerity：鲁莽，冒失（foolish or rash boldness）

24. between the gross, teeming world and the high and mighty Griersons：芸芸众生的世界与高贵有势的格里尔生家之间。teeming：full of creatures

25. in diffident deprecation：以委婉的语气表达不满的意见。diffident：害羞的，含蓄的（reserved）；deprecation：不赞成，反对（expressing disapproval）

26. graybeard：an old men

27. torso：躯干（the trunk of human body）

28. locust：洋槐树

29. the Griersons held themselves a little too high for what they really were：格里尔生一家人自视过高,并不了解自己的真实情况。

30. and such：诸如此类

31. We had long thought of them as a tableau：长久以来,我们把他们看成一幅画中的人物。tableau：舞台造型(a representation of a scene, painting, sculpture, etc. by a person or group silent and motionless)

32. a spraddled silhouette：叉开双腿站立的侧影

33. the two of them framed by the back-flung front door：一扇向后开的前门作为相框,嵌住了他们俩的身影。

34. vindicate：证明……是真实的(justify, comfirm)

35. materialize：appear.

36. it got about that . . .：人们就传开了……it 是形式主语,that-从句是真正的主语;get about：(消息、谣言)传开来(spread)

37. pauper：a very poor person

38. resort to：诉诸,采取(turn to sth. for help)

39. she would have to cling to that which had robbed her：她将紧紧抓住那个曾经抢夺她的人。

40. let the contracts：签订合同

41. nigger：a black person

42. ready：敏捷的(quick, intelligent)

43. cuss：curse

44. driving in the yellow-wheeled buggy and the matched team of bays from the livery stable：驾驶着黄轮轻便马车出游,黄轮车套上从马房中挑出的红棕色马,十分相称。buggy：轻型马车;bay:红棕色的马;livery stable：代养马房

45. *noblesse oblige*：贵人举止(the obligation of honorable, generous, and responsible behavior associated with high rank or birth)

46. fall out：quarrel

47. behind their hands：用手捂住嘴轻轻地说

48. rustling of craned silk and satin behind jalousies：百叶窗后面人们伸长脖子往外看时绸缎发出窸窣声。jalousie：百叶窗（a blind）

49. as if it had wanted that touch of earthiness to reaffirm her imperviousness：好像她的尊严还需要同世俗的接触来重新肯定她那不受任何影响的性格。imperviousness：不受影响（the quality of not being easily influenced or changed）

50. arsenic：砒霜

51. the flesh of which was strained across the temples and about the eyesockets as you imagine a lighthouse-keeper's face ought to look：脸上的肌肉在两边的太阳穴和眼窝处绷得很紧，那副面部表情是你想象中的灯塔守望人所应有的。

52. Baptist minister — Miss Emily's people were Episcopal：浸礼会牧师——艾米丽小姐的亲属是圣公会的。

53. divulge：泄露（disclose）

54. blowing-off：（以高声或长谈等）发泄（感情等）

55. cabal：阴谋小集团

56. circumvent：智取（outwit）

57. thwart：阻挠（prevent from happening or succeeding）

58. virulent：致命的（very powerful, quick-acting, and dangerous to life or health）

59. the collection plate：教堂里做礼拜时募捐用的盘子（the plate passed around among people attending the church service for the collection of money donated）

60. for good：for ever

61. like the carven torso of an idol in a niche：像神龛中的一个偶像的雕塑躯干

62. doddering：老态龙钟的（shaky, feeble from old age）

63. sibilant：作嘶嘶声的

64. bier：棺材

65. the ladies sibilant and macabre：妇女们唧唧喳喳地谈论着死亡。
    macabre：可怕的（causing fear, dislike, and shock, esp. because connected with death and the dead）

66. acrid pall：阴惨惨的氛围

67. deck：装饰（decorate, esp. with colorful or pretty things）

68. the valance curtains：床沿挂饰（short curtains around the frame of a bedstead）

69. monogram：姓名字母图案（a sign of identity composed of the combined initials of a name）

70. grimace：（表示痛苦、厌恶等的）怪相,鬼脸

71. cuckold：使戴绿帽子

72. inextricable：分不开的（which can not be separated）

73. indentation：压痕

Questions：

1. What is the significance of the title?

2. What is the conflict in this story?

3. Why did Emily kill Homer Barron?

4. What role does the Negro play in the story?

5. What details foreshadow the conclusion of the story? Could the ending be anticipated?

6. Discuss the character of Emily and the root of her tragic life.

Ernest Hemingway

(1899-1961)

Ernest Hemingway (1899—1961) was a novelist, short-story writer, and journalist. He was born in Oak Park, Illinois, a suburb of Chicago. His father was a doctor and was the first important influence on Ernest's life and writing. He was fond of hunting and fishing, and often took young Ernest with him on his trips, which helped to develop Ernest's interest in sports and adventure. The fact that his books abound with sports terms is partly traceable to his early life. During World War I, young Hemingway was recruited as an ambulance driver working with the Red Cross and went to France and later to Italy where he was severely wounded. This war experience affected his life and writing permanently, which led to his writings of two important novels: *The Sun Also Rises* (1926) and *A Farewell to My Arms* (1929). When the Spainish Civil War broke out, Hemingway went to Spain as a foreign correspondent. Out of this experience came his most popular novel, *For Whom the Bell Tolls* (1940).

Hemingway worked as a reporter, first with the Kansan City *Star* and later with the Canadian *Torontao Star*. As a journalist he trained himself in the economy of expression. His use of short sentences and paragraphs and vigorous and positive language, and the deliberate avoidance of gorgeous adjectives are some of the traces of his early journalistice practices. Hemingway's distinctive writing style is characterized by the deceptive economy in expression, the suppression of emotion, the almost indifferent handling of the extraordinary, and the understatement. This writing style attributes not only to his work as a jounalist, but also to the help from Sherwood Anderson, then called a writer's writer, and Gertrude Stein, an American experimentalist writer who spent most of her life in France, and who became a catalyst in the development of modern art and literature. For him Anderson was a guide in style while Stein was a mentor, giving him a lot of advice on his writing, especially in the use of simple language, rhythm, and repetition. Hemingway's style had a significant influence on the development of twentieth-century fiction writing. He was probably the most imitated American writer of the twentieth century.

Hemingway later developed his famous "Iceberg Theory" which is stated as follows: "If a writer of prose knows enough about what he is writing about he may omit things that will have a feeling of those things as strongly as though the writer had stated them. The dignity of movement of an iceberg is due to only one-eighth of it being above water. A good writer does not need to reveal every detail of a character or action." In other words, a story can communicate by subtext, for instance, Hemingway's *Hills Like White Elephants* (1927) never once mentions the word "abortion", though that is what the story's characters seem to be discussing.

Hemingway often wrote about war, bull fighting and hunting. The typical situations in his works are usually characterized by chaos, brutality and violence, by crime and death, and by sport, hard drinking and sexual promiscuity. Hemingway was recognized as the spokesman of the "lost generation", a term coined by Gertrude Stein, which refers to the post-World War I generation of American writers who were haunted by a sense of betrayal and emptiness brought about by the destructiveness of the war. Hemingway used it as an epigraph for his first important novel, *The Sun Also Rises*. Because of this novel's popularity, the term, "The Lost Generation", becomes the enduring term that has stayed associated with Hemingway and other writers of the 1920's.

In his stories of war, the bullfight, and the fight, Hemingway was primarily concerned about an individual's "moment of truth" and dealt with the threat of physical, emotional, or psychic death. His protagonists are typically stoic men who exhibit an ideal described as "grace under pressure". As Santiago, the protagonist of *The Old Man and the Sea* (1952), puts it at the end of the novel, "A man is not made for defeat . . . a man can be destroyed but not defeated."

Apart from novels, Hemingway also published some collections of short stories which include *In Our Time* (1925), *Men without Women* (1927), *Winner Take Nothing* (1933) and *The Snows of Kilimanjaro* (1936). "Soldier's Home" (1925), "Cat in the Rain" (1925), "A Clean, Well-Lighted Place" (1926), "Hills Like White Elephants", "The Killers" (1927) and "The Snows of Kilimanjaro" are Hemingway's finest short stories. Hemingway received the Pulitzer Prize in 1953 for *The Old Man and the Sea*, and the Nobel Prize for Literature in 1954 for his lifetime literary achievements. In 1961, he suffered from severe anxiety and depression, and killed himself with a shotgun.

"Hills Like White Elephants" is a short story by Ernest Hemingway. It was first published in the 1927 collection *Men Without Women*. The story happens between an American man and a girl called Jig at a train station in a river valley of Spain. They drink beer and a liquor called Anis del Toro and talk about an operation which the American is attempting to convince Jig to undergo while waiting for the train to Madrid. This short story is commonly studied in literature courses because it contains ingenious symbolism, efficient and powerful dialogue, and it deals with universal themes applied to a controversial topic, abortion, which is explored without ever being explicitly stated. These elements combine to make the story an apt introduction to Hemingway's minimalist narrative style, as expressed in his Iceberg Theory.

Hills Like White Elephants

Ernest Hemingway

The hills across the valley of the Ebro[1] were long and white. On this side there was no shade and no trees and the station was between two lines of rails in the sun. Close against the side of the station there was the warm shadow of the building and a curtain, made of strings of bamboo beads, hung across the open door into the bar, to keep out flies. The American and the girl with him sat at a table in the shade, outside the building. It was very hot and the express from Barcelona[2] would come in forty minutes. It stopped at this junction for two minutes and went on to Madrid.

"What should we drink?" the girl asked. She had taken off her hat and put it on the table.

"It's pretty hot. " the man said.

"Let's drink beer. "

"Dos cervezas[3]," the man said into the curtain.

"Big ones?" a woman asked from the doorway.

"Yes. Two big ones. "

The woman brought two glasses of beer and two felt pads[4]. She put the felt pads and the beer glasses on the table and looked at the man and the girl. The girl was looking off at the line of hills. They were white in the sun and the country was brown and dry.

"They look like white elephants," she said.

"I've never seen one. " The man drank his beer.

"No, you wouldn't have. "

"I might have," the man said. "Just because you say I wouldn't have doesn't prove anything. "

163

The girl looked at the bead curtain. "They've painted something on it," she said. "What does it say?"

"Anis del Toro. It's a drink."

"Could we try it?"

The man called "Listen" through the curtain. The woman came out from the bar.

"Four reales[5]."

"We want two Anis del Toro."

"With water?"

"Do you want it with water?"

"I don't know," the girl said. "Is it good with water?"

"It's all right."

"You want them with water?" asked the woman.

"Yes, with water."

"It tastes like licorice[6]," the girl said and put the glass down.

"That's the way with everything."

"Yes," said the girl. "Everything tastes of licorice. Especially all the things you've waited so long for, like absinthe[7]."

"Oh, cut it out."

"You started it," the girl said. "I was being amused. I was having a fine time."

"Well, let's try and have a fine time."

"All right. I was trying. I said the mountains looked like white elephants. Wasn't that bright?"

"That was bright."

"I wanted to try this new drink. That's all we do, isn't it—look at things and try new drinks?"

"I guess so."

The girl looked across at the hills.

"They're lovely hills," she said. "They don't really look like white elephants. I just meant the coloring of their skin through the trees."

"Should we have another drink?"

"All right."

The warm wind blew the bead curtain against the table.

"The beer's nice and cool," the man said.

"It's lovely." the girl said.

"It's really an awfully simple operation, Jig," the man said. "It's not really an operation at all."

The girl looked at the ground the table legs rested on.

"I know you wouldn't mind it, Jig. It's really not anything. It's just to let the air in."

The girl did not say anything.

"I'll go with you and I'll stay with you all the time. They just let the air in and then it's all perfectly natural."

"Then what will we do afterward?"

"We'll be fine afterward. Just like we were before."

"What makes you think so?"

"That's the only thing that bothers us. It's the only thing that's made us unhappy."

The girl looked at the bead curtain, put her hand out and took hold of two of the strings of beads.

"And you think then we'll be all right and be happy?"

"I know we will. You don't have to be afraid. I've known lots of people that have done it."

"So have I," said the girl. "And afterward they were all so happy."

"Well," the man said, "if you don't want to you don't have to. I wouldn't have you do it if you didn't want to. But I know it's perfectly simple."

"And you really want to?"

"I think it's the best thing to do. But I don't want you to do it if you don't really want to."

"And if I do it you'll be happy and things will be like they were and you'll love me?"

"I love you now. You know I love you."

"I know. But if I do it, then it will be nice again if I say things are like white elephants, and you'll like it?"

"I'll love it. I love it now but I just can't think about it. You know how I get when I worry."

"If I do it you won't ever worry?"

"I won't worry about that because it's perfectly simple."

"Then I'll do it. Because I don't care about me."

"What do you mean?"

"I don't care about me."

"Well, I care about you."

"Oh, yes. But I don't care about me. And I'll do it and then everything will be fine."

"I don't want you to do it if you feel that way."

The girl stood up and walked to the end of the station. Across, on the other side, were fields of grain and trees along the banks of the Ebro. Far away, beyond the river, were mountains. The shadow of a cloud moved across the field of grain and she saw the river through the trees.

"And we could have all this," she said. "And we could have everything and every day we make it more impossible."

"What did you say?"

"I said we could have everything."

"We can have everything."

"No, we can't."

"We can have the whole world. "

"No, we can't. "

"We can go everywhere. "

"No, we can't. It isn't ours any more. "

"It's ours. "

"No, it isn't. And once they take it away, you never get it back. "

"But they haven't taken it away. "

"We'll wait and see. "

"Come on back in the shade," he said. "You mustn't feel that way. "

"I don't feel any way," the girl said. "I just know things. "

"I don't want you to do anything that you don't want to do—"

"Nor that isn't good for me. " she said. "I know. Could we have another beer?"

"All right. But you've got to realize—"

"I realize," the girl said. "Can't we maybe stop talking?"

They sat down at the table and the girl looked across at the hills on the dry side of the valley and the man looked at her and at the table.

"You've got to realize," he said, "that I don't want you to do it if you don't want to. I'm perfectly willing to go through with it if it means anything to you. "

"Doesn't it mean anything to you? We could get along. "

"Of course it does. But I don't want anybody but you. I don't want anyone else. And I know it's perfectly simple. "

"Yes, you know it's perfectly simple. "

"It's all right for you to say that, but I do know it. "

"Would you do something for me now?"

"I'd do anything for you. "

"Would you please please please please please please please stop

167

talking?"

He did not say anything but looked at the bags against the wall of the station. There were labels on them from all the hotels where they had spent nights.

"But I don't want you to," he said. "I don't care anything about it."

"I'll scream," the girl said.

The woman came out through the curtains with two glasses of beer and put them down on the damp felt pads. "The train comes in five minutes," she said.

"What did she say?" asked the girl.

"That the train is coming in five minutes."

The girl smiled brightly at the woman, to thank her.

"I'd better take the bags over to the other side of the station," the man said. She smiled at him.

"All right. Then come back and we'll finish the beer."

He picked up the two heavy bags and carried them around the station to the other tracks. He looked up the tracks but could not see the train. Coming back, he walked through the barroom, where people waiting for the train were drinking. He drank an Anis at the bar and looked at the people. They were all waiting reasonably for the train. He went out through the bead curtain. She was sitting at the table and smiled at him.

"Do you feel better?" he asked.

"I feel fine," she said. "There's nothing wrong with me. I feel fine."

Notes:

1. Ebro: a river in northern Spain

2. the express from Barcelona: 从巴塞罗那开来的快速列车

168

3. Dos cervezas: (西班牙语) two beers

4. felt pads: 毡制杯垫

5. Four reales: 4 里亚尔。real: 里亚尔,旧时西班牙及其南美属地的货币单位

6. licorice: 欧亚甘草;甘草糖

7. absinthe: 苦艾酒

Questions:

1. Looking back on the story, list the evidence that tells what kind of operation Jig is confronting. How risky is it physically and emotionally?

2. How do the hills in the story spotlight Jig's decision? How does Jig see the setting as symbolic of her choices?

3. Discuss the themes of the story. How does Hemingway's use of symbols help to convey them?

4. What is the conflict between Jig and the American man? Has it been resolved at the end of the story?

5. Hemingway once suggested that his purpose in such a story is to tell the reader as little as possible directly yet to reveal characters' motives and their conflict. How does this principle operate in this story? Where would you like to have more information (besides "he said" and "she said")?

Eudora Welty

(1909-2001)

Eudora Welty (1909—2001) was an award-winning American writer who wrote about the American South. She was born in Jackson, Mississippi. She was educated at the Mississippi State College for Women (now called Mississippi University for Women), the University of Wisconsin-Madison, and Columbia Business School. During the 1930s, Welty worked as a photographer for the Works Progress Administration, a job that sent her all over the state of Mississippi photographing people from all economic and social classes. But Welty's true love was literature, not photography, and she soon devoted her energy to writing ficiton. Her first short story, "Death of a Traveling Salesman", appeared in 1936. Welty's first collection of short stories, *A Curtain of Green*, was published in 1941. Her novel, *The Optimist's Daughter*, won the Pulitzer Prize in 1972. She was a 6-time winner of the O. Henry Award for Short Stories, and her many awards also include the National Medal for Literature, and the American Book Award. In 1992, Welty was awarded the Rea Award for the Short Story for her lifetime contributions to the American short story. She never married. She died of pneumonia at the age of 92.

Throughout her long writing career, Welty wrote a memoir, 6 novels, and numerous short stories. Her major works include *A Curtain of Green*, *The Wide Net* (1943), *The Robber Bridegroom* (1942), *Delta Wedding* (1946), *The Golden Apples* (1949), *The Ponder Heart* (1954), *The Bride of Innesfallen* (1955), *Losing Battles* (1970), *The Optimist's Daughter*,

The Collected Stories of Eudora Welty (1980), and *One Writer's Beginnings* (1983). The characters in her stories include murderers, psychotics, suicides, deaf-mutes, the mentally retarded and the elderly as well as a multitude of people who used to be referred to as "common" by the southern upper class. Though often set in Mississippi, her fiction reveals truth about the human condition that transcend region. As the former U. S. President Jimmy Carter put it, "Welty's fiction, with its strong sense of place and triumphant comic spirit, illuminates the human condition. "

"A Worn Path" is one of Welty's most frequently anthologized short stories. It was first published in *Atlantic Monthly* in 1940 and won an O. Henry Prize in 1941. The story is one of the best examples of Welty's writing, which is known for its realistic portrayal of the American South. Welty has been praised for her masterly use of language, myth, and symbol in this deceptively simple story. It is the tale of Phoenix Jackson's journey through the woods of Mississippi to the town of Natchez to get medicine for her sick grandson. At first the story appears simple, but its mythic undertones and ambiguity gives a depth and richness that has been praised by critics. Welty once said that she was inspired to write the story after seeing an old African-American woman walking alone across the southern landscape. In the story, along the way, Phoenix encounters several obstacles and the story becomes a quest for her to overcome the trials she faces, which mirror her difficult situation in society at large. As she walks toward her destination, Phoenix struggles against the obstacles, exhaustion, and poor eyesight. She is the symbol of perseverance, endurance, and life in the face of hardship and death. Sympathy and even admiration pervade Welty's vivid and detailed depiction.

A Worn Path

Eudora Welty

It was December—a bright frozen day in the early morning. Far out in

171

the country there was an old Negro woman with her head tied in a red rag, coming along a path through the pinewoods. Her name was Phoenix Jackson. She was very old and small and she walked slowly in the dark pine shadows, moving a little from side to side in her steps, with the balanced heaviness and lightness of a pendulum in a grandfather clock. She carried a thin, small cane made from an umbrella, and with this she kept tapping the frozen earth in front of her. This made a grave and persistent noise in the still air, that seemed meditative like the chirping[1] of a solitary little bird.

She wore a dark striped dress reaching down to her shoe tops, and an equally long apron of bleached sugar sacks, with a full pocket: all neat and tidy, but every time she took a step she might have fallen over her shoelaces, which dragged from her unlaced shoes. She looked straight ahead. Her eyes were blue with age. Her skin had a pattern all its own of numberless branching wrinkles and as though a whole little tree stood in the middle of her forehead, but a golden color ran underneath, and the two knobs of her cheeks were illumined by a yellow burning under the dark. Under the red rag her hair came down on her neck in the frailest of ringlets, still black, and with an odor like copper.

Now and then there was a quivering in the thicket. Old Phoenix said, "Out of my way, all you foxes, owls, beetles, jack rabbits, coons and wild animals! ... Keep out from under these feet, little bob-whites. ... Keep the big wild hogs out of my path. Don't let none[2] of those come running my direction. I got a long way." Under her small black-freckled hand her cane, limber as a buggy whip[3], would switch at the brush as if to rouse up any hiding things.

On she went. The woods were deep and still. The sun made the pine needles almost too bright to look at, up where the wind rocked. The cones[4] dropped as light as feathers. Down in the hollow was the mourning dove—

it was not too late for him.

The path ran up a hill. "Seem like there is chains about my feet, time I get this far," she said, in the voice of argument old people keep to use with themselves. "Something always take[5] a hold of me on this hill? — pleads I should stay."

After she got to the top she turned and gave a full, severe look behind her where she had come. "Up through pines," she said at length. "Now down through oaks."

Her eyes opened their widest, and she started down gently. But before she got to the bottom of the hill a bush caught her dress.

Her fingers were busy and intent, but her skirts were full and long, so that before she could pull them free in one place they were caught in another. It was not possible to allow the dress to tear. "I in the thorny bush[6]," she said. "Thorns, you doing your appointed work. Never want to let folks pass, no sir. Old eyes thought you was[7] a pretty little green bush."

Finally, trembling all over, she stood free, and after a moment dared to stoop for her cane.

"Sun so high!" she cried, leaning back and looking, while the thick tears went over her eyes. "The time getting all gone here."

At the foot of this hill was a place where a log was laid across the creek.

"Now comes the trial," said Phoenix.

Putting her right foot out, she mounted the log and shut her eyes. Lifting her skirt, leveling her cane fiercely before her, like a festival figure in some parade, she began to march across. Then she opened her eyes and she was safe on the other side.

"I wasn't as old as I thought," she said.

But she sat down to rest. She spread her skirts on the bank around her and folded her hands over her knees. Up above her was a tree in a pearly cloud of mistletoe. She did not dare to close her eyes, and when a little boy brought her a plate with a slice of marble-cake[8] on it she spoke to him. "That would be acceptable," she said. But when she went to take it there was just her own hand in the air.

So she left that tree, and had to go through a barbed-wire fence[9]. There she had to creep and crawl, spreading her knees and stretching her fingers like a baby trying to climb the steps. But she talked loudly to herself: she could not let her dress be torn now, so late in the day, and she could not pay for having her arm or her leg sawed off if she got caught fast where she was.

At last she was safe through the fence and risen up out in the clearing. Big dead trees, like black men with one arm, were standing in the purple stalks of the withered cotton field. There sat a buzzard[10].

"Who you watching?"

In the furrow she made her way along.

"Glad this not the season for bulls," she said, looking sideways, "and the good Lord made his snakes to curl up and sleep in the winter. A pleasure I don't see no two-headed snake coming around that tree, where it come once. It took a while to get by him, back in the summer."

She passed through the old cotton and went into a field of dead corn. It whispered and shook and was taller than her head. "Through the maze[11] now," she said, for there was no path.

Then there was something tall, black, and skinny there, moving before her.

At first she took it for a man. It could have been a man dancing in the field. But she stood still and listened, and it did not make a sound. It was as silent as a ghost.

"Ghost," she said sharply, "who be you the ghost of? For I have heard of nary[12] death close by. "

But there was no answer—only the ragged dancing in the wind.

She shut her eyes, reached out her hand, and touched a sleeve. She found a coat and inside that an emptiness, cold as ice.

"You scarecrow," she said. Her face lighted. "I ought to be shut up for good," she said with laughter. "My senses is gone. I too old. I the oldest people I ever know. Dance, old scarecrow," she said, "while I dancing with you. "

She kicked her foot over the furrow, and with mouth drawn down, shook her head once or twice in a little strutting way. Some husks blew down and whirled in streamers about her skirts.

Then she went on, parting her way from side to side with the cane, through the whispering field. At last she came to the end, to a wagon track where the silver grass blew between the red ruts[13]. The quail were walking around like pullets[14], seeming all dainty[15] and unseen.

"Walk pretty," she said. "This the easy place. This the easy going. "

She followed the track, swaying through the quiet bare fields, through the little strings of trees silver in their dead leaves, past cabins silver from weather, with the doors and windows boarded shut[16], all like old women under a spell[17] sitting there. "I walking in their sleep," she said, nodding her head vigorously.

In a ravine she went where a spring was silently flowing through a hollow log. Old Phoenix bent and drank. "Sweet-gum makes the water sweet," she said, and drank more. "Nobody know who made this well, for it was here when I was born. "

The track crossed a swampy part where the moss hung as white as lace from every limb. "Sleep on, alligators[18], and blow your bubbles. " Then the track went into the road.

Deep, deep the road went down between the high green-colored banks. Overhead the live-oaks met, and it was as dark as a cave.

A black dog with a lolling tongue came up out of the weeds by the ditch. She was meditating, and not ready, and when he came at her she only hit him a little with her cane. Over she went in the ditch, like a little puff of milkweed[19].

Down there, her senses drifted away. A dream visited her, and she reached her hand up, but nothing reached down and gave her a pull. So she lay there and presently went to talking. "Old woman," she said to herself, "that black dog come up out of the weeds to stall you off[20], and now there he sitting on his fine tail, smiling at you."

A white man finally came along and found her—a hunter, a young man, with his dog on a chain.

"Well, Granny!" he laughed. "What are you doing there?"

"Lying on my back like a June-bug waiting to be turned over, mister," she said, reaching up her hand.

He lifted her up, gave her a swing in the air, and set her down. "Anything broken, Granny?"

"No sir, them old dead weeds is springy enough[21]," said Phoenix, when she had got her breath. "I thank you for your trouble."

"Where do you live, Granny?" he asked, while the two dogs were growling at each other.

"Away back yonder, sir, behind the ridge. You can't even see it from here."

"On your way home?"

"No sir, I going to town."

"Why, that's too far! that's as far as I walk when I come out myself, and I get something for my trouble." He patted the stuffed bag he carried, and there hung down a little closed claw. It was one of the bob-whites[22], with its beak hooked bitterly to show it was dead. "Now you go on home, Granny!"

"I bound to go to town, mister," said Phoenix. "The time come around."

He gave another laugh, filling the whole landscape. "I know you old colored people! Wouldn't miss going to town to see Santa Claus!"

But something held old Phoenix very still. The deep lines in her face went into a fierce and different radiation. Without warning, she had seen with her own eyes a flashing nickel fall out of the man's pocket onto the ground.

"How old are you, Granny?" he was saying.

"There is no telling[23], mister," she said, "no telling."

Then she gave a little cry and clapped her hands and said, "Git on away from here, dog! Look! Look at that dog!" She laughed as if in admiration. "He ain't scared of nobody[24]. He a big black dog." She whispered, "Sic him![25]"

"Watch me get rid of that cur," said the man. "Sic him, Pete! Sic him!"

Phoenix heard the dogs fighting, and heard the man running and throwing sticks. She even heard a gunshot. But she was slowly bending forward by that time, further and further forward, the lids stretched down over her eyes, as if she were doing this in her sleep. Her chin was lowered almost to her knees. The yellow palm of her hand came out from the fold of her apron. Her fingers slid down and along the ground under the piece of money with the grace and care they would have in lifting an egg from under a setting hen. Then she slowly straightened up, she stood erect, and the nickel was in her apron pocket. A bird flew by. Her lips moved. "God watching me the whole time. I come to stealing."

The man came back, and his own dog panted about them. "Well, I scared him off that time," he said, and then he laughed and lifted his gun and pointed it at Phoenix.

She stood straight and faced him.

"Doesn't the gun scare you?" he said, still pointing it.

"No, sir, I seen plenty go off closer by, in my day, and for less than what I done," she said, holding utterly still.

He smiled, and shouldered the gun. "Well, Granny," he said, "you must be a hundred years old, and scared of nothing. I'd give you a dime if I had any money with me. But you take my advice and stay home, and nothing will happen to you."

"I bound to go on my way, mister," said Phoenix. She inclined her head in the red rag. Then they went in different directions, but she could hear the gun shooting again and again over the hill.

She walked on. The shadows hung from the oak trees to the road like curtains. Then she smelled wood-smoke, and smelled the river, and she saw a steeple and the cabins on their steep steps. Dozens of little black children whirled around her. There ahead was Natchez shining. Bells were ringing. She walked on.

In the paved city it was Christmas time. There were red and green electric lights strung and crisscrossed everywhere, and all turned on in the daytime. Old Phoenix would have been lost if she had not distrusted her eyesight and depended on her feet to know where to take her.

She paused quietly on the sidewalk where people were passing by. A lady came along in the crowd, carrying an armful of red-, green- and silver-wrapped presents; she gave off perfume like the red roses in hot summer, and Phoenix stopped her.

"Please, missy, will you lace up my shoe?" She held up her foot.

"What do you want, Grandma?"

"See my shoe," said Phoenix. "Do all right for out in the country, but wouldn't look right to go in a big building. "

"Stand still then, Grandma," said the lady. She put her packages down on the sidewalk beside her and laced and tied both shoes tightly.

"Can't lace 'em with a cane," said Phoenix. "Thank you, missy. I doesn't mind asking a nice lady to tie up my shoe, when I gets out on the street. "

Moving slowly and from side to side, she went into the big building, and into a tower of steps, where she walked up and around and around until her feet knew to stop.

She entered a door, and there she saw nailed up on the wall the document that had been stamped with the gold seal and framed in the gold frame, which matched the dream that was hung up in her head.

"Here I be," she said. There was a fixed and ceremonial stiffness over her body.

"A charity case, I suppose," said an attendant who sat at the desk before her.

But Phoenix only looked above her head. There was sweat on her face, the wrinkles in her skin shone like a bright net.

"Speak up, Grandma," the woman said. "What's your name? We must have your history, you know. Have you been here before? What seems to be the trouble with you?"

Old Phoenix only gave a twitch to her face as if a fly were bothering her.

"Are you deaf?" cried the attendant.

But then the nurse came in.

"Oh, that's just old Aunt Phoenix," she said. "She doesn't come for herself—she has a little grandson. She makes these trips just as regular as clockwork. She lives away back off the Old Natchez Trace. " She bent down. "Well, Aunt Phoenix, why don't you just take a seat? We won't keep you standing after your long trip. " She pointed.

The old woman sat down, bolt upright in the chair.

"Now, how is the boy?" asked the nurse.

Old Phoenix did not speak.

"I said, how is the boy?"

But Phoenix only waited and stared straight ahead, her face very solemn and withdrawn into rigidity[26].

"Is his throat any better?" asked the nurse. "Aunt Phoenix, don't you hear me? Is your grandson's throat any better since the last time you came for the medicine?"

With her hands on her knees, the old woman waited, silent, erect and motionless, just as if she were in armor[27].

"You mustn't take up our time this way, Aunt Phoenix," the nurse said. "Tell us quickly about your grandson, and get it over. He isn't dead, is he?"

At last there came a flicker and then a flame of comprehension across her face, and she spoke.

"My grandson. It was my memory had left me. There I sat and forgot why I made my long trip. "

"Forgot?" The nurse frowned. "After you came so far?"

Then Phoenix was like an old woman begging a dignified forgiveness for waking up frightened in the night. "I never did go to school, I was too old at the Surrender[28]," she said in a soft voice. "I'm an old woman without an education. It was my memory fail me. My little grandson, he is just the same, and I forgot it in the coming. "

"Throat never heals, does it?" said the nurse, speaking in a loud, sure voice to old Phoenix. By now she had a card with something written on it, a little list. "Yes. Swallowed lye[29]. When was it? —January—two—three years ago?"

180

Phoenix spoke unasked now. "No, missy, he not dead, he just the same. Every little while his throat begin to close up again, and he not able to swallow. He not get his breath. He not able to help himself. So the time come around, and I go on another trip for the soothing medicine. "

"All right. The doctor said as long as you came to get it, you could have it," said the nurse. "But it's an obstinate case. "

"My little grandson, he sit up there in the house all wrapped up, waiting by himself," Phoenix went on. "We is the only two left in the world. He suffer and it don't seem to put him back[30] at all. He got a sweet look. He going to last. He wear a little patch quilt[31] and peep out holding his mouth open like a little bird. I remembers so plain now. I not going to forget him again, no, the whole enduring time. I could tell him from all the others in creation[32]. "

"All right. " The nurse was trying to hush her now. She brought her a bottle of medicine. "Charity," she said, making a check mark in a book.

Old Phoenix held the bottle close to her eyes, and then carefully put it into her pocket.

"I thank you," she said.

"It's Christmas time, Grandma," said the attendant. "Could I give you a few pennies out of my purse?"

"Five pennies is a nickel," said Phoenix stiffly.

"Here's a nickel," said the attendant.

Phoenix rose carefully and held out her hand. She received the nickel and then fished[33] the other nickel out of her pocket and laid it beside the new one. She stared at her palm closely, with her head on one side.

Then she gave a tap with her cane on the floor.

"This is what come to me to do," she said. "I going to the store and buy my child a little windmill they sells, made out of paper. He going to find it hard to believe there such a thing in the world. I'll march myself back where he waiting, holding it straight up in this hand."

She lifted her free hand, gave a little nod, turned around, and walked out of the doctor's office. Then her slow step began on the stairs, going down.

Notes:

1. chirping：叽叽喳喳叫

2. don't let none = don't let any：黑人英语中存在双重否定结构，当一个动词被否定时，句中的不定代词 something, somebody, some 变为 nothing, nobody 和 none, 这种双重否定仍然表示否定，而在标准英语中双重否定表示肯定。

3. limber as a buggy whip：像轻型马车的鞭子那样易弯曲

4. cone：松果, 球果

5. take = takes：在黑人英语中, 动词的一般现在时第三人称单数不加 "s"

6. I in the thorny bush = I'm in thorny bush：黑人英语中的"be"动词经常被省略

7. you was = you were：在黑人英语中, was 常代替 were

8. marble-cake：裱饰大理石花纹的蛋糕

9. barbed-wire fence：有刺铁丝网

10. buzzard：鸳（a large black bird that eats dead flesh）

11. maze：迷宫

12. nary：no, not any

13. rut：车辙

14. pullet：chick

15. dainty：small, pretty, and delicate

16. with the doors and windows boarded shut：门、窗被钉上木板堵死了

17. under a spell：在符咒的魔力下, 中了邪

18. alligator：短吻鳄

182

19. milkweed：马利筋（a kind of plant）

20. to stall you off：要拖延你

21. them old dead weeds is springy enough = these old dead weeds are springy enough：这些枯死的野草还是很有弹性的。

22. bob-white：山齿鹑（a kind of bird）

23. There is no telling：It's impossible to know.

24. He ain't scared of nobody = He isn't scared of anybody：他（狗）不怕任何人。ain't = is not, are not, am not, has not, have not, 常出现在黑人英语中

25. Sic him!：去咬他！sic = sick：attack（used esp. in commanding a dog）.

26. her face very solemn and withdrawn into rigidity：她脸色阴沉,板着脸。

27. in armor：身穿盔甲

28. the Surrender：1865 年 4 月 9 日南部邦联的李将军向北方联邦的格兰特将军投降,因而结束了美国内战（the surrender of General Lee of the Confederacy on April 9, 1865 to General Grant of the Union, thus ending the Civil War）

29. lye：碱液（a substance used for washing and for making soap）

30. put him back：discourage him

31. He wear a little patch quilt：他围着一条小百纳被。patch quilt：百纳被,黑人传统上使用的被子（a quilt with the cover made of small pieces of cloth of different colors and patterns, a quilt popular esp. among the black people）

32. I could tell him from all the others in creation：他刚生下我就能把他跟别的孩子分辨开来。

33. fish：掏出（draw or pull out as if fishing）

Questions:

1. Phoenix is a mythical bird that roses from its own ashes every 500 years to begin a new life cycle. Why does the writer give the old black woman such a name? Does it have any symbolic meaning in the story?

2. In what sense does Phoenix literally travel a worn path? How does the phrase refer more generally to her love for her grandson? What is the symbolic significance of the title?

3. Is Phoenix's grandson dead or still alive? Is it important to the portrayal of the character?

Bernard Malamud

(1914-1986)

Bernard Malamud (1914—1986) was one of the great American Jewish writers of the 20th century. He was born in Brooklyn, New York, to Russian Jewish immigrants. His parents, whom he described as gentle, honest, kindly people, were not highly educated and knew very little about literature or the arts. Malamud recalled, "There were no books that I remember in the house, no records, music, pictures on the wall." He received his B. A. degree from City College of New York in 1936. In 1942, he obtained a Master's degree from Columbia University. From 1940 to 1949 he taught high school. In 1949, he got a job teaching English at Oregon state University and began a long and distinguished career as a university teacher.

　　Malamud did not begin writing seriously until hearing of the horrors of the Holocaust, when 6 million Jewish people were put to death by the Germans during World War II. He also began reading about Jewish tradition and history. He wrote about Jews, especially the lower class Jewish people, but he is usually regarded as more than a "Jewish" writer. He used the Jew as a metaphor for humankind. He once remarked, "All men are Jews, though few men know it." He was a writer who explored, through the Jewish experience, universal human hopes, struggles, conflicts, and dilemmas. He emphasizes that humanity is his subject, that he uses Jews to communicate the universal just as William Faulkner created a universe from a corner of the American South. He

185

addresses the themes of sin, suffering, and redemption. His characters, while often awkward and isolated from society, evoke both pity and humor through their attempts at survival and salvation. Largely considered one of the foremost writers of moral fiction, Malamud is also considered a writer in the tradition of Anton Chekhov and Fyodor Dostoyevski. He pays attention to realistic, detailed descriptions of Jewish people's everyday life: their suffering, struggle, and hope. He won two National Book Awards and the Pulitzer Prize for his chronicles of human struggle.

Malamud's novels include *The Natural* (1952), *The Assistant* (1957), *The Fixer* (1966), *A New Life* (1961), *The Tenants* (1971), *Dubin's Lives* (1979), and *God's Grace* (1982). In 1967, *The Fixer* won both the National Book Award and the Pulitzer Prize. Malamud is also renowned for his short stories. His short-story collections are *The Magic Barrel* (1958), which won the National Book Award in 1959, *Idiots First* (1963), *Pictures of Fidelman* (1969), and *Rembrandt's Hat* (1973). *The Stories of Bernard Malamud* appeared in 1983.

"The First Seven Years" was published in Malamud's first collection of short stories, *The Magic Barrel*. The story is about Feld, a Jewish shoemaker who seeks a suitable husband for his daughter Miriam. But she is not interested in his choice of Max, a college student, because in her eyes Max is "nothing but a materialist". Feld soon discovers that his assistant, Sobel, a Polish Jewish refugee, is in love with Miriam, and that she returns his affections. Sobel likes to read and often gives Miriam books to read. Miriam sees spiritual qualities in Sobel, but in Feld's eyes Sobel is simply an old and ugly assistant and can't give her daughter a happy life. Feld is in poor health and Sobel is a good helper. Will Feld allow Sobel to marry Miriam? In the climax of the story, Feld tells Sobel that if he works for two more years, making seven in all, he can have the permission to marry Miriam. Hence the title of the story, which is an allusion to the Biblical story of how Jacob worked for Laban for seven years in order to marry his younger daughter Rachel, whom he loved.

The First Seven Years[1]

Bernard Malamud

Feld, the shoemaker, was annoyed that his helper, Sobel, was so insensitive to his reverie[2] that he wouldn't for a minute cease his fanatic pounding[3] at the other bench. He gave him a look, but Sobel's bald head was bent over the last[4] as he worked and he didn't notice. The shoemaker shrugged and continued to peer through the partly frosted window at the near-sighted haze of falling February snow. Neither the shifting white blur outside, nor the sudden deep remembrance[5] of the snowy Polish village where he had wasted his youth could turn his thoughts from Max the college boy, (a constant visitor in the mind since early that morning when Feld saw him trudging through the snowdrifts on his way to school[6]) whom he so much respected because of the sacrifices he had made throughout the years—in winter or direst[7] heat—to further his education. An old wish returned to haunt the shoemaker: that he had had a son instead of a daughter, but this blew away in the snow for Feld, if anything, was a practical man. Yet he could not help but contrast the diligence of the boy, who was a peddler's son, with Miriam's unconcern for an education. True, she was always with a book in her hand, yet when the opportunity arose for a college education, she had said no she would rather find a job. He had begged her to go, pointing out how many fathers could not afford to send their children to college, but she said she wanted to be independent. As for education, what was it, she asked, but books, which Sobel, who diligently read the classics, would as usual advise her on. Her answer greatly grieved her father.

187

A figure emerged from the snow and the door opened. At the counter the man withdrew from a wet paper bag a pair of battered[8] shoes for repair. Who he was the shoemaker for a moment had no idea, then his heart trembled as he realized, before he had thoroughly discerned the face, that Max himself was standing there, embarrassedly explaining what he wanted done to his old shoes. Though Feld listened eagerly, he couldn't hear a word, for the opportunity that had burst upon[9] him was deafening.

He couldn't exactly recall when the thought had occurred to him, because it was clear he had more than once considered suggesting to the boy that he go out with Miriam. But he had not dared speak, for if Max said no, how would he face him again? Or suppose Miriam, who harped so often on[10] independence, blew up in anger and shouted at him for his meddling[11]? Still, the chance was too good to let by: all it meant was an introduction. They might long ago have become friends had they happened to meet somewhere, therefore was it not his duty—an obligation—to bring them together, nothing more, a harmless connivance[12] to replace an accidental encounter in the subway, let's say, or a mutual friend's introduction in the street? Just let him once see and talk to her and he would for sure be interested. As for Miriam, what possible harm for a working girl in an office, who met only loud-mouthed salesmen and illiterate shipping clerks, to make the acquaintance of a fine scholarly boy? Maybe he would awaken in her a desire to go to college; if not—the shoe maker's mind at last came to grips with the truth[13]—let her marry an educated man and live a better life.

When Max finished describing what he wanted done with his shoes, Feld marked them, both with enormous holes in the soles which he pretended not to notice, with large white-chalk x's, and the rubber heels, thinned to the nails, he marked with o's, though it troubled him he might have mixed up the letters. Max inquired the price, and the shoemaker

188

cleared his throat and asked the boy, above Sobel's insistent hammering, would he please step through the side door there into the hall. Though surprised, Max did as the shoemaker requested, and Feld went in after him. For a minute they were both silent, because Sobel had stopped banging, and it seemed they understood neither was to say anything until the noise began again. When it did, loudly, the shoemaker quickly told Max why he had asked to talk to him.

"Ever since you went to high school," he said, in the dimly lit hallway, "I watched you in the morning go to the subway to school, and I said always to myself, this is a fine boy that he wants so much an education. "

"Thanks," Max said, nervously alert. He was tall and grotesquely thin, with sharply cut features, particularly a beaklike nose. He was wearing a loose, long slushy[14] overcoat that hung down to his ankles, looking like a rug draped over his bony shoulders[15], and a soggy[16], old brown hat, as battered as the shoes he had brought in.

"I am a business man," the shoemaker abruptly said to conceal his embarrassment, "so I will explain you right away why I talk to you. I have a girl, my daughter Miriam—she is nineteen—a very nice girl and also so pretty that everybody looks on her when she passes by in the street. She is smart, always with a book, and I thought to myself that a boy like you, an educated boy—I thought maybe you will be interested sometime to meet a girl like this. " He laughed a bit when he had finished and was tempted to say more but had the good sense not to.

Max stared down like a hawk. For an uncomfortable second he was silent, then he asked, "Did you say nineteen?"

"Yes. "

"Would it be all right to inquire if you have a picture of her?"

"Just a minute. " The shoemaker went into the store and hastily

189

returned with a snapshot that Max held up to the light.

"She's all right," he said.

Feld waited.

"And is she sensible—not the flighty[17] kind."

"She is very sensible."

After another short pause, Max said it was okay with him if he met her.

"Here is my telephone," said the shoemaker, hurriedly handing him a slip of paper. "Call her up. She comes home from work six o'clock."

Max folded the paper and tucked it away into his worn leather wallet.

"About the shoes," he said. "How much did you say they will cost me?"

"Don't worry about the price."

"I just like to have an idea."

"A dollar—dollar fifty. A dollar fifty," the shoemaker said.

At once he felt bad, for he usually charged two twenty-five for this kind of job. Either he should have asked the regular price or done the work for nothing.

Later, as he entered the store, he was startled by a violent clanging and looked up to see Sobel pounding with all his might upon the naked last. It broke, the iron striking the floor and jumping with a thump against the wall, but before the enraged shoemaker could cry out, the assistant had torn his hat and coat from the hook and rushed out into the snow.

So Feld, who had looked forward to anticipating how it would go with his daughter and Max, instead had a great worry on his mind. Without his temperamental[18] helper he was a lost man, especially since it was years now that he had carried the store alone. The shoemaker had for an age suffered from a heart condition that threatened collapse if he dared exert himself[19]. Five years ago, after an attack, it had appeared as though he would have

190

either to sacrifice his business upon the auction block[20] and live on a pittance[21] thereafter, or put himself at the mercy of some unscrupulous employee[22] who would in the end probably ruin him. But just at the moment of his darkest despair, this Polish refugee, Sobel, appeared one night from the street and begged for work. He was a stocky man, poorly dressed, with a bald head that had once been blond, a severely plain face and soft blue eyes prone to tears[23] over the sad books he read, a young man but old —no one would have guessed thirty. Though he confessed he knew nothing of shoemaking, he said he was apt and would work for a very little if Feld taught him the trade. Thinking that with, after all, a landsman[24], he would have less to fear than from a complete stranger, Feld took him on and within six weeks the refugee re-built as good a shoe as he, and not long thereafter expertly ran the business for the thoroughly relieved shoemaker.

Feld could trust him with anything and did, frequently going home after an hour or two at the store, leaving all the money in the till[25], knowing Sobel would guard every cent of it. The amazing thing was that he demanded so little. His wants were few; in money he wasn't interested— in nothing but books, it seemed—which he one by one lent to Miriam, together with his profuse, queer written comments, manufactured during his lonely rooming house[26] evenings, thick pads of commentary which the shoemaker peered at and twitched his shoulders over as his daughter, from her fourteenth year, read page by sanctified[27] page, as if the word of God were inscribed[28] on them. To protect Sobel, Feld himself had to see that he received more than he asked for. Yet his conscience bothered him for not insisting that the assistant accept a better wage than he was getting, though Feld had honestly told him he could earn a handsome salary if he worked elsewhere, or maybe opened a place of his own. But the assistant answered somewhat ungraciously, that he was not interested in going elsewhere, and though Feld frequently asked himself what keeps him here? Why does he stay? He finally answered it that the man, no doubt because of his terrible experiences as a refugee, was afraid of the world.

After the incident with the broken last, angered by Sobel's behavior, the shoemaker decided to let him stew[29] for a week in the rooming house, although his own strength was taxed[30] dangerously and the business suffered. However, after several sharp nagging warnings from both his wife and daughter, he went finally in search of Sobel, as he had once before, quite recently, when over some fancied slight[31]—Feld had merely asked him not to give Miriam so many books to read because her eyes were strained and red—the assistant had left the place in a huff[32], an incident which, as usual, came to nothing for he had returned after the shoemaker had talked to him, and taken his seat at the bench. But this time, after Feld had plodded through the snow to Sobel's house—he had thought of sending Miriam but the idea became repugnant[33] to him—the burly landlady at the door informed him in a nasal voice that Sobel was not at home, and though Feld knew this was a nasty lie, for where had the refugee to go? Still for some reason he was not completely sure of—it may have been the cold and his fatigue—he decided not to insist on seeing him. Instead he went home and hired a new helper.

Having settled the matter, though not entirely to his satisfaction, for he had much more to do than before, and so, for example, could no longer lie late in bed mornings because he had to get up to open the store for the new assistant, a speechless, dark man with an irritating rasp[34] as he worked, whom he would not trust with the key as he had Sobel. Furthermore, this one, though able to do a fair repair job, knew nothing of grades of leather or prices, so Feld had to make his own purchases; and every night at closing time it was necessary to count the money in the till, and lock up. However, he was not dissatisfied, for he lived much in his thoughts of Max and Miriam. The college boy had called her, and they arranged a meeting for this coming Friday night. The shoemaker would personally have preferred Saturday, which he felt would make it a date of the first magnitude[35], but he learned Friday was Miriam's choice, so he said nothing. The day of the week did not matter. What mattered was the aftermath. Would they like each other and want to be friends? He sighed at all the time that would have to go by before he knew for sure. Often he was tempted to talk to Miriam about the boy, to ask whether she thought she would like his type—he had told her only that he considered Max a nice boy and had suggested he call her—but the one time he tried she snapped at him[36]—justly—how should she know?

At last Friday came. Feld was not feeling particularly well so he stayed in bed, and Mrs. Feld thought it better to remain in the bedroom with him when Max called. Miriam received the boy, and her parents could hear their voices, his throaty one, as they talked. Just before leaving, Miriam brought Max to the bedroom door and he stood there a minute, a tall, slightly hunched figure wearing a thick, droopy suit, and apparently at ease as he greeted the shoemaker and his wife, which was surely a good sign. And Miriam, although she had worked all day, looked fresh and pretty. She was a large-framed girl with a well-shaped body, and she had a fine open face and soft hair. They made, Feld thought, a first-class couple.

Miriam returned after 11:30. Her mother was already asleep, but the shoemaker got out of bed and after locating his bathrobe went into the kitchen, where Miriam, to his surprise, sat at the table, reading.

"So where did you go?" Feld asked pleasantly.

"For a walk," she said, not looking up.

"I advised him," Feld said, clearing his throat, "he shouldn't spend so much money."

"I didn't care."

The shoemaker boiled up some water for tea and sat down at the table with a cupful and a thick slice of lemon.

"So how," he sighed after a sip, "did you enjoy?"

"It was all right. "

He was silent. She must have sensed his disappointment, for she added, "You can't really tell much the first time. "

"You will see him again?"

Turning a page, she said that Max had asked for another date.

"For when?"

"Saturday. "

"So what did you say?"

"What did I say?" she asked, delaying for a moment—"I said yes. "

Afterwards she inquired about Sobel, and Feld, without exactly knowing why, said the assistant had got another job. Miriam said nothing more and began to read. The shoe maker's conscience did not trouble him; he was satisfied with the Saturday date.

During the week, by placing here and there a deft question, he managed to get from Miriam some information about Max. It surprised him to learn that the boy was not studying to be either a doctor or lawyer but was taking a business course leading to a degree in accountancy. Feld was a little disappointed because he thought of accountants as bookkeepers and would have preferred "a higher profession". However, it was not long before he had investigated the subject and discovered that Certified Public Accountants[37] were highly respected people, so he was thoroughly content as Saturday approached. But because Saturday was a busy day, he was much in the store and therefore did not see Max when he came to call for Miriam. From his wife he learned there had been nothing especially revealing about their meeting. Max had rung the bell and Miriam had got her coat and left with him—nothing more. Feld did not probe, for his wife

194

was not particularly observant. Instead, he waited up for Miriam with a newspaper on his lap, which he scarcely looked at so lost was he in thinking of the future. He awoke to find her in the room with him, tiredly removing her hat. Greeting her, he was suddenly inexplicably afraid to ask anything about the evening. But since she volunteered nothing he was at last forced to inquire how she had enjoyed herself. Miriam began something noncommittal[38] but apparently changed her mind, for she said after a minute, "I was bored. "

When Feld had sufficiently recovered from his anguished disappointment to ask why, she answered without hesitation, "Because he's nothing more than a materialist. "

"What means this word?"

"He has no soul. He's only interested in things. "

He considered her statement for a long time but then asked, "Will you see him again?"

"He didn't ask. "

"Suppose he will ask you?"

"I won't see him. "

He did not argue; however, as the days went by he hoped increasingly she would change her mind. He wished the boy would telephone, because he was sure there was more to him than Miriam, with her inexperienced eye, could discern. But Max didn't call. As a matter of fact he took a different route to school, no longer passing the shoe maker's store, and Feld was deeply hurt.

Then one afternoon Max came in and asked for his shoes. The shoemaker took them down from the shelf where he had placed them, apart from the other pairs. He had done the work himself and the soles and heels were well built and firm. The shoes had been highly polished and somehow looked better than new. Max's Adam's apple[39] went up once when he saw

195

them, and his eyes had little lights in them[40].

"How much?" he asked, without directly looking at the shoemaker.

"Like I told you before," Feld answered sadly. "One dollar fifty cents."

Max handed him two crumpled bills and received in return a newly minted silver half dollar.

He left. Miriam had not been mentioned. That night the shoemaker discovered that his new assistant had been all the while stealing from him, and he suffered a heart attack.

Though the attack was very mild, he lay in bed for three weeks. Miriam spoke of going for Sobel, but sick as he was Feld rose in wrath against the idea. Yet in his heart he knew there was no other way, and the first weary day back in the shop thoroughly convinced him, so that night after supper he dragged himself to Sobel's rooming house.

He toiled up the stairs, though he knew it was bad for him, and at the top knocked at the door. Sobel opened it and the shoemaker entered. The room was a small, poor one, with a single window facing the street. It contained a narrow cot, a low table and several stacks of books piled haphazardly around on the floor along the wall[41], which made him think how queer Sobel was, to be uneducated and read so much. He had once asked him, Sobel, why you read so much? and the assistant could not answer him. Did you ever study in a college someplace? he had asked, but Sobel shook his head. He read, he said, to know. But to know what, the shoemaker demanded, and to know, why? Sobel never explained, which proved he read much because he was queer.

Feld sat down to recover his breath. The assistant was resting on his bed with his heavy back to the wall. His shirt and trousers were clean, and his stubby[42] fingers, away from the shoe maker's bench, were strangely pallid. His face was thin and pale, as if he had been shut in this room

196

since the day he had bolted from the store.

"So when you will come back to work?" Feld asked him.

To his surprise, Sobel burst out, "Never."

Jumping up, he strode over to the window that looked out upon the miserable street.

"Why should I come back?" he cried.

"I will raise your wages."

"Who cares for your wages!"

The shoemaker, knowing he didn't care, was at a loss what else to say.

"What do you want from me, Sobel?"

"Nothing."

"I always treated you like you was my son."

Sobel vehemently denied it. "So why you look for strange boys in the street they should go out with Miriam? Why you don't think of me?"

The shoe maker's hands and feet turned freezing cold. His voice became so hoarse he couldn't speak. At last he cleared his throat and croaked, "So what has my daughter got to do with a shoemaker thirty-five years old who works for me?"

"Why do you think I worked so long for you?" Sobel cried out. "For the stingy[43] wages I sacrificed five years of my life so you could have to eat and drink and where to sleep?"

"Then for what?" shouted the shoemaker.

"For Miriam," he blurted—"for her."

The shoemaker, after a time, managed to say, "I pay wages in cash, Sobel," and lapsed into silence[44]. Though he was seething with excitement[45] his mind was coldly clear, and he had to admit to himself he had sensed all along that Sobel felt his way. He had never so much as thought it consciously, but he had felt it and was afraid.

"Miriam knows?" he muttered hoarsely.

"She knows. "

"You told her?"

"No. "

"Then how does she know?"

"How does she know?" Sobel said. "Becauses she knows. She knows who I am and what is in my heart. "

Feld had a sudden insight. In some devious way, with his books and commentary, Sobel had given Miriam to understand that he loved her. The shoemaker felt a terrible anger at him for his deceit.

"Sobel, you are crazy," he said bitterly. "She will never marry a man so old and ugly like you. "

Sobel turned black with rage. He cursed the shoemaker, but then, though he trembled to hold it in, his eyes filled with tears and he broke into deep sobs. With his back to Feld, he stood at the window, fists clenched, and his shoulders shook with choked sobbing.

Watching him, the shoe maker's anger diminished. His teeth were on edge[46] with pity for the man, and his eyes grew moist. How strange and sad that a refugee, a grown man, bald and old with his miseries, who had by the skin of his teeth escaped Hitler's incinerators[47], should fall in love, when he had got to America, with a girl less than half his age. Day after day, for five years he had sat at his bench, cutting and hammering away[48], waiting for the girl to become a woman, unable to ease his heart with speech[49], knowing no protest but desperation.

"Ugly I didn't mean. " he said half aloud.

Then he realized that what he had called ugly was not Sobel but Miriam's life if she married him. He felt for his daughter a strange and gripping sorrow, as if she were already Sobel's bride, the wife, after all, of a shoemaker, and had in her life no more than her mother had had. And

198

all his dreams for her—why he had slaved and destroyed his heart with anxiety and labor—all these dreams of a better life were dead.

The room was quiet. Sobel was standing by the window reading, and it was curious that when he read he looked young.

"She is only nineteen," Feld said brokenly. "This is too young yet to get married. Don't ask her for two years more, till she is twenty-one, then you can talk to her."

Sobel didn't answer. Feld rose and left. He went slowly down the stairs but once outside, though it was an icy night the crisp falling snow whitened the street, he walked with a stronger stride.

But the next morning, when the shoemaker arrived, heavy-hearted, to open the store, he saw he needn't have come, for his assistant was already seated at the last, pounding leather for his love.

Notes:

1. The title alludes to the the Biblical story, "Jacob Marries Leah and Rachel" (Genesis 29:9, the Bible), which is as follows:

After Jacob had stayed with him for a whole month, Laban said to him, "Just because you are a relative of mine, should you work for me for nothing? Tell me what your wages should be?"

Now Laban had two daughters; the name of the older was Leah, and the name of the younger was Rachel. Leah had weak eyes, but Rachel was lovely in form, and beautiful. Jacob was in love with Rachel and said, "I'll work for you seven years in return for your younger daughter Rachel."

Laban said, "It's better that I give her to you than to some other man. Stay here with me." So Jacob served seven years to get Rachel, but they seemed like only a few days to him because of his love for her.

Then Jacob said to Laban, "Give me my wife. My time is completed, and I want to lie with her."

So Laban brought together all the people of the place and gave a feast. But when evening came, he took his daughter Leah and gave her to Jacob, and Jacob lay with her. And Laban gave his servant girl Zilpah to his daughter as her maidservant.

When morning came, there was Leah! So Jacob said to Laban, "What is this you have done to me? I served you for Rachel, didn't I? Why have you deceived me?"

Laban replied, "It is not our custom here to give the younger daughter in marriage before the older one. Finish this daughter's bridal week; then we will give you the younger one also, in return for another seven years of work."

And Jacob did so. He finished the week with Leah, and then Laban gave him his daughter Rachel to be his wife. Laban gave his servant girl Bilhah to his daughter Rachel as her maidservant. Jacob lay with Rachel also, and he loved Rachel more than Leah. And he worked for Laban another seven years.

2. reverie：幻想,白日梦(daydream)

3. cease his fanatic pounding：停止他疯狂的捶打

4. last：鞋楦(a piece of wood or metal shaped like a human foot, used by shoemakers and shoe repairers)

5. remembrance：回忆(the act of remembering)

6. trudging through the snowdrifts on his way to school：步履艰难地踩着厚厚的积雪,朝学校走去。snowdrift：雪堆(a deep bank or mass of snow piled up by the wind)

7. dire：极端的(extreme)

8. battered：破旧不堪的(worn out)

9. burst upon：突然来到(come suddenly)

10. harp on：talk about (something) repeatedly or continually

11. blew up in anger and shouted at him for his meddling：因为他管闲事而很生气,对他大声嚷嚷

12. connivance：纵容,默许(encouragement or permission of wrong doing)

13. the shoe maker's mind at last came to grips with the truth：鞋匠的思想最后还是面对现实。come to grips with：努力对付(deal with)

14. slushy：被雪水打湿的

15. looking like a rug draped over his bony shoulders：看起来就像一条披在他瘦削的双肩上的毯子。drape：披(cover with folds of cloth)

16. soggy：completely wet

17. flighty：轻浮的,朝三暮四的(often changing, esp. from one lover to another)

18. temperamental：喜怒无常的(having frequent changes of temper)

19. The shoemaker had for an age suffered from a heart condition that threatened collapse if he dared exert himself：鞋匠得心脏病很久了,如果他敢拼命工作,他的心脏就会崩溃。heart condition：心脏病(heart disease)；exert oneself：尽力(make a great effort)

20. on the auction block：拍卖(for sale at auction)

21. pittance：少量的收入(a small amount, esp. a very small amount of money)

22. put himself at the mercy of some unscrupulous employee：使自己完全受某个不择手段的雇员的支配。unscrupulous：不择手段的(not caring about honesty and fairness in getting what one wants)

23. prone to tears：爱流眼泪。prone to：易于发生……(likely to suffer)

24. landsman：同胞(compatriot)

25. till：(店铺中)放钱的抽屉(a drawer where money is kept in a shop)

26. rooming house：(按日或按星期出租房间的)公寓

27. sanctified：神圣的(made holy)

28. inscribed：被印,被刻写(printed, written)

29. let him stew：让他自作自受

30. tax：耗费（exhaust）

31. over some fancied slight：由于某次想象的冒犯。slight：冒犯,轻慢（insult）

32. in a huff：生气地（in anger）

33. repugnant：令人厌恶的（very unpleasant and offensive）

34. an irritating rasp：一把令人心烦的锉刀

35. magnitude：importance

36. she snapped at him：她斥责他。snap：speak rudely

37. Certified Public Accountants：注册会计师

38. noncommittal：含糊的,不表态的（not expressing a clear opinion）

39. Adam's apple：喉结

40. his eyes had little lights in them：他的两眼放光。

41. It contained a narrow cot, a low table ... haphazardly around on the floor along the wall：房间里有一张窄窄的帆布床,一个低矮的桌子,还有靠墙随意堆在地板上的几堆书。

42. stubby：短粗的（short and thick）

43. stingy：微薄的,极少的（small in quantity）

44. lapsed into silence：陷入了沉默。lapse：fall, slip or sink

45. seething with excitement：非常激动

46. on edge：僵直的,绷紧的（tense, stiff）

47. had by the skin of his teeth escaped Hitler's incinerators：差一点就死在希特勒的焚尸炉里。by the skin of one's teeth：差一点就没（just barely）；Hitler's incinerators：希特勒的焚尸炉,第二次世界大战时,纳粹杀死了几百万的欧洲犹太人,然后把尸体丢入焚尸炉里烧掉（During World War II, millions of Jews in Europe were murdered by the Nazis. Ovens were used to get rid of the victims's bodies.)

48. away：continuously

49. unable to ease his heart with speech：无法用语言来减轻他内心的痛苦

Questions:

1. Why does Miriam decline her father's offer of going to college? Discuss the characterization of Miriam.
2. Which man is more suitable for Miriam, Max, or Sobel? Why?
3. Feld asks himself why he should have "destroyed his heart with anxiety and labor" for the future. In his respect, what does he share with Sobel?
4. Is Feld's decision for Miriam's future that of a strictly practical man? Explain.
5. What new understanding of himself does Feld come to at the end of the story? Why do you think he returns home from Sobel's rooming house with a "stronger stride"?

John Cheever

(1912-1982)

John Cheever (1912—1982) is a master of short stories. He was born in Quincy, Massachusetts. His father owned a shoe factory and was relatively wealthy until he lost his business in the 1929 stock market crash and deserted his family. Young Cheever came to writing early. At the age of 17 he published his first short story. In 1929 he was expelled from school for smoking, which led to his writing of the story "Expelled". He submitted it to the magazine *The New Republic*, which published it in 1930. When World War II broke out, Cheever served in the army. After the war Cheever worked as a teacher and kept writing all the time.

Called the "Chekhov of the suburbs", Cheever is best known for his short stories dealing with the ironies of contemporary American life. His stories typically are subtle and finely worked comedies of manners, concerned with middle-class who live in the suburbs, presented with an ironic humour, which softened his basically dark vision. His characters tend to be less specific than symbolic, although the situations in his narratives are realistic and detailed. Cheever's work often portrays individuals who yearn for self-expression within a society whose values make it difficult to achieve this freedom. Cheever's main theme was the spiritual and emotional emptiness of life.

Cheever's works include short story collections *The Way Some People Live* (1943), *The Enormous Radio* (1954), *The Housebreaker of Shady Hill* (1958), *The Brigadier and the Golf Widow* (1964), *The World* of *Apples* (1973), and *The Stories of John Cheever* (1978) which won him the 1979 Pulitzer Prize in literature. As a novelist, Cheever is noted for *The Wapshot Chronicle* (1957) and its sequel, *The Wapshot Scandal* (1964); the first volume received a National Book Award in 1958. These novels deal with the wealthy, eccentric Wapshot family in suburban Massachusetts and expand on themes that Cheever explored in his shorter fiction. His later novels inclued *Bullet Park* (1969), *Falconer* (1977), and *Oh What a Paradise It Seems* (1982).

   The Death of Justina (1960) was one of Cheever's personal favorites. It is a reflection of the prosperous yet chaotic society contemporary with Cheever. It shows the writer's perceptions and ideas on death, which occurs in a wrong part of the city. Cheever presents this whole situation with irony. Moses is the narrator, an advertising man who lives in suburbia and who commutes to New York each day. Justina is a cousin of his wife, and while she is visiting, she dies suddenly on the sofa in their living room. The story has a certain wildly humorous tone that derives from the anger of the narrator as he details how he is refused permission to hold the funeral at his house because of the zoning laws, and how he threatens the mayor that if he is not given permission to hold the funeral at the house, he will bury Justina in the garden. Moses thinks the society where he lives is disappointing. He feels bitter and disillusioned. In this society the dead are despised, art is degraded, and dreams are lost. Justina's death triggers Moses' contemplation of American society and culture. Angered by the widespread disrespect of the dead among Americans, Moses makes this stunning comment at Justina's funeral: "How can a people who do not mean to understand death hope to understand love, and who will sound the alarm?"

The Death of Justina

John Cheever

So help me God[1] it gets more and more preposterous[2], it corresponds less and less to what I remember and what I expect as if the force of life were centrifugal[3] and threw one further and further away from one's purest memories and ambitions; and I can barely recall the old house where I was raised, where in midwinter Parma violets bloomed in a cold frame[4] near the kitchen door, and down the long corridor, past the seven views of Rome — up two steps and down three — one entered the library where all the books were in order, the lamps were bright, where there was a fire and a dozen bottles of good bourbon[5] locked in a cabinet with a veneer[6] like tortoise shell whose silver key my father wore on his watch chain. Fiction is art and art is the triumph over chaos (no less) and we can accomplish this only by the most vigilant exercise of choice, but in a world that changes more swiftly than we can perceive there is always the danger that our powers of selection will be mistaken and that the vision we serve will come to nothing. We admire decency and we despise death but even the mountains seem to shift in the space of a night and perhaps the exhibitionist[7] at the corner of Chestnut and Elm streets is more significant than the lovely woman with a bar of sunlight in her hair, putting a fresh piece of cuttlebone[8] in the nightingale's cage. Just let me give you one example of chaos and if you disbelieve me look honestly into your own past and see if you can't find a comparable experience ...

One Saturday the doctor told me to stop smoking and drinking and I did. I won't go into the commonplace symptoms of withdrawal[9] but I would like to point out that, standing at my window in the evening, watching the brilliant afterlight[10] and the spread of darkness, I felt, through the lack of these humble stimulants, the force of some primitive memory[11] in which the coming of night with its stars and its moon was apocalyptic[12]. I thought suddenly of the neglected graves of my three brothers on the mountainside and that death is a loneliness much crueler than any loneliness hinted at in life. The soul (I thought) does not leave the body but lingers with it through every degrading stage of decomposition and neglect[13], through heat, through cold, through the long winter nights when no one comes with a wreath[14] or a plant and no one says a prayer. This unpleasant premonition[15] was followed by anxiety. We were going out for dinner and I thought that the oil burner would explode in our absence and burn the house. The cook would get drunk and attack my daughter with a carving knife[16] or my wife and I would be killed in a collision[17] on the main highway, leaving our children bewildered orphans with nothing in life to look forward to but sadness. I was able to observe, along with these foolish and terrifying anxieties, a definite impairment of my discretionary poles[18]. I felt as if I were being lowered by ropes into the atmosphere of my childhood. I told my wife—when she passed through the living room—that I had stopped smoking and drinking but she didn't seem to care and who would reward me for my privations[19]? Who cared about the bitter taste in my mouth and that my head seemed to be leaving my shoulders? It seemed to me that men had honored one another with medals, statuary[20], and cups for much less and that abstinence[21] is a social matter. When I abstain from sin[22] it is more often a fear of scandal than a private resolve to improve on the purity of my heart, but here was a call for abstinence without the worldly enforcement of society, and death is not the threat that scandal is[23]. When it was time for us to go out I was so lightheaded[24] that I had to ask my wife to drive the car. On Sunday I sneaked seven cigarettes in various hiding places and drank two Martinis[25] in the downstairs coat closet. At breakfast on Monday my English muffin[26] stared up at me from the plate. I mean I saw a face there in the rough, toasted surface. The moment of recognition was fleeting[27], but it was deep, and I wondered who it had been. Was it a friend, an aunt, a sailor, a ski instructor, a bartender, or a conductor on a train? The smile faded off the muffin but it had been there for a second—the sense of a person, a life, a pure force of gentleness and censure[28]—and I am convinced that the muffin had contained the presence of some spirit. As you can see, I was nervous.

On Monday my wife's old cousin, Justina, came to visit her. Justina was a lively guest although she must have been crowding eighty[29]. On Tuesday my wife gave her a lunch party. The last guest left at three and a few minutes later Cousin Justina, sitting on the living-room sofa with a glass of good brandy, breathed her last[30]. My wife called me at the office and I said that I would be right out. I was clearing my desk when my boss, MacPherson, came in.

"Spare me a minute," he asked. "I've been bird dogging[31] all over the place, trying to track you down. Pierce had to leave early and I want you to write the last Elixircol commercial[32]."

"Oh, I can't, Mac," I said. "My wife just called. Cousin Justina is dead."

"You write that commercial," he said. His smile was satanic[33]. "Pierce had to leave early because his grandmother fell off a step-ladder."

Now I don't like fictional accounts of office life[34]. It seems to me that if you're going to write fiction you should write about mountain climbing and tempests at sea[35], and I will go over my predicament with MacPherson briefly, aggravated as it was by his refusal to respect and honor the death of dear old Justina[36]. It was like MacPherson. It was a good example of the way I've been treated. He is, I might say, a tall, splendidly groomed[37] man of about sixty who changes his shirt three times a day, romances[38] his secretary every afternoon between two and two-thirty and makes the habit of continuously chewing gum seem hygienic and elegant. I write his speeches for him and it has not been a happy arrangement for me. If the speeches are successful MacPherson takes all the credit[39]. I can see that his presence, his tailor[40] and his fine voice are all a part of the performance but it makes me angry never to be given credit for what was said[41]. On the other hand if the speeches are unsuccessful—if his presence and his voice can't carry the hour[42]—his threatening and sarcastic manner is surgical[43] and I am obliged to contain myself in the role of a man who can do no good in spite of the piles of congratulatory mail that my eloquence sometimes brings in. I must pretend—I must, like an actor, study and improve on my pretension[44]—to have nothing to do with his triumphs, and I must bow my head gracefully in shame when we have both failed. I am forced to appear grateful for injuries, to lie, to smile falsely and to play out a role as inane and as unrelated to the facts as a minor prince in an operetta[45], but if I speak the truth it will be my wife and my children who will pay in hardships for my outspokenness[46]. Now he refused to respect or even to admit the solemn fact of a death in our family and if I couldn't rebel it seemed as if I could at least hint at it[47].

The commercial he wanted me to write was for a tonic[48] called Elixircol and was to be spoken on television by an actress who was neither young nor beautiful but who had an appearance of ready abandon[49] and who was anyhow the mistress of one of the sponsor's uncles. *Are you growing old?* I wrote. *Are you falling out of love with your image in the looking glass[50]? Does your face in the morning seem rucked and seamed with alcoholic and sexual excesses[51] and does the rest of you appear to be a grayish-pink lump, covered all over with brindle[52] hair? Walking in the autumn woods do you feel that a subtle distance has come between you and the smell of wood smoke? Have you drafted your obituary[53]? Are you easily winded[54]? Do you wear a girdle[55]? Is your sense of smell fading, is your interest in gardening waning, is your fear of heights increasing, and are your sexual drives as ravening[56] and intense as ever and does your wife look more and more to you like a stranger with sunken[57] cheeks who has wandered into your bedroom by mistake? If this or any of this is true you need Elixircol, the true juice of youth. The small economy size (business with the bottle) costs seventy-five*

209

dollars and the giant family bottle comes at two hundred and fifty. It's a lot of scratch[58] *, God knows, but these are inflationary times*[59] *and who can put a price on youth*[60]*? If you don't have the cash borrow it from your neighborhood loan shark*[61] *or hold up*[62] *the local bank. The odds*[63] *are three to one that with a ten-cent water pistol and a slip of paper you can shake ten thousand out of any fainthearted teller*[64]*. Everybody's doing it. (Music up and out.)* I sent this in to MacPherson via Ralphie, the messenger boy, and took the 4: 16 home[65], traveling through a landscape of utter desolation.

Now my journey is a digression[66] and has no real connection to Justina's death but what followed could only have happened in my country and in my time and since I was an American traveling across an American landscape the trip may be part of the sum[67]. There are some Americans who, although their fathers emigrated from the Old World three centuries ago, never seem to have quite completed the voyage and I am one of these. I stand, figuratively[68], with one wet foot on Plymouth Rock[69], looking with some delicacy, not into a formidable and challenging wilderness but onto a half-finished civilization embracing glass towers, oil derricks[70], suburban continents and abandoned movie houses and wondering why, in this most prosperous, equitable, and accomplished world[71]—where even the cleaning women practice the Chopin preludes[72] in their spare time—everyone should seem to be so disappointed.

At Proxmire Manor I was the only passenger to get off the random meandering and profitless local[73] that carried its shabby lights off into the dusk like some game-legged watchman or beadle making his appointed rounds[74]. I went around to the front of the station to wait for my wife and to enjoy the traveler's fine sense of crisis. Above me on the hill were my home and the homes of my friends, all lighted and smelling of fragrant wood smoke like the temples in a sacred grove[75], dedicated to monogamy, feckless childhood, and domestic bliss[76] but so like a dream that I felt the lack of viscera[77] with much more than poignance[78]—the absence of that inner dynamism we respond to in some European landscapes[79]. In short, I was disappointed. It was my country, my beloved country, and there have been mornings when I could have kissed the earth that covers its many provinces and states. There was a hint of bliss; romantic and domestic bliss. I seemed to hear the jingle bells of the sleigh that would carry me to grand mother's house although in fact grandmother spent the last years of her life working as a hostess on an ocean liner and was lost in the tragic sinking of the S. S. Lorelei[80] and I was responding to a memory that I had not experienced. But the hill of light rose like an answer to some primitive dream of home-coming. On one of the highest lawns I saw the remains[81] of a snowman who still smoked a pipe and wore a scarf and a cap but whose form was wasting away[82] and whose anthracite eyes[83] stared out at the view with terrifying bitterness. I sensed some disappointing greenness of spirit in the scene although I knew in my bones, no less, how like yesterday it was that my father left the Old World to found a new[84]; and I thought of the forces that had brought stamina to the image: the cruel towns of Calabria with their cruel princes, the badlands northwest of Dublin, ghettos, despots, whore-houses, bread lines, the graves of children, intolerable hunger, corruption, persecution, and despair had generated these faint and mellow lights[85] and wasn't it all a part of the great migration that is the life of man?

My wife's cheeks were wet with tears when I kissed her. She was distressed, of course, and really quite sad. She had been attached to Justina. She drove me home, where Justina was still sitting on the sofa. I would like to spare you the unpleasant details but I will say that both her mouth and her eyes were wide open. I went into the pantry to telephone Dr. Hunter. His line was busy. I poured myself a drink—the first since

211

Sunday—and lighted a cigarette. When I called the doctor again he answered and I told him what had happened. "Well, I'm awfully sorry to hear about it, Moses," he said. "I can't get over until after six and there isn't much that I can do. This sort of thing has come up[86] before and I'll tell you all I know. You see, you live in Zone B—two-acre lots[87]; no commercial enterprises and so forth. A couple of years ago some stranger bought the old Plewett Mansion and it turned out that he was planning to operate it as a funeral home. We didn't have any zoning provision[88] at the time that would protect us and one was rushed through the village council at midnight and they overdid it. It seems that you not only can't have a funeral home in Zone B—you can't bury anything there and you can't die there. Of course it's absurd, but we all make mistakes, don't we? Now there are two things you can do. I've had to deal with this before: You can take the old lady and put her into the car and drive her over to Chestnut Street, where Zone C begins. The boundary is just beyond the traffic light by the high school. As soon as you get her over to Zone C, it's all right. You can just say she died in the car. You can do that or if this seems distasteful[89] you can call the mayor and ask him to make an exception to the zoning laws. But I can't write you out a death certificate until you get her out of that neighborhood and of course no undertaker[90] will touch her until you get a death certificate."

"I don't understand," I said, and I didn't, but then the possibility that there was some truth in what he had just told me broke against me or over me like a wave, exciting mostly indignation[91]. "I've never heard such a lot of damned foolishness in my life," I said. "Do you mean to tell me that I can't die in one neighborhood and that I can't fall in love in another and that I can't eat ... "

"Listen. Calm down, Moses. I'm not telling you anything but the facts and I have a lot of patients waiting. I don't have the time to listen to

212

you fulminate[92]. If you want to move her, call me as soon as you get her over to the traffic light. Otherwise, I'd advise you to get in touch with the mayor or someone on the village council[93]. " He cut the connection. I was outraged but this did not change the fact that Justina was still sitting on the sofa. I poured a fresh drink and lit another cigarette.

Justina seemed to be waiting for me and to be changing from an inert into a demanding figure[94]. I tried to imagine carrying her out to the station wagon but I couldn't complete the task in my imagination and I was sure that I couldn't complete it in fact. I then called the mayor but this position in our village is mostly honorary and as I might have known he was in his New York law office and was not expected home until seven. I could cover her, I thought, that would be a decent thing to do, and I went up the back stairs to the linen closet and got a sheet. It was getting dark when I came back into the living room but this was no merciful twilight. Dusk seemed to be playing directly into her hands[95] and she gained power and stature with the dark. I covered her with a sheet and turned on a lamp at the other end of the room but the rectitude[96] of the place with its old furniture, flowers, paintings, etc., was demolished by her monumental shape[97]. The next thing to worry about was the children, who would be home in a few minutes. Their knowledge of death, excepting[98] their dreams and intuitions of which I know nothing, is zero and the bold figure in the parlor was bound to be traumatic[99]. When I heard them coming up the walk I went out and told them what had happened and sent them up to their rooms. At seven I drove over to the mayor's.

He had not come home but he was expected at any minute and I talked with his wife. She gave me a drink. By this time I was chain-smoking[100]. When the mayor came in we went into a little office or library, where he took up a position behind a desk, putting me in the low chair of a supplicant[101]. "Of course I sympathize with you, Moses," he said, "it's an awful thing to have happened, but the trouble is that we can't give you a zoning exception without a majority vote of the village council and all the members of the council happen to be out of town. Pete's in California and Jack's in Paris and Larry won't be back from Stowe[102] until the end of the week. "

I was sarcastic. "Then I suppose Cousin Justina will have to gracefully decompose[103] in my parlor until Jack comes back from Paris. "

"Oh, no," he said, "oh no. Jack won't be back from Paris for another month but I think you might wait until Larry comes from Stowe. Then we'd have a majority, assuming of course that they would agree to your appeal[104]. "

"For Christ's sake," I snarled.

"Yes, yes," he said, "it is difficult, but after all you must realize that this is the world you live in and the importance of zoning can't be over-estimated[105]. Why, if a single member of the council could give out zoning exception, I could give you permission right now to open a saloon in your garage, put up neon lights, hire an orchestra and destroy the neighborhood and all the human and commercial values we've worked so hard to protect. "

"I don't want to open a saloon in my garage," I howled. "I don't want to hire an orchestra. I just want to bury Justina. "

"I know, Moses, I know," he said. "I understand that. But it's just that it happened in the wrong zone and if I make an exception for you I'll have to make an exception for everyone and this kind of morbidity, when it gets out of hand, can be very depressing[106]. People don't like to live in a neighborhood where this sort of thing goes on all the time. "

"Listen to me," I said. "You give me an exception and you give it to me now or I'm going home and dig a hole in my garden and bury Justina myself. "

214

"But you can't do that, Moses. You can't bury anything in Zone B. You can't even bury a cat."

"You're mistaken," I said. "I can and I will. I can't function as[107] a doctor and I can't function as an undertaker, but I can dig a hole in the ground and if you don't give me my exception, that's what I'm going to do."

"Come back, Moses, come back," he said. "Please come back. Look, I'll give you an exception if you'll promise not to tell anyone. It's breaking the law, it's a forgery[108] but I'll do it if you promise to keep it a secret."

I promised to keep it a secret, he gave me the documents and I used his telephone to make the arrangements. Justina was removed a few minutes after I got home but that night I had the strangest dream. I dreamed that I was in a crowded supermarket. It must have been night because the windows were dark. The ceiling was paved with fluorescent light[109]—brilliant, cheerful but, considering our prehistoric memories, a harsh link in the chain of light that binds us to the past. Music was playing and there must have been at least a thousand shoppers pushing their wagons among the long corridors of comestibles and victuals[110]. Now is there—or isn't there—something about the posture we assume when we push a wagon that unsexes[111] us? Can it be done with gallantry? I bring this up because the multitude of shoppers seemed that evening, as they pushed their wagons, penitential[112] and unsexed. There were all kinds, this being my beloved country. There were Italians, Finns, Jews, Negroes, Shropshire-men, Cubans—anyone who had heeded the voice of liberty—and they were dressed with that sumptuary abandon that European caricaturists record with such bitter disgust[113]. Yes, there were grandmothers in shorts, big-butted[114] women in knitted pants and men wearing such an assortment of[115] clothing that it looked as if they had dressed hurriedly in a burning

215

building. But this, as I say, is my own country and in my opinion the caricaturist who vilifies[116] the old lady in shorts vilifies himself. I am a native and I was wearing buckskin jump boots[117], chino pants[118] cut so tight that my sexual organs were discernible and a rayon-acetate pajama top printed with representations of the Pinta, the Nina and the Santa Maria in full sail[119]. The scene was strange—the strangeness of a dream where we see familiar objects in an unfamiliar light—but as I looked more closely I saw that there were some irregularities. Nothing was labeled. Nothing was identified or known. The cans and boxes were all bare. The frozen-food bins were full of brown parcels but they were such odd shapes that you couldn't tell if they contained a frozen turkey or a Chinese dinner. All the goods at the vegetable and the bakery counters were concealed in brown bags and even the books for sale had no titles. In spite of the fact that the contents of nothing was known, my companions of the dream—my thousands of bizarrely dressed compatriots[120]—were deliberating gravely over[121] these mysterious containers as if the choices they made were critical. Like any dreamer, I was omniscient[122], I was with them and I was withdrawn, and stepping above the scene for a minute I noticed the men at the check-out counters[123]. They were brutes[124]. Now sometimes in a crowd, in a bar or a street, you will see a face so full-blown in its obdurate resistance to the appeals of love, reason and decency, so lewd, so brutish and unregenerate, that you turn away[125]. Men like these were stationed at the only way out and as the shoppers approached them they tore their packages open—I still couldn't see what they contained—but in every case the customer, at the sight of what he had chosen, showed all the symptoms of the deepest guilt; that force that brings us to our knees. Once their choice had been opened to their shame they were pushed—in some cases kicked—toward the door and beyond the door I saw dark water and heard a terrible noise of moaning and crying in the air. They waited at the door in

216

groups to be taken away in some conveyance[126] that I couldn't see. As I watched, thousands and thousands pushed their wagons through the market, made their careful and mysterious choices and were reviled[127] and taken away. What could be the meaning of this?

We buried Justina in the rain the next afternoon. The dead are not, God knows, a minority, but in Proxmire Manor their unexalted kingdom is on the outskirts, rather like a dump[128], where they are transported furtively as knaves and scoundrels[129] and where they lie in an atmosphere of perfect neglect. Justina's life had been exemplary, but by ending it she seemed to have disgraced us all. The priest was a friend and a cheerful sight, but the undertaker and his helpers, hiding behind their limousines, were not; and aren't they at the root of most of our troubles[130], with their claim that death is a violet-flavored kiss? How can a people who do not mean to understand death hope to understand love, and who will sound the alarm[131]?

I went from the cemetery back to my office. The commercial was on my desk and MacPherson had written across it in grease pencil: *Very funny, you broken-down bore[132]. Do again.* I was tired but unrepentant and didn't seem able to force myself into a practical posture of usefulness and obedience. I did another commercial. *Don't lose your loved ones,* I wrote, *because of excessive radioactivity. Don't be a wallflower[133] at the dance because of strontium 90[134] in your bones. Don't be a victim of fallout[135]. When the tart[136] on Thirty-sixth Street gives you the big eye does your body stride off in one direction and your imagination in another? Does your mind follow her up the stairs and taste her wares in revolting detail while your flesh goes off to Brooks Brothers[137] or the foreign exchange desk of the Chase Manhattan Bank[138]? Haven't you noticed the size of the ferns, the lushness of the grass, the bitterness of the string beans and the brilliant markings on the new breeds of butterflies[139]? You have been inhaling lethal atomic waste[140] for the last twenty-five years and only Elixircol can save you.* I gave this to

Ralphie and waited perhaps ten minutes when it was returned, marked again with grease pencil. *Do*, he wrote, *or you'll be dead.* I felt very tired. I put another piece of paper into the machine and wrote: *The Lord is my shepherd; therefore can I lack nothing. He shall feed me in a green pasture and lead me forth beside the waters of comfort. He shall convert my soul and bring me forth in the paths of righteousness for his Name's sake. Yea, though I walk through the valley of the shadow of death I will fear no evil for thou art with me; thy rod and thy staff comfort me. Thou shalt prepare a table before me in the presence of them that trouble me; thou hast anointed my head with oil and my cup shall be full. Surely thy loving-kindness and mercy shall follow me all the days of my life and I will dwell in the house of the Lord for ever*[141]. I gave this to Ralphie and went home.

Notes:

1. So help me God: (赌咒时用语)千真万确,我担保(I'm speaking the truth, on my honor)

2. preposterous: 荒谬的(absurd)

3. centrifugal: 离心的(moving outward from the center)

4. Parma violets bloomed in a cold frame: 帕尔马(意大利北部城市)紫罗兰在冷床里开花。cold frame: 冷床(保护幼苗免受寒害的罩子)

5. bourbon: 一种烈性威士忌酒

6. veneer: 饰面薄板

7. exhibitionist: 裸露症患者

8. cuttlebone: 墨鱼骨

9. the commonplace symptoms of withdrawal: 戒掉烟酒嗜好后的常见的生理反应。symptoms of withdrawal: 脱瘾症状(the painful or unpleasant effects which are the result of breaking or stopping a habit, esp. the taking of a drug)

10. afterlight: 余晖,晚霞(afterglow)

11. I felt, through the lack of these humble stimulants, the force of some primitive memory：由于缺少这些低廉的刺激物,我感觉到了某种原始记忆的力量。humble stimulants 这里指烟酒刺激物

12. apocalyptic：预言将来的大灾难的(telling of great misfortunes in the future)

13. through every degrading stage of decomposition and neglect：经过尸体分解和遭忽略的每个丧失体面的阶段

14. wreath：花圈

15. premonition：预感,预兆(a feeling that something, esp. something unpleasant, is going to happen)

16. carving knife：雕刻刀

17. collision：相撞,撞车事故

18. a definite impairment of my discretionary poles：我的思维辨别能力确实受到损害。discretionary：辨别力的,判断力的

19. privation：(生活必需品的)缺乏(lack or loss of the necessary things or the main conforts of life),这里指烟酒习惯的戒断

20. statuary：雕像,塑像(statues)

21. abstinence：戒酒(the act of keeping away from pleasant things, esp. from alcoholic drink)

22. abstain from sin：戒绝犯罪,这里指戒酒、戒烟。abstain：戒除,避免(keep oneself from doing something)

23. death is not the threat that scandal is：死亡对人的威胁不如被人讲闲话来的厉害。

24. lightheaded：(发热或饮酒后)头脑不清醒的,脚步不稳的,头晕目眩的(unable to think clearly or move steadily, e. g. during fever or after drinking alcohol)

25. Martini：马丁尼酒(a cocktail made by mixing gin and vermouth)

26. English muffin：英国松饼(a small thick round breadlike cake, usu. eaten hot with butter)

27. fleeting：短暂的,飞逝的(passing quickly)

28. censure：指责(strong expression of disapproval)

29. crowding eighty：快 80 岁了。crowding：very close to.

30. breathed her last：死了

31. bird dogging：到处寻找(hunting like a bird dog)

32. Elixircol commercial：长生不老药"青春露"的广告词。Elixircol 是作者虚构的一种药品,以讽刺美国商业界的市场销售术

33. satanic：邪恶的,无情的(extremely cruel or evil)

34. fictional accounts of office life：小说中有关办公室生活的描述

35. tempests at sea：海上的暴风雨

36. I will go over my predicament with MacPherson . . . and honor the death of dear old Justina：我将简要地回顾一下我与 MacPherson 在一起的处境,尽管这种处境由于他拒绝尊重亲爱的老贾斯蒂娜之死而恶化。

37. splendidly groomed：打扮光鲜的

38. romance：与……谈情说爱(try to have an affair with)

39. takes all the credit：拿去所有的功劳

40. his tailor：他的衣着

41. it makes me angry never to be given credit for what was said：我为他写了演说稿,却从不给一点功劳,让我很生气。

42. carry the hour：赢得听众的欢迎

43. surgical：像外科手术刀一样锋利

44. pretension：假装

45. to play out a role as inane and as unrelated to the facts as a minor prince in an operetta：扮演一个像小歌剧中的次要亲王那样毫无意义、与事实无关联的角色。inane：无意义的,无比愚蠢(meaningless, extremely stupid)；operetta：小歌剧(a short cheerful musical play that includes dancing and in which many of the words are spoken)

46. pay in hardships for my outspokenness：因为我的坦率直言而吃苦遭殃

47. as if I could at least hint at it：我似乎至少可以做个造反的姿态

48. tonic：滋补品（a medicine that increases mental or physical strength, health, or well-being）

49. ready abandon：放纵情欲。abandon：放纵（the state when one's feelings and actions are uncontrolled）

50. falling out of love with your image in the looking glass：不爱镜中自己的形象。fall out of：放弃；looking glass：镜子

51. seem rucked and seamed with alcoholic and sexual excesses：似乎因为酗酒和纵欲过度布满皱纹、褶子。rucked：变皱的（wrinkled）；seamed：起皱纹的（marked with wrinkles）

52. brindle：斑纹，斑点

53. drafted your obituary：起草你的讣告

54. easily winded：容易呼吸急促。wind：使喘不上气（cause to be breathless or have difficulty in breathing）

55. wear a girdle：（因为发胖）穿紧身褡。girdle：紧身褡（a firm undergarment for women, worn round the waist and hips, that supports and shapes the stomach, hips, and bottom）

56. ravening：贪求的，欲望很大的（voracious）

57. sunken：凹陷的

58. a lot of scratch：lots of money

59. inflationary times：通货膨胀的时代

60. who can put a price on youth?：谁能给青春标价呢？

61. loan shark：放高利贷者

62. hold up：抢劫（rob by using the threat of violence）

63. odds：可能性，机会（the possibility that something will or will not happen）

64. fainthearted teller：胆小的出纳。fainthearted：胆小的（cowardly）

65. took the 4:16 home：乘 4 点 16 分的车回家

66. digression：离题（wandering away from the main topic）

67. part of the sum：整体中的一部分

68. figuratively：比喻地,象征地

69. Plymouth Rock：普利茅斯岩石,是 1620 年英国清教徒初次登陆美洲时的地点

70. derrick：铁架塔

71. in this most prosperous, equitable, and accomplished world：在这个最繁荣、公平和完美的世界

72. the Chopin preludes：肖邦的前奏曲

73. the random meandering and profitless local：指班次稀少、路线曲折而赢利很少的区间火车

74. some game-legged watchman or beadle making his appointed rounds：某个巡视猎场的看守人或按指定线路游行的游行领队

75. a sacred grove：神圣的小树林

76. dedicated to monogamy, feckless childhood, and domestic bliss：致力于一夫一妻制,无忧忧虑的童年和家庭幸福。feckless：什么都不在乎的

77. viscera：内脏,脏腑（如心、肺、胃等）,在本小说中意为"内容"

78. poignance：辛酸（a state of deeply felt distress or sorrow）

79. the absence of that inner dynamism we respond to in some European landscapes：缺乏我们在欧洲的一些景观相应的精神活力

80. the S. S. Lorelei：罗瑞莱号轮船,罗瑞莱为德国传说中的一女妖,出没莱茵河岩石上,以其美貌和歌声诱惑船夫触礁沉没。轮船以她的名字命名,可能是作者的杜撰。

81. remains：尸体（a dead body）

82. wasting away：逐渐变小,变消瘦

83. anthracite eyes：black eyes

84. a new：a new world

85. I thought of the forces that had brought stamina to the image ... had generated these faint and mellow lights：我想起了那些使这个形象得以持久的种种因素：卡拉布里亚地区残暴的亲王们统治的无情小镇，都伯林西北部的荒地，平民区，暴君，妓院，领救济食品的队伍，儿童的坟墓，无法忍受的饥饿，腐败，迫害，和绝望点燃的这些暗淡、柔和的灯光。stamina：持久力（endurance）；Calabria：卡拉布里亚，意大利南部一地区

86. come up：happened

87. two-acre lots：2 英亩的地

88. zoning provision：划分地区的法律条款

89. distasteful：unpleasant

90. undertaker：殡仪事务承办人

91. broke against me or over me like a wave, exciting mostly indignation：像海浪一样撞击我，或者把我淹没，激起的主要是愤慨

92. fulminate：严厉谴责（declare one's opposition very strongly and angrily）

93. the village council：村委会

94. changing from an inert into a demanding figure：从一动不动的体态变成请求的体态

95. playing directly into her hands：上了她的圈套，让她捞到了好处

96. rectitude：正直（moral integrity）

97. demolished by her monumental shape：被她硕大的身姿所破坏

98. excepting：除……外（excluding）

99. the bold figure in the parlor was bound to be traumatic：赫然出现在客厅的尸体肯定会对他们造成精神创伤。bold：醒目的（striking to the eye）；bound：肯定的（certain）；traumatic：造成精神创伤的（deeply and unforgettably shocking）

100. chain-smoking：一支接一支地抽烟

101. supplicant：恳求者，哀求者（a person begging for something, esp.

from someone in power or from God）

102. Stowe：纽约州的一个城镇

103. decompose：腐烂（decay）

104. assuming of course that they would agree to your appeal：假设他们当然会同意你的请求

105. the importance of zoning can't be over-estimated：地区划分具有十分重大的意义

106. this kind of morbidity, when it gets out of hand, can be very depressing：这种不正常的情况，一旦控制不住，可能是非常令人沮丧的。

107. function as：起……作用（fulfil the duty of, be）

108. forgery：伪造罪（the crime of falsely making or changing writing or a signature）

109. fluorescent light：荧光灯

110. comestibles and victuals：各种食物和饮料。comestible：something to be eaten as food（该词常用复数）；victuals：food and drink

111. unsex：使失去性征

112. penitential：后悔的

113. they were dressed with that sumptuary abandon ... with such bitter disgust：他们衣着随便，关于这一点欧洲的漫画家十分厌恶地记录了下来。

114. big-butted：大屁股的

115. an assortment of：all kind of

116. vilify：毁谤，中伤（say bad things about someone or something without good cause, esp. in order to influence others unavorably）

117. buckskin jump boots：鹿皮做的伞兵军靴。jump boots：also known as paratrooper boots 伞兵军靴

118. chino pants：西方流行的一种紧身裤

119. a rayon-acetate pajama top printed ... and the Santa Maria in full

sail：醋酯人造丝睡衣的上装印着张着满帆的平塔号、尼娜号和桑塔玛利亚号帆船。the Pinta, the Nina, the Santa Maria 是哥伦布第一次横渡大西洋驶向美洲时所使用的普通贸易商船。

120. bizarrely dressed compatriots：穿着奇怪的同胞

121. deliberating gravely over：正严肃地仔细考虑

122. omniscient：无所不知的（knowing everything）

123. the check-out counters：商场出口处的付款柜台

124. brute：禽兽，残忍无情的人（a brutal person）

125. you will see a face so full-blown in its obdurate resistance ... that you turn away：你会看到一张凶神恶煞的脸，这张脸对仁爱、理性和尊严的呼吁完全无动于衷，那么下流，没有人性，不知悔改，以至于你转过身去。obdurate：顽固的（stubbon）

126. conveyance：交通工具（a vehicle）

127. were reviled：被辱骂

128. their unexalted kingdom is on the outskirts, rather like a dump：他们不受尊重的王国在郊区，颇像个垃圾场

129. where they are transported furtively as knaves and scoundrels：他们像流氓和恶棍一样被偷偷地运到这里

130. at the root of most of our troubles：我们大多数烦恼的根源

131. sound the alarm：拉响警报信号

132. you broken-down bore：你这个讨厌的废物

133. wallflower：舞会中呆坐一旁没人请跳舞的女子

134. strontium 90：锶 90（放射性同位素）

135. fallout：放射性坠尘

136. tart：妓女（a prostitute）

137. Brooks Brothers：布克兄弟（美国高级服装店）

138. the Chase Manhattan Bank：美国大通银行

139. the size of the ferns, the lushness of the grass, the bitterness of the string beans and the brilliant markings on the new breeds of

butterflies：蕨类植物之硕大,青草之繁茂,红花菜豆之苦涩,新蝴蝶之耀眼斑纹。这些都是受放射性元素伤害的动植物。

140. inhaling lethal atomic waste：一直在吸入含放射性废料的空气

141. The Lord is my shepherd; therefore can I lack nothing. ... I will dwell in the house of the Lord for ever：这是《圣经》的《诗篇》第23篇的全文,译文如下：耶和华是我的牧者,我必不致缺乏。他使我躺卧在青草地上,领我在可安歇的水边。他使我的灵魂苏醒,为自己的名引导我走义路。我虽然行过死荫的幽谷,也不怕遭害,因为你与我同在;你的杖,你的竿,都安慰我。在我敌人面前,你为我摆设筵席;你用油膏了我的头,使我的福杯满溢。我一生一世必有恩惠慈爱随着我;我且要住在耶和华的殿中,直到永远。

Questions：

1. Why does Moses first stop and then resume smoking and drinking?

2. How does the writer depict American society? Is he satisfied with his life in this society? How are the dead and death treated in society?

3. Do you think Elixircol will sell well? If you were Moses, how would you write the commercial?

4. How do you interpret Moses' dream of the supermarket?

5. Discuss the themes that are explored in the story.

John Updike

(1932-)

John Updike (1932—) is a famous American writer. His most famous work is his Rabbit series: *Rabbit, Run* (1960) ; *Rabbit Redux* (1971) ; *Rabbit Is Rich* (1981) ; *Rabbit at Rest* (1990) ; and *Rabbit Remembered* (2000). *Rabbit is Rich* and *Rabbit at Rest* both won Pulitzer Prizes for Updike. Besides, he won the National Book Award, the National Book Critics Circle Award, the Rosenthal Award, and the Howells Medal. He received the National Medal of Art from President George H. W. Bush in 1989, and in 2003 was presented with the National Medal for the Humanities from President George W. Bush. He is one of a very few Americans to receive both of these honors.

Describing his subject as " the American small town, Protestant middle class", Updike is well known for his careful craftsmanship and prolific writing, having published more than 60 books, including novels, collections of short stories, poems, essays and criticism. His works often explore sex, faith, and death, and their inter-relationships. He favors realism and naturalism in his writing. In most of his novels and short stories the hero is typically an everyman one can find on the streets. Throughout Updike's works, one finds the gentle observations of American life and customs. His works are often viewed as a commentary on the moral and social fabric of American life.

Updike was born in Reading, Pennsylvania, and was raised in nearby Shillington, a small town where his father was a high school science teacher. The area surrounding Reading has provided the setting for many of his stories, with the invented towns of Brewer and Olinger standing in for Reading and Shillington. An only child, Updike and his parents shared a house with his grandparents for much of his childhood. In the Depression Updike's grandfather lost his fortune and his father lost his job as a travelling salesman. When he was 13, the family moved to his mother's birthplace, a stone farmhouse on an 80-acre farm near Plowville, eleven miles from Shillington, where he continued to attend school. His mother was a writer and encouraged him to write. Many of these childhood memories found their way into the following short story "My Father on the Verge of Disgrace". Thus this story, like some of his other short stories, has a strongly autobiographical flavor.

Updike graduated from Harvard University in 1954, and spent a year in England studying art. After his return to the United States, he worked on the staff of The New Yorker, where many of his short stories have appeared. Updike has been recognized as a master of the short story. His short stories are collected in The Same Door (1959) , Pigeon Feathers and other Stories (1962) , The Music School (1966) , Bech: A Book (1970) ; Museums and Women (1972) ; Too Far to Go (1979) ; Bech is Back (1982) ; Trust Me (1987) ; Licks of Love: Short Stories and a Sequel (2000) ; and The Collected Stories: 1953—1975 (2003) . "My Father on the Verge of Disgrace" was published in 1998 and was collected in Licks of Love in 2000. This short story is about a father's struggle to support his family and the son's maturation in a small town in Pennsylvania. It presents the poor life of an ordinary American family in the Great Depression and portrays a boy's mixed emotions toward his father who works as a school teacher but steals money from the high school sports receipts in his care. As the boy grows up, he understands his father better and comes to know that "part of being human is being on the verge of disgrace".

My Father on the Verge of Disgrace

John Updike

It filtered even into my childhood dreams, the fear. The fear that he would somehow fall from his precarious ledge of respectability[1], a ledge where we all stood with him. "We all": his dependents—my mother, her parents, myself. The house we lived in was too big for us: my grandfather had bought it in 1922, when he felt prosperous enough to retire. Within the decade, the stock market crash[2] took all his savings. He sat in one corner of the big house, the little "sunroom" that looked toward the front yard, the hedge[3] and the street with its murmuring traffic. My grandmother, bent over and crippled by arthritis[4], hobbled about in the kitchen and out into the back yard, where she grew peas and kept chickens. My mother had her nook[5] upstairs, at a little desk with wicker sides, where she did not like to be interrupted, and my father was generally out somewhere in the town. He was a tall, long-legged man who needed to keep moving. The year I was born, he had lost his job, as salesman in the mid-Atlantic territory for a line of quality English china[6]. Only after three years—anxious years for him, but for me just a few smells and radiant visions retained by my infant memory[7]—did he succeed in getting another job, as a high school teacher. It was as a schoolteacher that I always knew him. Wearing a suit, his shirt pocket holding a pack of cigarettes and a mechanical pencil and a fountain pen, he loomed[8] to me as a person of eminence[9] in the town; it was this sense of his height that led, perhaps, to my fear that he would somehow topple[10].

One of my dreams, borrowing some Depression imagery[11] from the cartoons in the newspaper, had him clad in a barrel[12] and, gray-faced,

229

being harried down the town hall steps by the barking apparitions of local officialdom[13]. The crowd began to throw things, and my attempt at explaining, at pleading for him, got caught up in my throat. In this present day of strip malls[14] and towns that are mere boundaries on a developer's map, it is hard to imagine the core of authority that existed then in small towns, at least in the view of child—the power of righteousness and enforcement that radiated from the humorless miens of the central men[15]. They were not necessarily officials—the town was too small to have many of those. And the police chief was a perky[16], comically small man who inspired fear not even in first-graders, as he halted traffic to let them cross the street to the elementary school. But certain local merchants, a clergyman or two, the undertaker whose green-awninged mansion dominated the main intersection, across from a tavern and a drug-store, not to mention the druggist and the supervising principal of the school where my father taught, projected an aura of potential condemnation and banishment[17].

To have this power, you had to have been born in the town, or at least in the locality, and my father had not been. His accent, his stride, were slightly different. This was Pennsylvania, and he was from New Jersey. My mother came from the area, and she may have married my father in hopes of escaping it. But the land of six decades ago was less permeable than it is now; it exerted a grip[18]. Fate, or defeat, returned my parents to my grand father's big house, a house where only I, growing up day by day, felt perfectly at home.

I was proud of my schoolteacher father. If his suit was out of press and his necktie knotted awry, I was too new to the world to notice. He combed his hair back and, in the style of his generation, parted it near the middle. In our kitchen, he would bolt his orange juice (squeezed on one of those ribbed glass sombreros and then poured off through a strainer) and his toast

230

(the toaster a simple tin box, a kind of little hut with slit and slanted sides, that rested over a gas burner and browned one side of the bread, in stripes, at a time)[19], and then he would stride, so hurriedly that his necktie flew back over his shoulder, down through our yard, past the grapevines hung with buzzing Japanese beetle traps, to the yellow brick building, with its tall smokestack and wide playing fields, where he taught. Though the town had some hosiery and hat factories tucked around in its blocks of row housed, the high school was the most impressive building on my horizon. To me, it was the center of the universe. I enjoyed the gleams of recognition that fell to me from my father's high visibility. His teaching colleagues greeted me on the street with a smile; other adults seemed to know me and included me in a sort of ironical forbearance. He was not a drinker—his anxious stomach was too tender for that—but he had the waywardly sociable habits of a drinker. He needed people, believed in their wisdom and largesse, as none of the rest of us who lived in the house did: four recluses and an extrovert[20]. Imitating my mother, I early developed a capacity to entertain myself, with paper and the images it bore. When school—the elementary school, at the other end of town, along the main street—took me into its classes, I felt, in relation to my classmates, slightly timid.

He called me "young America", as if I were more bumptious than I was. He pushed me about the town with a long stick he had made, whose fork gripped the back of my red wagon, so that all I had to do was sit in it and steer. No more births followed mine. My bedroom was a narrow back room, with a bookshelf and some framed illustrations, by Vernon Grant, of nursery rhymes[21]; it overlooked the back yard and adjoined my parents' bedroom. I could hear them talk at night; even when the words were indistinct, the hiss of unhappiness, of obscure hot pressures, came through the walls. "*That son of a bitch*," my father would say, of some man whose

231

name I had missed. "*Out to get me,*" I would hear. Who could this enemy be, I would wonder, while my mother's higher, more rhythmic voice would try to seal over the wound, whatever it was, and I would be lulled into sleep, surrounded by my toys, my Big Little Books, my stacked drawings crayoned on the rough dun-colored paper supplied at school, the Vernon Grant figures presiding above the bookshelf—a band of cheerful, long-nosed angels who lived in shoes and tumbled downhill. Paper, I felt, would protect me. Sometimes in my parents' room there were quarrels, stifled sobs from my melodious mother and percussive rumbling from my father, these troubles were like a thunderstorm that whipped and thumped the house for half an hour and then rolled off into the sky to the east[22].

One center of trouble, I remember, was a man called Otto Werner, which Otto pronounced as if the *W* were a *V*. Among the Pennsylvania Germans, he was exceptionally German, with a toothbrush mustache, a malicious twinkle in his eye, and an erect, jerky way of carrying himself. He too was a schoolteacher, but not in our town's system. He and my father, on weekends and in the summer, traveled to Philadelphia, an hour and a half away, to accumulate credits toward a master's degree. Having a master's would improve my father's salary by a few sorely needed dollars.

The first scandal that attached itself to Otto concerned his standing on the steps of some building at the University of Pennsylvania and shouting, "*Heil, Hitler!*" The United States was not yet in the war, and a pro-German Bund[23] openly met in our local city of Brewer, but still it was an eccentric and dangerous thing to do. Otto was, my father admitted, "a free spirit". But he owned a car, and we did not. We once did—a green Model A that figures in my earliest memories—but somewhere in the thirties it disappeared. In a town so compact one could walk anywhere within twenty minutes, and in a region webbed with trolley tracks and train tracks, the deprivation did not seem radical[24]. Once the war came, even those who

232

owned cars couldn't drive them.

A worse scandal than "*Heil, Hitler!*" had to do with a girl at the high school. My father carried a few notes from Otto to her, and it turned out they were love notes, and he was aiding and abetting the corruption of a minor[25]. The girl's parents got involved, and members of the school board were informed. Not only could my father get fired, I understood; he could go to jail for his part in this scandal. As I lay in my bed at night I could hear my parents talking in a ragged, popping murmur like the noise of something frying; I could feel the heat, and my father twisting in his agony, and the other adults in the house holding their breath. Had there been trysts, and had my father carried the notes that arranged them? It was like him; he was always doing people unnecessary favors. Once he walked out into a snowstorm to go and apologize to a boy in one of his classes with whom he had been impatient, or sarcastic. "I hate sarcasm," he said. "Everybody in this part of the world uses it, but it hurts like hell to be on the receiving end[26]. Poor kid, I thought he stunk the place up to get my goat, but upon sober reflection I believe it was just one more case of honest stupidity[27]." His subject was chemistry, with its many opportunities for spillage, breakage, smells, and small explosions.

The scandal with the girl somehow died away. Perhaps the notes he carried were innocent. Perhaps he persuaded the principal and the school board that he, at least, was innocent. There had been a romance, because within a year or two the girl, graduated now, married Otto. The couple moved to the Southwest but occasionally would visit my parents. When my mother became a widow, living alone in a farmhouse ten miles from the town, the couple would visit her as part of their annual eastern pilgrimage. Though twenty years younger, Mrs. Werner went plump early, and her hair turned white, so the age difference became less and less noticeable. They had bought a Winnebago[28] and would pull up alongside the barn and Otto would limp across the yard to greet my mother merrily, that twinkle still in his eye. My mother would be merry in turn, having forgotten, it seemed, all the woe he once brought us. In trying to recall the heat in the old house, the terror he had caused, I have forgotten the most interesting thing about him: he had only one leg. The other was a beige prosthesis that gave him his jerky walk, a sharp hitch as if he were tossing something with his right hip[29]. Remembering this makes him seem less dangerous: how could the world ever punish a one-legged man for shouting "*Heil, Hitler!*" or for falling in love with a teenager from another school system?

The country ran on dimes and quarters[30]. A hamburger cost ten cents, and I paid ten cents to get into the movie-house, until a war tax made it eleven. The last year of the war, a month before V-E Day[31] and Hitler's vanishing—*poof*! —from his underground bunker, I turned thirteen, and old Mrs. Naftzinger in the little glass booth somehow knew it. An adult ticket cost twenty-seven cents, and that was too much for me to go twice a week. The economics of my grand father's house seemed simple: my father brought home his pay every other week in a brown envelope, and the money was dumped in a little red-and-white recipe box that sat on top of the icebox. Anybody who needed money fished it out of the box; each lunchtime I was allowed six cents, a nickel and a penny, to buy a Tastykake[32] on the way back to elementary school. My grandfather did the packaged-food shopping at Tyse Segner's store, a few houses away. Tyse, who lived in the back rooms and upstairs with his wife, was a man of my grandfather's generation—a rather ill-tempered one, I thought, considering all the candy he had behind his counter and could eat for free whenever he wanted. My mother usually bought fresh meat and vegetables at Bud Hoffert's Acme, two blocks away, past the ice plant, up on Second Street. Bud wore rimless glasses and a bloody apron. My grandmother did the cooking but never shopped; nor did my father—he just brought home, as he said, "the bacon". The little tin recipe box never became quite empty; I never had to do without a noontime Tastykake. I moved a kitchen chair next to the icebox to stand on while I fished the nickel and the penny from the box, beneath a clutter of folded dollars and scattered quarters. When the tin bottom began to show, more coins and bills somehow appeared, to tide us over, and these, it slowly dawned on me, were borrowed from the high school sports receipts[33].

My father had charge of them, as an extracurricular duty: at football games he would sit at a gap in the ropes, selling tickets and making change from a flat green box whose little compartments were curved to let your fingers scoop up the coins. At basketball games he would sit with the box at a little table just inside the school's mighty front portals, across from the glass case of silver trophies and around the corner from the supervising principal's office. The green box would come home with him, many nights, for safekeeping. The tickets fascinated me—the great wheels of them, as wide as dinner plates but thicker. They came in two distinct colors, blue for adults and orange for students, and each ticket was numbered. It was another kind of money. Each rectangle of the thin, tightly coiled cardboard possessed, at the right time, a real value, brought into play by a sports event; money and time and cardboard and people's desire to see were magically interwoven. My father was magical, converting into dollars and quarters and dimes the Tuesday and Friday night basketball crowds and the outdoor crowd that straggled out of the town's streets onto the football field on Saturday afternoons. (It was easy to sneak under the ropes, but many grownups didn't bother, and solemnly paid.) The tickets, numbered into the hundreds, were worth nothing until my father presided at his little table. He always made the balance right when he got his paycheck, or so he assured my mother. She had begun to get alarmed, and her alarm spread to me.

My memories of their conversations, the pressure of them, have me leaning my face against the grain of the wooden icebox, a zinc-lined cabinet whose dignity dominated our kitchen as it majestically digested, day after day, a succession of heavy ice blocks fetched in a straw-lined truck and carried with tongs into the house by a cheerful man with a leathern apron down his back, to ward off the wet and the chill[34]. I could feel the coldness on my cheek through the zinc and wood as my parents' faces revolved above me and their voices clung to my ears.

"Embezzlement[35]," my mother said, a word I knew only from the radio. "What good will you be to any of us in jail?"

"I make it square, right to the penny. Square on the button, every other week, when I get my envelope."

"Suppose Danny Haas some week decides to deposit the receipts on a Friday instead of a Monday? He'd ask, and you'd be short."

Danny Haas, I knew, taught senior-high math and headed up the school athletics program; a short man who smoked cigars and wore suits with broad stripes, he nevertheless was one of the righteous at the town's core. My tall father and he sometimes clowned together, because of their height discrepancy, but it was clear to me who had the leverage, the connections, the power to bring down[36].

"He won't, Lucy," my father was saying. Whenever he used my mother's name, it was a sign that he wanted to end the conversation. "Danny's like all these Dutchmen, a slave to habit. Anyway, we're not talking Carnegie-Mellon bucks[37] here, we're talking relative peanuts[38]." How much, indeed? A ten-dollar bill, in those days, looked like a fortune to me; I never saw a twenty, not even when the recipe box was fullest.

"Nobody will think it's peanuts if it's missing."

My father became angry, as much as he ever did. "What can I do, Lucy? We live poor as dump dogs anyway." The phrase "dump dogs" had

236

to be one he had brought from his other life, when he lived in another state and was a boy like me. He went on, venting grievances seldom expressed in my hearing. "We've got a big place here to heat. We can't all go naked. The kid keeps growing. My brown suit is wearing out. Mom does what she can in her garden, but I've got five mouths to feed." He called my grandmother Mom and exempted her, I felt, from the status of pure burden. My mother's work at her wicker desk produced no money, my grandfather in his pride had bought too big a house, and I—I didn't even go out and shovel snow for neighbors in a storm, because I was so susceptible to colds[39]. My father was warming to his subject. "Count'em—five! *Nihil ex nihilo*[40], Dad used to say." Dad was his own father, dead before I was born. "You don't get something for nothing," he translated. "There are no free rides in this life."

My mother feebly used the word *economize*, another radio word, but even I could feel it was hopeless; how could I go without my Tastykake, when nobody else in my class was that poor? My father had to go on stealing from the school, and would someday be chased in his barrel down the town hall steps.

During the war things eased a bit. Men were scarce, and he got summer jobs that did not aggravate his hernia[41]; he was made a timekeeper for a railroad work crew. The tracks were humming and needed to be kept up. In the history books our time in the war looks short: less than four years from Pearl Harbor to V-J Day[42]. Yet it seemed to go on forever, while I inched up through the grades of elementary school. It became impossible to imagine a world without the war, without the big headlines and the ration tokens and coupons and the tin-can drives and Bing Crosby and Dorothy La-mour selling War Bonds at rallies[43]. I reached seventh grade, a junior-high grade, housed in the grand yellow brick building where my father taught.

237

I was too young for chemistry, but there was no missing his high head and long stride in the halls. Sharing the waxed, locker-lined halls with him all day, being on his work premises, as it were, did not eradicate my anxiety that he would be brought low. The perils surrounding him became realer to me. We students filled the halls with a ruthless, trampling sound. My father was a notoriously poor disciplinarian[44]; he was not German enough, and took too little pleasure in silence and order. Entire classes, rumor reached me from the upper grades, were wasted in monologues in which he tried to impart the lessons that life had taught him—you don't get something for nothing, there are no free rides. These truths were well illustrated in the workings of chemistry, so perhaps he wasn't as far off the point as the students thought. They played a game of getting him going and thus sparing themselves classwork for the day. He would suddenly throw a blackboard eraser up toward the ceiling and with a boyish deftness catch it, saying, "What goes up must come down." He told the momentarily silenced students, "You're on top of Fools' Hill now, but you'll come down the other side." He did not conceal from them his interest in the fruitful possibilities of disorder; so many great chemical discoveries, after all, were accidents. He loved chemistry. "Water is the universal solvent," I often heard him pronounce, as if it were a truly consoling formula, like "This too will pass away." Who is to say his message did not come through all the classroom confusion—the notes being passed, the muttered asides of the class clown, the physical tussles at the rear of the room[45]?

He was the faculty clown, to my discomfort. His remarks in assembly always got the students laughing, and in the spring, in the annual faculty assembly program, he participated in a, to me, horrifying performance of the Pyramus and Thisby episode of A *Midsummer Night's Dream*[46]. Gotten up as a gawky, dirndle-clad, lipsticked Thisby, in a reddish blond wig with pigtails[47], my father climbed a little stepladder to reach the chink in

238

the wall. The Wall was played by thickset football coach, tank Geiger, wearing a football helmet and a sheet painted to resemble masonry.

I had noticed in the privacy of our home how my father's legs, especially where his stockings rubbed, were virtually hairless compared with those of other men. Now the sight of his hairless legs, bare for all to see, as he mounted the ladder—the students around me howling at every mincing step he took upward—made me think his moment to topple had come. Mr. Geiger held up at arm's height a circle-forming thumb and forefinger to represent the chink in the wall; on the opposite side of the wall, little Mr. Haas climbed his ladder a step higher than my father, to put his face on the same level. "O, kiss me," he recited, "through the hole of this vile wall." Mr. Geiger mugged in mock affront, and the auditorium rocked[48]. My father, in his high Thisby voice, answered, "I kiss the wall's hole, not your lips at all," and his and Mr. Haas's faces slowly met through the third teacher's fingers. The screams of disbelieving hilarity around me made my ears burn. This had to be ruinous, I thought. This was worse than any of my dreams.

But the next day my father loped through the halls with his head high, his hair parted in the middle as usual, in his usual shiny suit, and school life continued. "Burning," went another of his chemical slogans, "destroys nothing. It just shuffles the molecules."

At the war's end, we moved form the house that was too big to a small farmhouse ten miles away. It was my mother's idea of economizing. The antique small-town certainties I had grown up among were abruptly left behind. No more wood icebox, no more tin toaster, no more Vernon Grant nursery rhymes framed above my bed, no more simply running down through the yard to the eighth grade. My father and I were thrown together in a state of daily exile, getting into the car—we had to acquire a car— before the frost had left the windshield and returning, many nights, after dusk, our headlights the only ones on the pitted dirt road home. He still took the ticket money at the basketball games and, as another extracurricular duty, coached the swimming team, which, since the school had no pool, practiced at the YMCA[49] in the city of Brewer's dingy and menacing downtown. The ten-year-old car we acquired kept giving us adventures: flat tires, broken axles, fearful struggles to put on tire chains at the base of a hill in the midst of a snowstorm. We sometimes didn't make it home, and walked and hitchhiked to shelter—the homes of fellow teachers, or what my father cheerfully called "fleabag" hotels. We became, during those years of joint commuting, a kind of team—partners in peril, fellow sufferers on the edge of disaster. It was dreadful but somehow authentic to be stuck in a stalled car with only four dollars between us, in the age before ATMs. It was —at least afterward, in the hotel, where my father had successfully begged the clerk to call Danny Haas to vouch for us—bliss, a rub against basic verities[50], an instance of survival.

I stood in sardonic, exasperated silence during his conversations with hotel clerks, garage mechanics, luncheonette waitresses, strangers on the street, none of whom were accustomed to encountering such a high level of trust. It was no mistake that he had wound up in education; he believed that everyone had something to teach him. His suppliant air humiliated me, but I was fourteen, fifteen; I was at his mercy, and he was at the mercy of the world. I saw him rebuffed and misunderstood. Flecks of foam would appear at the corners of his mouth as he strove to communicate; in my helpless witnessing I was half blinded by impatience and what now seems a mist of love, a pity bulging toward him like some embarrassing warpage of my own face[51].

He enjoyed human contact even at its least satisfactory, it slowly came to me. "I just wanted to see what he would say," he would explain after some futile tussle with, say, the policeman in charge of the municipal garage to which our nonstarting car had been towed, parked as it had been in a loading zone by the railroad platform; the cop refused to grasp the distinction between my father's good intentions and the car's mechanical misbehavior. "I used to land in the damnedest little towns," he would tell me, of his days selling china. "In upstate New York, West Virginia, wherever, you'd just get off the train with your sample case and go into any store where you saw china and try to talk them into carrying your line[52], which usually cost a bit more than the lines they had. You never knew what would happen. Some of them, at these dumps in the back of nowhere, would come up with the most surprising orders—tall orders. This was before the Depression hit, of course. I mean, it hit in '29, but there was a grace period before it took hold[53]. And then you were born. Young America. Your mother and I, it knocked us for a loop, we had never figured on ourselves as parents[54]. I don't know why not—it happens all the time. Making babies is the number one priority for human nature. When I'm standing up there trying to pound the periodic table into their jiggling heads I sometimes think, these poor devils, they just want to be making babies.

My own developing baby-making yen took the form, first, of learning to smoke. You couldn't get anywhere in the high school society of the late forties without smoking. I had bought a pack—Old Golds, I think, because of the boubloons[55]—at the Brewer railroad station, while my father was coaching the swimming team. Though the first drags did, in his phrase, knock me for a loop, I stuck with it; my vagabond life as his satellite left me with a lot of idle time in luncheonette booths. One winter morning when I was fifteen, I asked him if I could light up a cigarette in the car on the way to school. He himself had stopped, on his doctor's advice. But he didn't say no to me, and more than thirty years after I too quit, I still remember those caustic, giddying drags mixed with the first grateful whiffs of warmth from the car heater, while the little cracking radio played its medley of the Ink Spots and farm reports[56]. His tacit permission, coming from a schoolteacher, would have been viewed, we both knew, as something of a disgrace. But it was my way of becoming a human being, and part of being human is being on the verge of disgrace.

Moving to the country had liberated us both, I see now, from the small-town grid and those masters of righteousness. The shopping fell to us, and my father favored a roadside grocery store that was owned and run, it was rumored, by a former Brewer gangster. Like my father, Arty Callahan was tall, melancholy, and slightly deaf; his wife was an overweight, wisecracking woman whose own past, it was said, was none too savory[57]. My father loved them, and loved the fifteen minutes of delay their store gave him on the return home. Both Mr. and Mrs. Callahan took him in the right way, it seemed to me, with not too much of either amusement or gravity; they were, all three, free spirits and understood one another. While he talked to them, acting out, in gestures and phrases that had become somewhat stylized, his sense of daily peril, I would sit at a small Formica-topped table[58] next to the magazine rack and leaf through *Esquire*[59], looking for Varga girls[60]. I would sneak a look at Arty Callahan's profile, so noncommittally clamped over his terribly false teeth[61], and wonder how many men he had killed. The only gangsterish thing he did was give me ten dollars—a huge amount for an hour's work— for tutoring his son in algebra on Saturdays, when I was old enough to drive the car there.

We had traded in our car for a slightly newer and more dependable one, though still a prewar model. By the time I went off to college I no longer feared—I no longer dreamed—that my father would be savaged by society. He was fifty by then, a respectable age. Living his life beside him for five years, I had seen that his flirtation with disgrace was only that, not a ruinous infatuation. Nothing but death could topple him, and even that not very far, not in my mind.

Notes:

1. The fear that he would somehow fall from his precarious ledge of respectability: 担心他会从体面但危险的高位上掉下来,令自己和家人名誉扫地。precarious: unsafe; ledge: 壁架(a narrow flat shelf or surface, esp. one on the edge of an upright object); respectability: 体面(the quality of being respectable)

2. the stock market crash: 1929 年美国股市的崩溃(The stock market of the U. S. collapsed on Thursday, October 24, 1929. The stock market crash ruined thousands of Americans. It marked the beginning of the Great Depression—a long, slow, painful fall to the worst economic crisis in American history. The Depression brought suffering to millions of people. Many corporations were bankrupted; many workers lost their jobs. The Depression did not end until the early 1940s.)

3. hedge: 树篱(a fence or boundary formed of shrubs or small trees)

4. arthritis: 关节炎

5. nook:(房间的)角落(a small space in a corner of a room)

6. as salesman in the mid-Atlantic territory for a line of quality English china: 在中大西洋区域推销一种高级的英国瓷器。中大西洋区域包括以下 8 个州:New York, Pennsylvania, New Jersey, Delaware, Maryland, Virginia, West Virginia 和 the District of Columbia。territory: 领土,区域,这里指销售员的推销区

7. just a few smells and radiant visions retained by my infant memory:只是儿时记忆所保留的一些气味和发光的幻觉

8. loom: 赫然耸现(appear in an impressively exaggerated form)

9. eminence: 著名,卓越(the quality of being famous and of a high rank,

esp. in science, the arts, etc.)

10. topple：倒下（become unsteady and fall down）

11. imagery：画像（images）

12. ...had him clad in a barrel：给他身上套了个木桶。clad in：穿
……衣服的（covered or clothed in）

13. being harried down the town hall steps by the barking apparitions of
local officialdom：被当地官员的幽灵咆哮着赶下市政厅的台阶。
harry：驱赶（to force to move along by harassing）；apparition：ghost；
officialdom：官员（总称）（officials as a group）

14. strip malls：（繁忙道路旁的）购物中心

15. the power of righteousness and enforcement that radiated from the
humorless miens of the central men：从这些重要人士一本正经的神
态中流露出来的公正不阿和严格执法的权力

16. perky：confidently cheerful

17. the undertaker whose green-awninged mansion dominated...
condemnation and banishment：那个墓葬承办人（他那栋装有绿色帆
布雨篷的大厦耸立于主交叉路口，大厦对面是个小酒馆和一家药
店），更不必说那个药店店主和那个我爸爸所任教学校的主管校
长，制造了一种可能谴责和驱逐的气氛。

18. But the land of six decades ago was less permeable than it is now; it
exerted a grip：但是60年前的土地比现在更难渗透，它具有一种控
制力。permeable：可渗透的（capable of being passed through or
permeated, especially by liquids or gases）；   grip：紧抓，控制（a
grasp, hold, or control）

19. In our kitchen, he would bolt his orange juice（squeezed on one of
those ribbed glass sombreros and then poured off through a strainer）
and toast...in stripes, at a time）：在我们的厨房，他会快速喝掉
橙汁（在一个有凸起条纹的形似墨西哥草帽的玻璃容器上挤出来，
然后通过一个滤网倒出来），匆匆吞下烤面包（烤面包机是个简单

244

的铁盒,一种小箱子,两侧倾斜,上面有狭长的切口。面包机放在一个煤气炉上,把长条形面包的两面烤成棕色,一次烤一面)。bolt:狼吞虎咽(eat quickly);ribbed:有凸起条纹的(having a pattern of long thin raised lines);sombrero:墨西哥草帽

20. believed in their wisdom and largesse, as none of the rest of us who lived in the house did: four recluses and an extrovert: 相信他们的智慧和慷慨,而家里其他人谁也不会这样做:4个隐居者和一个性格外向的人。

21. some framed illustrations, by Vernon Grant, of nursery rhymes: 一些装在镜框里的、由费农·格兰特画的儿歌插图。Vernon Grant (1902—1990): 费农·格兰特, 美国杂志和书籍插图画家, 创作了家乐氏公司的早餐玉米片卡通人物 Snap, Crackle 和 Pop (a magazine and book illustrator who was the creator of the Kellogg's cereal characters Snap, Crackle and Pop)

22. stifled sobs from my melodious mother . . . and then rolled off into the sky to the east: 声音悦耳的母亲努力抑制的抽泣声,父亲低沉有力的咕哝声;这些烦恼就像一场雷雨,鞭打和冲击房屋半小时,然后向东滚滚而去,消失在天空中。percussive:有强大冲击力的(having powerful impact);rumble:用低沉的声音说话,咕哝(speak in a low rolling tone)

23. pro-German Bund: 20 世纪 30 年代美国亲纳粹德国的德美同盟会(a pro-Nazi German-American organization of the 1930s)

24. in a region webbed with trolley tracks and train tracks, the deprivation did not seem radical: 在一个到处铺设着有轨电车和铁路轨道的地区,没有车似乎并不十分严重。deprivation: a lack or loss; radical: extreme.

25. abetting the corruption of a minor: 怂恿一个未成年人的堕落。abet: encourage; minor: 未成年人(a person below the age at which they are fully responsible in law for their actions)

26. but it hurts like hell to be on the receiving end：但这大大伤害了受到挖苦的一方。like hell：very much

27. he stunk the place up to get my goat . . . just one more case of honest stupidity：他把那个地方弄得臭气熏天就是为了激怒我,但经过冷静的考虑,我认为这不过是他干的又一件诚实而愚蠢的事。stunk是 stink 的过去式和过去分词;stink up：使臭气熏天(cause to give a strong bad smell)；get one's goat：使人恼怒(make sb. extremely annoyed)

28. Winnebago：美国 Winnebago 公司生产的房车(a model of motor home produced by Winnebago Industries Inc.)

29. a beige prosthesis that gave him . . . with his right hip：一条使他走起路来一颠一颠的米黄色假肢,每走一步就要猛拉一下腿,好像他在用右边的臀部抛掷什么东西。

30. dimes and quarters：美元或加元硬币,小钱。dime：一角硬币(a coin of the United States worth one tenth of a dollar)；quarter：2 角 5 分硬币(a coin worth a quarter of a dollar)

31. V-E Day：欧洲胜利日。[On the 7th May 1945 Germany surrendered and the 8th May was declared V-E Day (Victory in Europe).]

32. Tastykake：美国 Tasty Baking Company 生产的糕点商标,小说中指的可能是该牌子的一种蛋糕

33. When the tin bottom began to show . . . the high school sports receipt：当锡盒的底部开始显露时,不知怎么的,又会出现更多的硬币和钞票,帮助我们渡过难关,而这些钱,我慢慢地明白,是从高中体育活动的收入中借来的。

34. have me leaning my face against . . . ward off the wet and the chill：使我把脸靠在木制的冰箱上。这是个内壁涂了一层锌的柜子,摆在厨房里,高贵无比,它日复一日高贵地消化着接连不断送来的大冰块。冰块先是用垫了稻草的卡车运来,然后用钳子夹进房子。运冰人是个快活的人,他系着一条皮围裙,皮围裙从后背垂下,以抵

挡潮湿和寒冷。grain：纹理（the arrangement of fibers in wood）

35. embezzlement：盗用/挪用公款（the act of stealing money that is placed in one's care）

36. My tall father and he ... the power to bring down：因为他们两人身高的差异,有时候身材高大的父亲和他在一起扮演小丑,但我明白,谁有手段、关系和权势叫人身败名裂。

37. Carnegie-Mellon bucks：大数额的钱（big money）。Carnegie：Andrew Carnegie(1835—1919),美国钢铁企业家,百万富翁,慈善家（American industrialist, millionaire, and philanthropist）；Mellon：Andrew William Mellon (1855—1937),美国金融家,企业家,慈善家,20 世纪 20 年代初美国最大富豪之一

38. relative peanuts：相对而言区区一点小钱。peanuts：微不足道的一小笔钱（a sum of money so small that it is not worth considering）

39. because I was so susceptible to colds：因为我非常容易感冒。susceptible to：易被……感染的（likely to suffer from）

40. *Nihil ex nihilo*：拉丁文,意思是"从无生不出有来"（Latin, meaning "out of nothing comes nothing"）

41. aggravate his hernia：加重他的疝气

42. from Pearl Harbor to V-J Day：从珍珠港事件到日本投降日。[Pearl Harbor：On 7 December 1941, Japanese naval and air forces attacked the American Pacific Fleet base at Pearl Harbor on the Hawaiian island of Oahu. No declaration of war was made. The attack brought the United States of America into the Second World War. V-J Day：On 15th August 1945, Japan surrendered. This day was declared V-J Day (Victory in Japan).]

43. the ration tokens and coupons ... selling War Bonds at rallies：配给标志和票证,捐献洋铁罐的运动,Bing Crosby 和 Dorothy Lamour 在群众集会上卖战时公债。Bing Crosby（1903—1977）：美国著名电影演员和歌星。Dorothy Lamour（1914—1996）：美国著名女演员

和歌手。二战期间,两人经常为慰问军队和推销战时公债到各地演出。

44. notoriously poor disciplinarian：人人皆知的不会抓纪律的老师。disciplinarian：执行纪律者（a person who can make people obey orders or who believes in firm discipline）

45. the notes being passed, the muttered asides … tussles at the rear of the room：纸条传来传去,爱开玩笑的学生低声说话,教室后面的打架。aside：小声说的话；旁白（an utterance meant to be inaudible to someone；*especially*：an actor's speech heard by the audience but supposedly not by other characters）；tussle：扭打（a rough struggle or fight）

46. the Pyramus and Thisby episode of *A Midsummer Night's Dream*：《仲夏夜之梦》关于 Pyramus 和 Thisby 的那一出戏。*A Midsummer Night's Dream* 是莎士比亚的著名浪漫喜剧。Pyramus 和 Thisby 原是罗马诗人奥维德（Ovid）在《变形记》（*Metamorphoses*）中讲述的一个巴比伦爱情故事中的男女主角,莎士比亚把这个故事用在他的这部喜剧中。

47. Gotten up as a gawky, dirndle-clad, lipsticked Thisby, in a reddish blond wig with pigtails：化装成一个笨拙的、身穿紧身连衣裙、嘴唇涂了口红的 Thisby,头上戴着一个编了两根辫子的微红金色假发。

48. Mr. Geiger mugged in mock affront, and the auditorium rocked：Mr. Geiger 假装有意冒犯地做了个鬼脸,整个礼堂的人于是哄堂大笑,笑得前仰后合。

49. YMCA：Young Men's Christian Association 基督教青年会

50. a rub against basic verities：接触到基本的真相

51. a pity bulging toward him like some embarrassing warpage of my own face：就像自己的脸令人尴尬地变了形,我对他充满了无限的同情。warpage：扭曲；变形（a twist or curve that has developed in something originally flat or straight）

248

52. talk them into carrying your line：说服他们代售你的产品

53. but there was a grace period before it took hold：在大萧条发生前有一个过渡期。take hold：生效（take effect）

54. it knocked us for a loop，we ... as parents：你的降生使我们不知所措，我们还从来没有打算为人父母。knock sb. for a loop：使震惊（dumbfound，amaze）；figure on：打算（plan）

55. boubloon：都布隆，从前西班牙金币的名称（a gold coin formerly used in Spain and Spanish America）

56. those caustic，giddying drags ... its medley of the Ink Spots and farm reports：吸的那些辣辣的、令人头晕的烟，夹带着汽车加热器散发的令人愉快的温暖气息。沙沙作响的收音机里播放着"墨迹斑斑"乐团的歌曲，不时还夹播农场报道。the Ink Spots："墨迹斑斑"乐团（an African-American vocal group prominent in the late 1930s and '40s）

57. none too savory：一点也不体面。savory：体面（morally respectable）

58. Formica-topped table：贴了福米卡家具塑料贴面的桌子。Formica：福米卡家具塑料贴面（商标名称，用作桌子和柜台的能耐高温和抗化学物质的桌面）

59. *Esquire*：《老爷》杂志（the original and leading men's lifestyle magazine in the United States of America）

60. Varga girls：1940 年首次刊登在《老爷》杂志上的广告女郎宣传画，成为风靡全美的性感女神

61. noncommittally clamped over his terribly false teeth：暧昧地紧紧裹住了他那一口可怕的假牙

Questions：

1. What did the child fear? Why did he have such a fear?
2. What did the child think of "the core of authority"?
3. Why did the parents sometimes quarrel?

4. Was the father a good teacher? Why or why not?

5. In order to support the family, what else did the father do apart from teaching of chemistry?

6. Which particular event shows that the child began to mature?

7. How does the writer portray the character of the father?

Alice Walker

(1944-)

Alice Walker (1944—) is recognized as a leading African-American writer. She has produced an acclaimed and varied body of work, including poetry, novels, short stories, essays, and criticism. Her writings portray the struggle of black people throughout history, and are praised for their insightful and fascinating portraits of black life, in particular the experiences of black women in a sexist and racist society. She won wide recognition with her novel *The Color Purple*, which is about a poor black Southern woman's painful journey toward self-realization. This novel won for her the three most prestigious prizes of American literature in 1983: Pulitzer Prize, National Book Award and National Book Critics Circle Awards. Her reputation was further increased through the film adaptation by Steven Spielberg in 1985.

Walker was born in Eatonton, Georgia. Her parents were sharecroppers. When she was eight years old, she lost sight of one eye because of an accident. Despite the damage to her eye, she managed to finish high school and went to study at Spelman College in Atlanta and Sarah Lawrence College in the Bronx, New York. During her junior year she traveled to Africa as an exchange student. In 1965 she received her B. A. from Sarah Lawrence College. She was active in the Civil Rights Movement of the 1960s. She brings her travel experience in Africa and memories of the American civil rights movement to an examination of the experience of African Americans, mainly in the South, and of Africans. A self-described "womanist", — her term for a black feminist, she has maintained a strong focus on feminist issues within African-American culture.

Among her other novels are *Meridian* (1976), *The Temple of My Familiar* (1989), *By the Light of My Father's Smile* (1994), and *Now Is the Time to Open Your Heart* (2004). Her short-story collections include *In Love and Trouble: Stories of Black Women* (1973), *You Can't Keep a Good Woman Down* (1981) and the partially autobiographical *The Way Forward Is with a Broken Heart* (2000). She has also written poetry, such as *Revolutionary Petunias and Other Poems* (1973), *Her Blue Body Everything We Know: Earthling Poems 1965—1990* (1991), and *Absolute Trust in the Goodness of the Earth* (2003). Many of her essays are collected in *In Search of Our Mother's Gardens: Womanist Prose* (1984), *Living by the Word* (1988) and *Anything We Love Can Be Saved* (1997).

"Everyday Use", a short story from *In Love and Trouble*, was written during the heyday of the Black Power movement, when African Americans were trying to gain racial equality and called for self-determination and racial dignity. African American short stories of this period often dealt with problematic issues like separation, integration and redefinition of the African American past. Blacks were seeking their cultural roots in Africa, the slogan "Black is beautiful" and the Afro hair style arose. "Everyday Use" is Alice Walker's answer to the social discourse of that time, especially concerning the African American concept of heritage and identity.

"Everyday Use", set around the year 1970, is about a poor black mother and her two daughters Dee and Maggie, and their different attitudes toward the black heritage. Dee, educated, beautiful, but arrogant, has changed her name, adopted the ideas of the Black Power movement and criticizes her family for the way they "still live". Maggie, simple-minded, disfigured and slow, has learned how to quilt from her elders, which is a symbol of the continuation of black tradition. The story reaches its climax when the mother refuses to give Dee some old quilts because they were already meant to be a wedding present for Maggie. These quilts are the central image of the story and represent the concept of heritage. By her act of refusal, the mother decides that Maggie's practical approach to heritage is better than Dee's superficial, cold concept of heritage.

Everyday Use

for your grandma

Alice Walker

I will wait for her in the yard that Maggie and I made so clean and wavy yesterday afternoon. A yard like this is more comfortable than most people know. It is not just a yard. It is like an extended living room. When the hard clay is swept clean as a floor and the fine sand around the edges lined with tiny, irregular grooves[1], anyone can come and sit and look up into the elm tree[2] and wait for the breezes that never come inside the house.

Maggie will be nervous until after her sister goes: she will stand hopelessly in corners, homely and ashamed of the burn scars down her arms and legs, eying her sister with a mixture of envy and awe. She thinks her sister has held life always in the palm of one hand, that "no" is a word the world never learned to say to her.

You've no doubt seen those TV shows where the child who has "made it" is confronted, as a surprise, by her own mother and father, tottering in weakly from backstage[3]. (A pleasant surprise, of course: What would they do if parent and child came on the show only to curse out and insult each other?) On TV mother and child embrace and smile into each other's faces. Sometimes the mother and father weep, the child wraps them in her arms[4] and leans across the table to tell how she would not have made it without their help. I have seen these programs.

Sometimes I dream a dream in which Dee and I are suddenly brought together on a TV program of this sort. Out of a dark and soft-seated limousine[5] I am ushered into[6] a bright room filled with many people. There I meet a smiling, gray, sporty man like Johnny Carson[7] who shakes my hand and tells me what a fine girl I have. Then we are on the stage and Dee is embracing me with tears in her eyes. She pins on my dress a large orchid, even though she has told me once that she thinks orchids are tacky flowers[8].

In real life I am a large, big-boned woman with rough, man-working hands. In the winter I wear flannel nightgowns to bed and overalls during the day. I can kill and clean a hog as mercilessly as a man. My fat keeps me hot in zero weather. I can work outside all day, breaking ice to get water for washing; I can eat pork liver cooked over the open fire minutes after it comes steaming from the hog. One winter I knocked a bull calf straight in the brain between the eyes with a sledge hammer and had the meat hung up to chill before nightfall. But of course all this does not show on television. I am the way my daughter would want me to be: a hundred pounds lighter, my skin like an uncooked barley pancake. My hair glistens in the hot bright lights. Johnny Carson has much to do to keep up with my quick and witty tongue.

But that is a mistake. I know even before I wake up. Who ever knew a Johnson with a quick tongue? Who can even imagine me looking a strange white man in the eye? It seems to me I have talked to them always with one foot raised in flight, with my head turned in whichever way is farthest from them. Dee, though. She would always look anyone in the eye. Hesitation

254

was no part of her nature.

"How do I look, Mama?" Maggie says, showing just enough of her thin body enveloped in pink skirt and red blouse for me to know she's there, almost hidden by the door.

"Come out into the yard," I say.

Have you ever seen a lame animal, perhaps a dog run over by some careless person rich enough to own a car, sidle[9] up to someone who is ignorant enough to be kind to him? That is the way my Maggie walks. She has been like this, chin on chest, eyes on ground, feet in shuffle, ever since the fire that burned the other house to the ground.

Dee is lighter than Maggie, with nicer hair and a fuller figure. She's a woman now, though sometimes I forget. How long ago was it that the other house burned? Ten, twelve years? Sometimes I can still hear the flames and feel Maggie's arms sticking to me, her hair smoking and her dress falling off her in little black papery flakes. Her eyes seemed stretched open, blazed open by the flames reflected in them. And Dee. I see her standing off under the sweet gum tree she used to dig gum out of; a look of concentration on her face as she watched the last dingy gray board of the house fall in toward the red-hot brick chimney. Why don't you do a dance around the ashes? I'd wanted to ask her. She had hated the house that much.

I used to think she hated Maggie, too. But that was before we raised the money, the church and me, to send her to Augusta to school. She used to read to us without pity; forcing words, lies, other folks' habits, whole lives upon us two, sitting trapped and ignorant underneath her voice. She washed us in a river of make-believe, burned us with a lot of knowledge we didn't necessarily need to know. Pressed us to her with the serious way she read, to shove us away at just the moment, like dim-wits[10], we seemed about to understand.

Dee wanted nice things. A yellow organdy[11] dress to wear to her graduation from high school; black pumps[12] to match a green suit she'd made from an old suit somebody gave me. She was determined to stare down any disaster in her efforts. Her eyelids would not flicker for minutes at a time. Often I fought off the temptation to shake her. At sixteen she had a style of her own: and knew what style was.

I never had an education myself. After second grade the school was closed down. Don't ask me why: in 1927 colored[13] asked fewer questions than they do now. Sometimes Maggie reads to me. She stumbles along good-naturedly but can't see well[14]. She knows she is not bright. Like good looks and money, quickness passed her by. She will marry John Thomas (who has mossy[15] teeth in an earnest face) and then I'll be free to sit here and I guess just sing church songs to myself. Although I never was a good singer. Never could carry a tune. I was always better at a man's job. I used to love to milk till I was hooked in the side in '49. Cows are soothing and slow and don't bother you, unless you try to milk them the wrong way.

I have deliberately turned my back on the house. It is three rooms, just like the one that burned, except the roof is tin; they don't make shingle[16] roofs anymore. There are no real windows, just some holes cut in the sides, like the portholes[17] in a ship, but not round and not square, with rawhide holding the shutters up on the outside[18]. This house is in a pasture, too, like the other one. No doubt when Dee sees it she will want to tear it down. She wrote me once that no matter where we "choose" to live, she will manage to come see us. But she will never bring her friends. Maggie and I thought about this and Maggie asked me, "Mama, when did Dee ever have any friends?"

She had a few. Furtive boys in pink shirts hanging about on washday after school. Nervous girls who never laughed. Impressed with her they worshiped the well-turned phrase, the cute shape, the scalding humor that erupted like bubbles in lye[19]. She read to them.

When she was courting Jimmy T she didn't have much time to pay to us, but turned all her faultfinding power on him. He flew to marry a cheap city girl from a family of ignorant flashy people. She hardly had time to re-compose herself[20].

When she comes I will meet—but there they are!

Maggie attempts to make a dash for the house, in her shuffling way, but I stay her with my hand. "Come back here," I say. And she stops and tries to dig a well in the sand with her toe.

It is hard to see them clearly through the strong sun. But even the first glimpse of leg out of the car tells me it is Dee. Her feet were always neat-looking, as if God himself had shaped them with a certain style. From the other side of the car comes a short, stocky man. Hair is all over his head a foot long and hanging from his chin like a kinky mule tail[21]. I hear Maggie suck in her breath. "Uhnnnh," is what it sounds like. Like when you see the wriggling end[22] of a snake just in front of your foot on the road. "Uhnnnh."

Dee next. A dress down to the ground, in this hot weather. A dress so loud[23] it hurts my eyes. There are yellows and oranges enough to throw back the light of the sun. I feel my whole face warming from the heat waves it throws out. Earrings gold, too, and hanging down to her shoulders. Bracelets dangling[24] and making noises when she moves her arm up to shake the folds of the dress out of her armpits. The dress is loose and flows, and as she walks closer, I like it. I hear Maggie go "Uhnnnh" again. It is her sister's hair. It stands straight up like the wool on a sheep. It is black as night and around the edges are two long pigtails that rope about like small lizards disappearing behind her ears.

"Wa-su-zo-Tean-o[25]!" she says, coming on in that gliding way the dress makes her move. The short stocky fellow with the hair to his navel[26] is all grinning and he follows up with "Asalamalakim[27], my mother and sister!" He moves to hug Maggie but she falls back, right up against the back of my chair. I feel her trembling there and when I look up I see the perspiration[28] falling off her chin.

"Don't get up," says Dee. Since I am stout it takes something of a push. You can see me trying to move a second or two before I make it. She turns, showing white heels through her sandals, and goes back to the car. Out she peeks next with a Polaroid[29]. She stoops down quickly and lines up picture after picture of me sitting there in front of the house with Maggie cowering[30] behind me. She never takes a shot without making sure the house is included. When a cow comes nibbling around the edge of the yard she snaps it and me and Maggie and the house. Then she puts the Polaroid in the back seat of the car, and comes up and kisses me on the forehead.

Meanwhile Asalamalakim is going through motions with Maggie's hand. Maggie's hand is as limp as a fish, and probably as cold, despite the sweat, and she keeps trying to pull it back. It looks like Asalamalakim wants to shake hands but wants to do it fancy. Or maybe he don't[31] know how people shake hands. Anyhow, he soon gives up on Maggie.

"Well," I say. "Dee."

"No, Mama," she says. "Not 'Dee', Wangero Leewanika Kemanjo[32]!"

"What happened to 'Dee'?" I wanted to know.

"She's dead," Wangero said. "I couldn't bear it any longer, being named after the people who oppress me."

"You know as well as me you was[33] named after your aunt Dicie," I said. Dicie is my sister. She named Dee. We called her "Big Dee" after Dee was born.

"But who was she named after?" asked Wangero.

"I guess after Grandma Dee," I said.

"And who was she named after?" asked Wangero.

"Her mother," I said, and saw Wangero was getting tired. "That's about as far back as I can trace it," I said. Though, in fact, I probably could have carried it back beyond the Civil War through the branches.

"Well," said Asalamalakim, "there you are. "

"Uhnnnh," I heard Maggie say.

"There I was not," I said, "before 'Dicie' cropped up[34] in our family, so why should I try to trace it that far back?"

He just stood there grinning, looking down on me like somebody inspecting a Model A car. Every once in a while he and Wangero sent eye signals over my head.

"How do you pronounce this name?" I asked.

"You don't have to call me by it if you don't want to. " said Wangero.

"Why shouldn't I?" I asked. "If that's what you want us to call you, we'll call you. "

"I know it might sound awkward at first," said Wangero.

"I'll get used to it. " I said. "Ream it out again[35]. "

Well, soon we got the name out of the way. Asalamalakim had a name twice as long and three times as hard. After I tripped over it[36] two or three times he told me to just call him Hakim-a-barber. I wanted to ask him was he a barber, but I didn't really think he was, so I didn't ask.

"You must belong to those beef-cattle peoples down the road," I said. They said "Asalamalakim" when they met you, too, but they didn't shake hands. Always too busy: feeding the cattle, fixing the fences, putting up salt-lick shelters, throwing down hay. When the white folks poisoned some of the herd the men stayed up all night with rifles in their hands. I walked a mile and a half just to see the sight.

Hakim-a-barber said, "I accept some of their doctrines, but farming and raising cattle is not my style." (They didn't tell me, and I didn't ask, whether Wangero (Dee) had really gone and married him.)

We sat down to eat and right away he said he didn't eat collards[37] and pork was unclean. Wangero, though, went on through the chitlins[38] and corn bread, the greens and everything else. She talked a blue streak[39] over the sweet potatoes. Everything delighted her. Even the fact that we still used the benches her daddy made for the table when we couldn't afford to buy chairs.

"Oh, Mama!" she cried. Then turned to Hakim-a-barber. "I never knew how lovely these benches are. You can feel the rump prints[40]," she said, running her hands underneath her and along the bench. Then she gave a sigh and her hand closed over Grandma Dee's butter dish. "That's it!" she said. "I knew there was something I wanted to ask you if I could have." She jumped up from the table and went over in the corner where the churn[41] stood, the milk in it clabber[42] by now. She looked at the churn and looked at it.

"This churn top is what I need;" she said. "Didn't Uncle Buddy whittle[43] it out of a tree you all used to have?"

"Yes." I said.

"Uh huh," she said happily. "And I want the dasher[44], too."

"Uncle Buddy whittle that, too?" asked the barber.

Dee (Wangero) looked up at me.

"Aunt Dee's first husband whittled the dash," said Maggie so low you almost couldn't hear her. "His name was Henry, but they called him Stash."

"Maggie's brain is like an elephant's," Wangero said, laughing. "I can use the churn top as a centerpiece for the alcove table[45]," she said, sliding a plate over the churn, "and I'll think of something artistic to do with the dasher. "

When she finished wrapping the dasher the handle stuck out. I took it for a moment in my hands. You didn't even have to look close to see where hands pushing the dasher up and down to make butter had left a kind of sink[46] in the wood. In fact, there were a lot of small sinks; you could see where thumbs and fingers had sunk into the wood. It was beautiful light yellow wood, from a tree that grew in the yard where Big Dee and Stash had lived.

After dinner Dee (Wangero) went to the trunk at the foot of my bed and started rifling through[47] it. Maggie hung back in the kitchen over the dishpan. Out came Wangero with two quilts. They had been pieced by Grandma Dee and then Big Dee and me had hung them on the quilt frames on the front porch and quilted them. One was in the Lone Star pattern. The other was Walk Around the Mountain. In both of them were scraps[48] of dresses Grandma Dee had worn fifty and more years ago. Bits and pieces of Grandpa Jarrell's Paisley shirts. And one teeny faded blue piece, about the size of a penny matchbox, that was from Great Grandpa Ezra's uniform that he wore in the Civil War.

"Mama," Wangero said sweet as a bird. "Can I have these old quilts?"

I heard something fall in the kitchen, and a minute later the kitchen door slammed.

"Why don't you take one or two of the others?" I asked. "These old things was[49] just done by me and Big Dee from some tops your grandma pieced before she died. "

"No," said Wangero. "I don't want those. They are stitched around the borders by machine. "

"That'll make them last better," I said.

"That's not the point," said Wangero. "These are all pieces of

261

dresses Grandma used to wear. She did all this stitching by hand. Imagine!" She held the quilts securely in her arms, stroking them.

"Some of the pieces, like those lavender ones, come from old clothes her mother handed down to her," I said, moving up to touch the quilts. Dee (Wangero) moved back just enough so that I couldn't reach the quilts. They already belonged to her.

"Imagine!" she breathed again, clutching them closely to her bosom.

"The truth is," I said, "I promised to give them[50] quilts to Maggie, for when she marries John Thomas. "

She gasped like a bee had stung her.

"Maggie can't appreciate these quilts!" she said. "She'd probably be backward enough to put them to everyday use. "

"I reckon[51] she would," I said. "God knows I been saving 'em for long enough with nobody using 'em. I hope she will!" I didn't want to bring up how I had offered Dee (Wangero) a quilt when she went away to college. Then she had told me they were old-fashioned, out of style.

"But they're priceless!" she was saying now, furiously; for she has a temper. "Maggie would put them on the bed and in five years they'd be in rags. Less than that!"

"She can always make some more," I said. "Maggie knows how to quilt. "

Dee (Wangero) looked at me with hatred. "You just will not understand. The point is these quilts, these quilts!"

"Well," I said, stumped[52]. "What would you do with them?"

"Hang them," she said. As if that was the only thing you could do with quilts.

Maggie by now was standing in the door. I could almost hear the sound her feet made as they scraped over each other.

"She can have them, Mama," she said, like somebody used to never

262

winning anything, or having anything reserved for her. "I can 'member Grandma Dee without the quilts."

I looked at her hard. She had filled her bottom lip with checkerberry snuff[53] and it gave her face a kind of dopey, hangdog look[54]. It was Grandma Dee and Big Dee who taught her how to quilt herself. She stood there with her scarred hands hidden in the folds of her skirt. She looked at her sister with something like fear but she wasn't mad at her. This was Maggie's portion. This was the way she knew God to work.

When I looked at her like that something hit me in the top of my head and ran down to the soles of my feet. Just like when I'm in church and the spirit of God touches me and I get happy and shout. I did something I never had done before: hugged Maggie to me, then dragged her on into the room, snatched the quilts out of Miss Wangero's hands and dumped them into Maggie's lap. Maggie just sat there on my bed with her mouth open.

"Take one or two of the others," I said to Dee.

But she turned without a word and went out to Hakim-a-barber.

"You just don't understand," she said, as Maggie and I came out to the car.

"What don't I understand?" I wanted to know.

"Your heritage," she said. And then she turned to Maggie, kissed her, and said, "You ought to try to make something of yourself, too, Maggie. It's really a new day for us. But from the way you and Mama still live you'd never know it."

She put on some sunglasses that hid everything above the tip of her nose and her chin.

Maggie smiled; maybe at the sunglasses. But a real smile, not scared. After we watched the car dust settle I asked Maggie to bring me a dip of snuff. And then the two of us sat there just enjoying, until it was time to go in the house and go to bed.

263

Notes：

1. lined with tiny, irregular grooves：布满一条条不规则的小沟

2. elm tree：榆树

3. tottering in weakly from backstage：步履蹒跚地从后台进来。totter：步履蹒跚（walk with weak unsteady steps）

4. the child wraps them in her arms：孩子搂着他们

5. limousine：豪华大轿车（a big expensive comfortable car）

6. ushered into：领进（brought into by showing the way）

7. Johnny Carson（1925—2005）：美国电视节目主持人,曾主持美国国家广播公司（NBC）深夜时段著名脱口秀节目《今夜秀》30年（host of an American late-night talk show, NBC's "The Tonight Show" for nearly 30 years）

8. she thinks orchids are tacky flowers：她认为兰花是俗气的花。tacky：俗气的（marked by lack of style or good taste）

9. sidle：侧身而行（move sideways）

10. dim-wit：a stupid person

11. organdy：玻璃纱（very thin rather stiff cotton material, used esp. for women's dresses）

12. pump：轻软平底鞋

13. colored：black people

14. She stumbles along good-naturedly but can't see well：她脾气好、结结巴巴地读着,但（对读的东西）不是太明白。stumble：蹒跚而行；结巴（walk unsteadily；speak or read aloud in a clumsy way）

15. mossy：长满苔藓的（covered with moss）

16. shingle：木瓦板（a small thin piece of building material, esp. wood, laid in rows to cover a roof or wall）

17. porthole：船或飞机的舷窗

18. with rawhide holding the shutters up on the outside：用生牛皮把窗板

264

朝外顶起来

19. the scalding humor that erupted like bubbles in lye：像洗涤液里的泡泡那样突然冒出的辛辣幽默

20. re-compose herself：make herself calm again

21. like a kinky mule tail：像一条卷曲的骡子尾巴

22. the wriggling end：扭动的尾巴

23. loud：花里胡哨的，招摇的（having unpleasantly bright colors or too strong patterns）

24. Bracelets dangling：臂上的手镯叮当作响

25. Wa-su-zo-Tean-o：a Luganda phrase showing how the Buganda people of Uganda say "Good Morning". It can be translated as something like "I hope you have slept well".

26. navel：肚脐

27. Asalamalakim：祝您平安（an African greeting meaning "Peace be with you"）

28. perspiration：汗水（sweat）

29. Out she peeks next with a Polaroid：接着她拿起一架"拍立来"照相机瞄过来。peek：窥视，看一眼（take a quick look at something）

30. cowering：退缩（shrinking from fear）

31. don't：doesn't

32. Wangero Leewanika Kemanjo：a mixture of names from more than one ethnic group in East Africa, possibly indicating that Dee is confused and has only superficial knowledge of Africa and all it stands for.

33. was：were

34. crop up：happen or appear unexpectedly

35. Ream it out again：给我再念一遍吧

36. After I tripped over it：在我把它念错了后。trip：make a mistake.

37. collard：羽衣甘蓝菜

38. chitlins：猪的小肠

39. a blue streak：滔滔不绝的一番话

40. the rump prints：屁股印迹

41. churn：（制造黄油的）搅乳器（a container in which milk is shaken until it becomes butter）

42. clabber：变稠,凝固（thicken）

43. whittle：削,切

44. dasher：搅拌装置

45. I can use the churn top as a centerpiece for the alcove table：我可以将这搅乳器盖子放在凹室餐桌中央做装饰品。centerpiece：中心装饰品

46. sink：小坑,小槽

47. rifling through：searching quickly through

48. scraps：small pieces

49. was：were

50. them：these

51. reckon：think

52. stumped：感到为难的（baffled）

53. checkerberry snuff：蔓虎刺浆果鼻烟

54. it gave her face a kind of dopey, hangdog look：这使她看起来有一种迟钝而又羞愧的神色

Questions：

1. Why does Dee want the old quilts? What does she intend to do with them?

2. What do you learn about Maggie at the opening of the story?

3. What are you told about Dee by the kinds of pictures she takes?

4. What are the essential differences between Dee's life and Maggie's life?

5. What are the essential differences between Dee's character and

Maggie's?

6. Who is the real center of the story? Explain.

Ursula K. Le Guin

(1929-)

Ursula K. Le Guin (1929—) is a writer of science fiction and fantasy, poet and author of critical essays. Le Guin was born and raised in Berkeley, California. She grew up in an academic atmosphere. Her father was a famous anthropologist, who published work on Native Americans. He was granted the first Ph. D. in Anthropology in the United States in 1901 (Columbia University). Le Guin's mother was a psychologist and writer of children's stories. Le Guin received her B. A. from Radcliffe College in 1951, and M. A. from Columbia University in 1952. She later studied in France, where she met her husband, historian Charles Le Guin. They were married in 1953 and have three children. She currently lives in Portland, Oregon.

Le Guin is best known for science fiction and fantasy classics *The Left Hand of Darkness* (1969), *The Dispossessed* (1974), *The Lathe of Heaven* (1971), and *the Earthsea Saga* (1968—2001). In addition to novels, her work includes short stories, screenplays, essays, poetry, literature for children and young adults. Respected in academic circles, Le Guin's literary work is noteworthy for its lyrical and often precise use of language, for its investigation of alternative societies, and for inciting social awareness through intricately woven tales. Her work is heavily flavored by her early exposure to anthropology, her work as a poet, her deep interest in Taoism, and her own "thoughtful feminism". She has received several Hugo and Nebula awards, and was awarded the

Gandalf Grand Master award in 1979 and the Science Fiction and Fantasy Writers of America Grand Master Award in 2003. She has received eighteen Locus Awards, more than any other author. Her novel *The Farthest Shore*(1972) won the National Book Award for Children's Books in 1973. She received the Library of Congress *Living Legends* award in the "Writers and Artists" category in April 2000 for her significant contributions to America's cultural heritage.

Le Guin became interested in literature when she was very young. At the age of eleven she submitted her first story to the magazine *Astounding Science Fiction* (it was rejected). Her earliest writings (little published at the time, but some appeared in adapted form much later in *Orsinian Tales* and *Malafrena*) were non-fantastic stories of imaginary countries. Searching for a publishable way to express her interests, she returned to her early interest in science fiction and began to be published regularly in the early 1960s. She became famous after the publication of her novel *The Left Hand of Darkness*, which won the Hugo and Nebula awards. Over nearly 50 years she has published 17 novels, 11 children's books, more than 100 short stories, two collections of essays, five volumes of poetry, two volumes of translation and screenplays of her works. Much of Le Guin's science fiction belongs to the subcategory known as soft science fiction for its great emphasis on the social sciences, including sociology and anthropology. Through her tales and complex characters, she has explored the themes of sexism, racism, nationalism, unchecked technological progress and the flaws in popular utopian visions.

"She Unnames Them" is a short story first published in *The New Yorker*, 21 January 1985. In the *Bible*, God gives Adam the power to name the animals of the earth. With this naming comes man's supposed right of dominion over the animals, the birds, and the fish. In "She Unnames Them" Eve deconstructs the linguistic world of man, opposing his unquestionable right to name, that is, to linguistically mark the world around him. This short story depicts how unnaming helps Eve and the

269

animals get rid of subordination and develop a better human-nature relationship. The story is often studied from the perspectives of theology, linguistics and ecological feminism.

She Unnames Them

Ursula K. Le Guin

Most of them accepted namelessness with the perfect indifference with which they had so long accepted and ignored their names. Whales and dolphins, seals and sea otters consented with particular grace and alacrity, sliding into anonymity as into their element[1]. A faction of yaks[2], however, protested. They said that "yak" sounded right, and that almost everyone who knew they existed called them that. Unlike the ubiquitous creatures such as rats and fleas[3] who had been called by hundreds or thousands of different names since Babel[4], the yaks could truly say, they said, that they had a name. They discussed the matter all summer. The councils of elderly females finally agreed that though the name might be useful to others it was so redundant from the yak point of view that they never spoke it themselves and hence might as well dispense with it[5]. After they presented the argument in this light[6] to their bulls, a full consensus was delayed only by the onset of severe early blizzards[7]. Soon after the beginning of the thaw[8], their agreement was reached and the designation "yak" was returned to the donor.

Among the domestic animals, few horses had cared what anybody called them since the failure of Dean Swift's attempt to name them from their own vocabulary. Cattle, sheep, swine, asses, mules, and goats, along with chickens, geese, and turkeys, all agreed enthusiastically to give their names back to the people to whom—as they put it—they belonged.

270

A couple of problems did come up with pets. The cats, of course, steadfastly denied ever having had any name other than those self-given, unspoken, ineffably[9] personal names which, as the poet named Eliot said, they spend long hours daily contemplating—though none of the contemplators has ever admitted that what they contemplate is in fact their names, and some onlookers have wondered if the object of that meditative gaze might not in fact be the Perfect, or Platonic, Mouse[10]. In any case, it is a moot point[11] now. It was with the dogs, and with some parrots, lovebirds, ravens, and mynahs, that the trouble arose. These verbally talented individuals insisted that their names were important to them, and flatly refused to part with them[12]. But as soon as they understood that the issue was precisely one of individual choice, and that anybody who wanted to be called Rover, or Froufrou, or Polly, or even Birdie in the personal sense, was perfectly free to do so, not one of them had the least objection to parting with the lower case (or, as regards German creatures, uppercase) generic appellations "poodle", "parrot", "dog", or "bird", and all the Linnaean qualifiers[13] that had trailed along behind them for two hundred years like tin cans tied to a tail.

The insects parted with their names in vast clouds and swarms of ephemeral syllables buzzing and stinging and humming and flitting and crawling and tunnelling away.

As for the fish of the sea, their names dispersed[14] from them in silence throughout the oceans like faint, dark blurs of cuttlefish ink, and drifted off on the currents[15] without a trace.

None were left now to unname, and yet how close I felt to them when I saw one of them swim or fly or trot or crawl across my way or over my skin, or stalk me in the night, or go along beside me for a while in the day. They seemed far closer than when their names had stood between myself and them like a clear barrier: so close that my fear of them and their

271

fear of me became one same fear. And the attraction that many of us felt, the desire to smell one another's smells, feel or rub or caress one another's scales or skin or feathers or fur, taste one another's blood or flesh, keep one another warm—that attraction was now all one with the fear, and the hunter could not be told from the hunted, nor the eater from the food.

This was more or less the effect I had been after. It was somewhat more powerful than I had anticipated, but I could not now, in all conscience[16], make an exception for myself. I resolutely put anxiety away, went to Adam, and said, "You and your father lent me this—gave it to me, actually. It's been really useful, but it doesn't exactly seem to fit very well lately. But thanks very much! It's really been very useful."

It is hard to give back a gift without sounding peevish or ungrateful, and I did not want to leave him with that impression of me. He was not paying much attention, as it happened, and said only, "Put it down over there, O. K.?" and went on with what he was doing.

One of my reasons for doing what I did was that talk was getting us nowhere, but all the same I felt a little let down[17]. I had been prepared to defend my decision. And I thought that perhaps when he did notice he might be upset and want to talk. I put some things away and fiddled around[18] a little, but he continued to do what he was doing and to take no notice of anything else. At last I said, "Well, goodbye, dear. I hope the garden key turns up."

He was fitting parts together, and said, without looking around, "O. K., fine, dear. When's dinner?"

"I'm not sure," I said. "I'm going now. With the—" I hesitated, and finally said, "with them, you know," and went out. In fact, I had only just then realized how hard it would have been to explain myself. I could not chatter away as I used to do, taking it all for granted. My words

272

must be as slow, as new, as single, as tentative as the steps I took going down the path away from the house, between the dark-branched, tall dancers[19] motionless against the winter shining.

Notes:

1. Whales and dolphins, seals and sea otters consented with particular grace and alacrity, sliding into anonymity as into their element: 鲸鱼和海豚、海豹和海獭都非常优雅、欣然地同意了,舒适、自然地进入了无名状态,如同进入它们熟悉的生活环境。alacrity: 欣然(cheerful readiness and quickness); element: 自然的、适宜的环境(a situation that is familiar, enjoyable, or suitable)

2. A faction of yaks: 一部分牦牛

3. Unlike the ubiquitous creatures such as rats and fleas: 不像老鼠和跳蚤这样无处不在的生物

4. Babel: 巴别城,巴别塔(According to the biblical account, Babel was a city that united humanity, all speaking a single language and migrating from the east; it was the home city of the great king Nimrod, and the first city to be built after the Great Flood. The people decided their city should have a tower so immense that it would have "its top in the heavens". However, the Tower of Babel was not built for the worship and praise of God, but was dedicated to the glory of man, with a motive of making a "name" for the builders: "Then they said, 'Come, let us build ourselves a city, and a tower with its top in the heavens, and let us make a name for ourselves; otherwise we shall be scattered abroad upon the face of the whole earth.'" [Genesis 11:4]. God, seeing what the people were doing, gave each person a different language to confuse them and scattered the people throughout the earth. — Wikipedia)

5. hence might as well dispense with it: 因此不妨把它废弃不用。

dispense with：摒弃（get rid of）

6. in this light：依照这种看法

7. a full consensus was delayed only by the onset of severe early blizzards：只是由于猛烈的早期暴风雪开始了,才推迟讨论,达成完全一致的意见

8. thaw：融雪期（a period of warm weather during which snow and ice melt）

9. ineffably：说不出的

10. the Perfect, or Platonic, Mouse：完美的,或理想中的老鼠

11. a moot point：争论未决的问题（an undecided question）

12. and flatly refused to part with them：断然拒绝舍弃它们。part with：放弃,舍弃（stop having）

13. the Linnaean qualifiers：林奈的修饰语。（当前,生物的命名采用双名制,即瑞典科学家林奈于 18 世纪 50 年代创造出统一的生物命名系统,即双名法。按照这个系统,每种生物的名称均由两个拉丁词构成,前面一个是属名,后面一个是种名。这种方法后来被国际学术界所接受。属名是名词;种名是修饰语,可以是形容词、名词的所有格、分词。于是,每一个物种只能有一个名称。）Linnaean：林奈的,是 Linnaeus 的形容词。Carl Linnaeus：林奈（1707— 1778,瑞典文为 Carl von Linne）,瑞典植物学家、冒险家,首先构想出定义生物属种的原则,并创造出统一的生物命名系统。

14. disperse：消散（vanish）

15. current：水流,海流

16. in all conscience：当然,一定

17. let down：disappointed

18. fiddle around：逗留,无目的地行动

19. the dark-branched, tall dancers：那些长着黑色枝丫的、高高的树木

Questions:

1. Why does Eve give up her God-given power to have "dominion" over the world? What is the relationship between dominion and naming?

2. How do you interpret Eve's act of unnaming? How do the newly unnamed creatures react to their unnamed status?

3. Why does Eve abandon Adam? What role is Eve expected to assume in the patriarchal society? Comment on the man-woman relationship presented by Le Guin in the story.

William Gibson

(*1948-*)

William Gibson (1948—) is one of the most well known North American science fiction writers. He has written more than twenty short stories and nine critically acclaimed novels (one in collaboration). He coined the term "cyberspace" in his short story "Burning Chrome" and later popularized the concept in his first novel, *Neuromancer* (1984). His work is praised by critics for its depictions of late capitalism and its rewriting of subjectivity, human consciousness and behaviour made newly problematic by technology. His thought has been cited as an influence on science fiction authors, design, academia, cyberculture, and technology.

Gibson was born in the coastal city of Conway, South Carolina and spent most of his childhood in Wytheville, Virginia, a small town in the Appalachians where his parents had been born and raised. His family moved frequently during Gibson's youth due to his father's position as manager of a large construction company. While Gibson was still a young child, his father died. As a shy, clumsy teenager, he often read science fiction. After spending his adolescence at a private boarding school in Arizona, Gibson avoided the draft during the Vietnam War by emigrating to Canada in 1968, where he became immersed in the counterculture and after settling in Vancouver eventually became a full-time writer. He retains dual citizenship.

Gibson started to write short stories which were published in popular science fiction magazines. "Fragments of a Hologram Rose" (1977), "Johnny Mnemonic" (1981), "The Gernsback Continuum" (1981) and other early short stories were collected in *Burning Chrome* in 1986. The themes, settings and characters developed in these stories culminated in his first novel, *Neuromancer*, which garnered critical and commercial success, virtually initiating the cyberpunk literary genre.

Gibson published *Neuromancer* in 1984 and became the first novel to win three major science fiction awards (the Nebula Award, the Philip K. Dick Award, and the Hugo Award), an unprecedented achievement described by the Mail & Guardian as "the sci-fi writer's version of winning the Goncourt, Booker and Pulitzer prizes in the same year". *Neuromancer* gained unprecedented critical and popular attention outside science fiction and in 2005 *Time* magazine included it in their list of the 100 best English-language novels written since 1923.

Although much of Gibson's reputation has remained associated with *Neuromancer*, his work has continued to develop. After expanding on *Neuromancer* with two more novels (*Count Zero*, 1986; *Mona Lisa Overdrive*, 1988) to complete the dystopic *Sprawl trilogy*, Gibson became an important author of another science fiction sub-genre—steampunk—with the 1990 alternate history novel *The Difference Engine*, written with Bruce Sterling. In the 1990s he composed the *Bridge trilogy* of novels, which focused on sociological observations of near-future urban environments and late capitalism. His most recent novels—*Pattern Recognition* (2003) and *Spook Country* (2007)—are set in a contemporary world and have put his work onto mainstream bestseller lists for the first time.

"The Gernsback Continuum" is a short story about a photographer who has been given the assignment of photographing old, futuristic architecture. "Gernsback" alludes to Hugo Gernsback, a pulp science fiction writer and publisher during the early 20th century. "Continuum" is an alternate reality containing the possible future of the world represented

277

by the architecture—a future that could have been, but was not. The title is a comparison between the imagined future of Hugo Gernsback, and the new images and style of Cyberpunk. Gernsback's science fiction and Cyberpunk, a subset of science fiction, both have the futuristic setting as the key ingredient. But there is a significant difference in that cyberpunk claims to realistically portray the future while the Gernsback's science fiction merely glorifies the roles of science and technology in the future. Gernsback forsaw a future of technically perfect superstructures in a completely modernized society while in "The Gernsback Continuum" Gibson sardonically applies this setting, and examines the individual that is suffocating in this global modernism. "The Gernsback Continuum" is an anti-utopian, postmodern story. Its closing dialogue, in which the narrator is asked, " 'Hell of a world we live in, huh?' " and responds that it could be worse—" 'it could be perfect' "—can stand as the typical postmodern response to modernism's grand ambitions.

The Gernsback Continuum[1]

William Gibson

Mercifully, the whole thing is starting to fade, to become an episode. When I do still catch the odd glimpse, it's peripheral[2]; mere fragments of mad-doctor chrome[3], confining themselves to the corner of the eye. There was that flying-wing liner[4] over San Francisco last week, but it was almost translucent[5]. And the shark-fin roadsters[6] have gotten scarcer, and freeways discreetly avoid unfolding themselves into the gleaming eighty-lane monsters I was forced to drive last month in my rented Toyota. And I know that none of it will follow me to New York; my vision is narrowing to a single wavelength of probability. I've worked hard for that. Television helped a lot.

278

I suppose it started in London, in that bogus Greek taverna[7] in Battersea Park Road, with lunch on Cohen's corporate tab[8]. Dead steam-table food and it took them thirty minutes to find an ice bucket for the retsina[9]. Cohen works for Barris-Watford, who publish big, trendy[10] "trade" paperbacks: illustrated histories of the neon sign, the pinball machine[11], the windup toys[12] of Occupied Japan. I'd gone over to shoot a series of shoe ads; California girls with tanned legs and frisky Day-Glo jogging shoes[13] had capered[14] for me down the escalators of St. John's Wood and across the platforms of Tooting Bec. A lean and hungry young agency had decided that the mystery of London Transport would sell waffle-tread nylon runners[15]. They decide; I shoot. And Cohen, whom I knew vaguely from the old days in New York, had invited me to lunch the day before I was due out of Heathrow. He brought along a very fashionably dressed young woman named Dialta Downes, who was virtually chinless and evidently a noted pop-art historian. In retrospect, I see her walking in beside Cohen under a floating neon sign that flashes THIS WAY LIES MADNESS in huge sans-serif capitals[16].

Cohen introduced us and explained that Dialta was the prime mover[17] behind the latest Barris-Watford project, an illustrated history of what she called "American Streamlined Moderne". Cohen called it "raygun Gothic". Their working title was *The Airstream Futuropolis: The Tomorrow That Never Was*[18].

There's a British obsession with the more baroque[19] elements of American pop culture, something like the weird cowboys-and-Indians fetish of the West Germans or the aberrant French hunger for old Jerry Lewis films[20]. In Dialta Downes this manifested itself in a mania[21] for a uniquely American form of architecture that most Americans are scarcely aware of. At first I wasn't sure what she was talking about, but gradually it began to dawn on[22] me. I found myself remembering Sunday morning television in the Fifties.

Sometimes they'd run old eroded newsreels as filler on the local station[23]. You'd sit there with a peanut butter sandwich and a glass of milk, and a static-ridden Hollywood baritone[24] would tell you that there was A Flying Car in Your Future. And three Detroit engineers would putter[25] around with this big old Nash[26] with wings, and you'd see it rumbling furiously down some deserted Michigan runway. You never actually saw it take off, but it flew away to Dialta Downes's never-never land, true home of a generation of completely uninhibited technophiles[27]. She was talking about those odds and ends[28] of "futuristic" Thirties and Forties architecture you pass daily in American cities without noticing; the movie marquees ribbed to radiate some mysterious energy[29], the dime stores faced with fluted aluminum[30], the chrome-tube chairs gathering dust in the lobbies of transient hotels. She saw these things as segments of a dreamworld, abandoned in the uncaring present; she wanted me to photograph them for her.

The Thirties had seen the first generation of American industrial designers; until the Thirties, all pencil sharpeners had looked like pencil sharpeners—your basic Victorian mechanism, perhaps with a curlicue of decorative trim[31]. After the advent of the designers, some pencil sharpeners looked as though they'd been put together in wind tunnels. For the most part, the change was only skin-deep; under the streamlined chrome shell, you'd find the same Victorian mechanism. Which made a certain kind of sense[32], because the most successful American designers had been recruited from the ranks of Broadway theater designers. It was all a stage set, a series of elaborate props[33] for playing at living in the future.

Over coffee, Cohen produced a fat manila envelope full of glossies[34]. I saw the winged statues that guard the Hoover Dam, forty-foot concrete hood ornaments leaning steadfastly into an imaginary hurricane. I saw a dozen

280

shots of Frank Lloyd Wright's Johnson's Wax Building, juxtaposed with the covers of old *Amazing Stories* pulps, by an artist named Frank R. Paul; the employees of Johnson's Wax must have felt as though they were walking into one of Paul's spray-paint pulp utopias[35]. Wright's building looked as though it had been designed for people who wore white togas and Lucite sandals[36]. I hesitated over one sketch of a particularly grandiose prop-driven airliner[37], all wing, like a fat symmetrical boomerang[38] with windows in unlikely places. Labeled arrows indicated the locations of the grand ballroom and two squash courts[39]. It was dated 1936.

"This thing couldn't have flown . . . ?" I looked at Dialta Downes.

"Oh, no, quite impossible, even with those twelve giant props; but they loved the look, don't you see? New York to London in less than two days, first-class dining rooms, private cabins, sun decks, dancing to jazz in the evening . . . The designers were populists[40], you see; they were trying to give the public what it wanted. What the public wanted was the future. "

I'd been in Burbank for three days, trying to suffuse a really dull-looking rocker with charisma[41], when I got the package from Cohen. It is possible to photograph what isn't there; it's damned hard to do, and consequently a very marketable talent. While I'm not bad at it, I'm not exactly the best, either, and this poor guy strained my Nikon's credibility[42]. I got out, depressed because I do like to do a good job, but not totally depressed, because I did make sure I'd gotten the check for the job, and I decided to restore myself with the sublime artiness[43] of the Barris-Watford assignment. Cohen had sent me some books on Thirties design, more photos of streamlined buildings, and a list of Dialta Downes's fifty favorite examples of the style in California.

Architectural photography can involve a lot of waiting; the building becomes a kind of sundial, while you wait for a shadow to crawl away from a detail you want, or for the mass and balance of the structure to reveal itself in a certain way. While I was waiting, I thought myself in Dialta Downes's America. When I isolated a few of the factory buildings on the ground glass of the Hasselblad, they came across with a kind of sinister totalitarian dignity, like the stadiums Albert Speer built for Hitler. But the rest of it was relentlessly tacky: ephemeral[44] stuff extruded[45] by the collective American subconscious of the Thirties, tending mostly to survive along depressing strips[46] lined with dusty motels, mattress wholesalers, and small used-car lots. I went for the gas stations in a big way.

During the high point of the Downes Age, they put Ming the Merciless in charge of designing California gas stations. Favoring the architecture of his native Mongo, he cruised up and down the coast erecting raygun emplacements in white stucco[47]. Lots of them featured superfluous central towers ringed with those strange radiator flanges that were a signature motif of the style[48], and made them look as though they might generate potent bursts of raw technological enthusiasm, if you could only find the switch that turned them on. I shot one in San Jose[49] an hour before the bulldozers arrived and drove right through the structural truth of plaster and lathing[50] and cheap concrete.

"Think of it," Dialta Downes had said, "as a kind of alternate America: a 1980 that never happened. An architecture of broken dreams."

And that was my frame of mind as I made the stations of her convoluted[51] socioarchitectural cross in my red Toyota—as I gradually tuned in to[52] her image of a shadowy America-that-wasn't, of Coca-Cola plants like beached submarines[53], and fifth-run movie houses like the temples of some lost sect[54] that had worshiped blue mirrors and geometry. And as I moved among these secret ruins, I found myself wondering what the inhabitants of that lost future would think of the world I lived in. The

282

Thirties dreamed white marble and slipstream[55] chrome, immortal crystal and burnished[56] bronze, but the rockets on the covers of the Gernsback pulps had fallen on London in the dead of night, screaming. After the war, everyone had a car—no wings for it—and the promised superhighway to drive it down, so that the sky itself darkened, and the fumes ate the marble and pitted[57] the miracle crystal. . . .

And one day, on the outskirts of Bolinas, when I was setting up to shoot a particularly lavish example of Ming's martial architecture, I penetrated a fine membrane, a membrane of probability. . . .

Ever so gently, I went over the Edge—

And looked up to see a twelve-engined thing like a bloated boomerang, all wing, thrumming its way east with an elephantine grace[58], so low that I could count the rivets[59] in its dull silver skin, and hear—maybe—the echo of jazz.

I took it to Kihn.

Merv Kihn, free-lance journalist with an extensive line[60] in Texas pterodactyls[61], redneck UFO contactees[62], bush-league Loch Ness monsters, and the Top Ten conspiracy theories in the loonier reaches[63] of the American mass mind.

"It's good," said Kihn, polishing his yellow Polaroid shooting glasses on the hem of his Hawaiian shirt, "but it's not *mental*; lacks the true quill[64]. "

"But I saw it, Mervyn. " We were seated poolside in brilliant Arizona sunlight. He was in Tucson waiting for a group of retired Las Vegas civil servants whose leader received messages from Them on her microwave oven. I'd driven all night and was feeling it.

"Of course you did. Of course you saw it. You've read my stuff; haven't you grasped my blanket[65] solution to the UFO problem? It's simple, plain and country simple: people"—he settled the glasses carefully

283

on his long hawk nose and fixed me with his best basilisk[66] glare—"see . . .
things. People see things. Nothing's there, but people see them anyway.
Because they need to, probably. You've read Jung, you should know the
score[67]. . . . In your case, it's so obvious: You admit you were thinking
about this crackpot[68] architecture, having fantasies. . . . Look, I'm sure
you've taken your share of drugs[69], right? How many people survived the
Sixties in California without having the odd hallucination? All those nights
when you discovered that whole armies of Disney technicians had been
employed to weave animated holograms of Egyptian hieroglyphs into the
fabric of your jeans[70], say, or the times when—"

"But it wasn't like that. "

"Of course not. It wasn't like that at all; it was 'in a setting of clear
reality', right? Everything normal, and then there's the monster, the
mandala, the neon cigar. In your case, a giant Tom Swift airplane. It
happens *all the time*. You aren't even crazy. You know that, don't you?"
He fished[71] a beer out of the battered foam cooler beside his deck chair.

"Last week I was in Virginia. Grayson County. I interviewed a
sixteen-year-old girl who'd been assaulted by a *bar hade*. "

"A what?"

"A bear head. The severed[72] head of a bear. This *bar hade*, see, was
floating around on its own little flying saucer, looked kind of like the
hubcaps[73] on cousin Wayne's vintage Caddy[74]. Had red, glowing eyes like
two cigar stubs and telescoping[75] chrome antennas poking up[76] behind its
ears. " He burped[77].

"It assaulted her? How?"

"You don't want to know; You're obviously impressionable. 'It was
cold' "—he lapsed into[78] his bad southern accent—" 'and metallic. ' It
made electronic noises. Now that is the real thing, the straight goods from
the mass unconscious, friend; that little girl is a witch. There's just no

284

place for her to function in this society. She'd have seen the devil, if she hadn't been brought up on 'The Bionic Man' and all those 'Star Trek' reruns[79]. She is clued into the main vein[80]. And she knows that it happened to her. I got out ten minutes before the heavy UFO boys showed up with the polygraph[81]. "

I must have looked pained, because he set his beer down carefully beside the cooler and sat up.

"If you want a classier[82] explanation, I'd say you saw a semiotic[83] ghost. All these contactee stories, for instance, are framed in a kind of sci-fi imagery[84] that permeates our culture. I could buy aliens, but not aliens that look like Fifties' comic art. They're semiotic phantoms, bits of deep cultural imagery that have split off and taken on a life of their own, like the Jules Verne airships[85] that those old Kansas farmers were always seeing. But you saw a different kind of ghost, that's all. That plane was part of the mass unconscious, once. You picked up on that, somehow. The important thing is not to worry about it. "

I did worry about it, though.

Kihn combed his thinning blond hair and went off to hear what they had had to say over the radar range lately, and I drew the curtains in my room and lay down in air-conditioned darkness to worry about it. I was still worrying about it when I woke up. Kihn had left a note on my door; he was flying up north in a chartered plane[86] to check out a cattle-mutilation rumor[87] (" muties ", he called them; another of his journalistic specialties).

I had a meal, showered, took a crumbling diet pill that had been kicking around in the bottom of my shaving kit[88] for three years, and headed back to Los Angeles.

The speed limited my vision to the tunnel of the Toyota's headlights. The body could drive, I told myself, while the mind maintained.

285

Maintained and stayed away from the weird peripheral window dressing of amphetamine[89] and exhaustion, the spectral, luminous vegetation[90] that grows out of the corners of the mind's eye along late-night highways. But the mind had its own ideas, and Kihn's opinion of what I was already thinking of as my "sighting" rattled endlessly through my head in a tight, lopsided orbit[91]. Semiotic ghosts. Fragments of the Mass Dream, whirling past in the wind of my passage. Somehow this feedback-loop aggravated the diet pill, and the speed-vegetation along the road began to assume the colors of infrared[92] satellite images, glowing shreds[93] blown apart in the Toyota's slipstream.

I pulled over, then, and a half-dozen aluminum beer cans winked goodnight as I killed the headlights. I wondered what time it was in London, and tried to imagine Dialta Downes having breakfast in her Hampstead flat, surrounded by streamlined chrome figurines and books on American culture.

Desert nights in that country are enormous; the moon is closer. I watched the moon for a long time and decided that Kihn was right. The main thing was not to worry. All across the continent, daily, people who were more normal than I'd ever aspired to be saw giant birds, Bigfeet, flying oil refineries[94]; they kept Kihn busy and solvent[95]. Why should I be upset by a glimpse of the 1930s pop imagination loose over Bolinas? I decided to go to sleep, with nothing worse to worry about than rattlesnakes and cannibal hippies[96], safe amid the friendly roadside garbage of my own familiar continuum. In the morning I'd drive down to Nogales and photograph the old brothels[97], something I'd intended to do for years. The diet pill had given up.

The light woke me, and then the voices.

The light came from somewhere behind me and threw shifting shadows inside the car. The voices were calm, indistinct, male and female, engaged in conversation.

My neck was stiff and my eyeballs felt gritty in their sockets[98]. My leg had gone to sleep, pressed against the steering wheel. I fumbled for my glasses in the pocket of my work shirt and finally got them on.

Then I looked behind me and saw the city.

The books on Thirties design were in the trunk; one of them contained sketches of an idealized city that drew on *Metropolis* and *Things to Come*[99], but squared everything, soaring up through an architect's perfect clouds to zeppelin docks and mad neon spires[100]. That city was a scale model[101] of the one that rose behind me. Spire stood on spire in gleaming ziggurat steps[102] that climbed to a central golden temple tower ringed with the crazy radiator flanges of the Mongo gas stations. You could hide the Empire State Building in the smallest of those towers. Roads of crystal soared between the spires, crossed and recrossed by smooth silver shapes like beads of running mercury[103]. The air was thick with ships: giant wing-liners, little darting silver things (sometimes one of the quicksilver[104] shapes from the sky bridges rose gracefully into the air and flew up to join the dance), mile-long blimps[105], hovering dragonfly things that were gyrocopters[106]...

I closed my eyes tight and swung around in the seat. When I opened them, I willed myself to see the mileage meter[107], the pale road dust on the black plastic dashboard[108], the overflowing ashtray[109].

"Amphetamine psychosis[110]," I said. I opened my eyes. The dash was still there, the dust, the crushed filtertips. Very carefully, without moving my head, I turned the headlights on.

And saw them.

They were blond. They were standing beside their car, an aluminum avocado with a central shark-fin rudder jutting up from its spine[111] and smooth black tires like a child's toy. He had his arm around her waist and was gesturing toward the city. They were both in white: loose clothing,

287

bare legs, spotless white sun shoes. Neither of them seemed aware of the beams of my headlights. He was saying something wise and strong, and she was nodding, and suddenly I was frightened, frightened in an entirely different way. Sanity had ceased to be an issue; I knew, somehow, that the city behind me was Tucson[112]—a dream Tucson thrown up out of the collective yearning of an era. That it was real, entirely real. But the couple in front of me lived in it, and they frightened me.

They were the children of Dialta Downes's '80-that-wasn't; they were Heirs to the Dream. They were white, blond, and they probably had blue eyes. They were American. Dialta had said that the Future had come to America first, but had finally passed it by. But not here, in the heart of the Dream. Here, we'd gone on and on, in a dream logic that knew nothing of pollution, the finite bounds of fossil fuel[113], or foreign wars it was possible to lose. They were smug, happy, and utterly content with themselves and their world. And in the Dream, it was their world.

Behind me, the illuminated city: Searchlights swept the sky for the sheer joy of it. I imagined them thronging the plazas of white marble[114], orderly and alert, their bright eyes shining with enthusiasm for their floodlit[115] avenues and silver cars.

It had all the sinister fruitiness of Hitler Youth propaganda.

I put the car in gear and drove forward slowly, until the bumper was within three feet of them. They still hadn't seen me. I rolled the window down and listened to what the man was saying. His words were bright and hollow as the pitch in some Chamber of Commerce brochure[116], and I knew that he believed in them absolutely.

"John," I heard the woman say, "we've forgotten to take our food pills." She clicked two bright wafers[117] from a thing on her belt and passed one to him. I backed onto the highway and headed for Los Angeles, wincing and shaking my head.

288

I phoned Kihn from a gas station. A new one, in bad Spanish Modern. He was back from his expedition and didn't seem to mind the call.

"Yeah, that is a weird one. Did you try to get any pictures? Not that they ever come out, but it adds an interesting *frisson*[118] to your story, not having the pictures turn out. ..."

But what should I do?

"Watch lots of television, particularly game shows and soaps. Go to porn movies. Ever see *Nazi Love Motel*? They've got it on cable, here. Really awful. Just what you need."

What was he talking about?

"Quit yelling and listen to me. I'm letting you in on a trade secret[119]: Really bad media can exorcise your semiotic ghosts. If it keeps the saucer people off my back, it can keep these Art Deco futuroids off yours[120]. Try it. What have you got to lose?"

Then he begged off, pleading an early-morning date with the Elect.

"The who?"

"These oldsters from Vegas; the ones with the microwaves."

I considered putting a collect call through to London[121], getting Cohen at Barris-Watford and telling him his photographer was checked out for a protracted season[122] in the Twilight Zone. In the end, I let a machine mix me a really impossible cup of black coffee and climbed back into the Toyota for the haul to Los Angeles.

Los Angeles was a bad idea, and I spent two weeks there. It was prime Downes country; too much of the Dream there, and too many fragments of the Dream waiting to snare me. I nearly wrecked the car on a stretch of overpass near Disneyland, when the road fanned out like an origami trick and left me swerving through a dozen minilanes of whizzing chrome teardrops with shark fins[123]. Even worse, Hollywood was full of

289

people who looked too much like the couple I'd seen in Arizona. I hired an Italian director who was making ends meet doing darkroom work and installing patio decks[124] around swimming pools until his ship came in; he made prints of all the negatives I'd accumulated on the Downes job. I didn't want to look at the stuff myself. It didn't seem to bother Leonardo, though, and when he was finished I checked the prints, riffling through them like a deck of cards[125], sealed them up, and sent them air freight[126] to London. Then I took a taxi to a theater that was showing *Nazi Love Motel*, and kept my eyes shut all the way.

Cohen's congratulatory wire was forwarded to me[127] in San Francisco a week later. Dialta had loved the pictures. He admired the way I'd "really gotten into it", and looked forward to working with me again. That afternoon I spotted a flying wing over Castro Street, but there was something tenuous[128] about it, as though it were only half there. I rushed into the nearest newsstand and gathered up as much as I could find on the petroleum crisis and the nuclear energy hazard. I'd just decided to buy a plane ticket for New York.

"Hell of a world we live in, huh?" The proprietor[129] was a thin black man with bad teeth and an obvious wig. I nodded, fishing in my jeans for change, anxious to find a park bench where I could submerge myself in hard evidence of the human near-dystopia we live in[130]. "But it could be worse, huh?"

"That's right," I said, "or even worse, it could be perfect."

He watched me as I headed down the street with my little bundle of condensed catastrophe.

Notes:

1. The Gernsback Continuum: 根斯巴克连续体。Gernsback: 根斯巴克 (1884—1967), 美国发明家、出版家、科幻小说主要奠基人, 科幻小说雨果奖即由其名命名（Gernsback refers to Hugo Gernsback, an American inventor, writer and magazine publisher, best remembered for publications that included the first science fiction magazine. His bold and vivid stories shaped the collective imagination of the future. His contributions to the genre as publisher were so significant that, along with H. G. Wells and Jules Verne, he is sometimes popularly called "The Father of Science Fiction"; in his honor, the annual Science Fiction Achievement awards are named the "Hugos".) continuum: 连续体（something which is without parts and the same from beginning to end）

2. peripheral: 外围的（not central or closely related）

3. chrome: 铬

4. flying-wing liner: 飞翼班机

5. translucent: 半透明的

6. the shark-fin roadsters: 鲨鱼鳍双座敞篷汽车

7. that bogus Greek taverna: 那一家冒牌希腊餐厅。bogus: 假的（pretended）; taverna: 希腊餐厅（refers to a small restaurant serving Greek cuisine, not to be confused with "tavern"）

8. with lunch on Cohen's corporate tab: 午餐由科恩的公司付账。tab: a bill, esp. for a meal or drinks.

9. retsina: 一种松香味希腊葡萄酒

10. trendy: very fashionable

11. the pinball machine: 弹子机

12. the windup toys: 发条玩具

13. frisky Day-Glo jogging shoes: 活泼的"狄格洛"荧光跑步鞋。Day-Glo: [商标]"狄格洛"荧光加色剂（一种在日间也会闪出绚丽色彩的荧光色剂）

14. caper: jump about in a happy playful manner

15. waffle-tread nylon runners: 格子底尼龙跑鞋。tread: 鞋底

16. in huge sans-serif capitals：一串无衬线大写字母。sans-serif：（印刷中的）无衬线的字体

17. prime mover：主要的推动者

18. *The Airstream Futuropolis*：*The Tomorrow That Never Was*：《气流未来城：从未实现的明天》

19. baroque：巴洛克风格的（in a highly decorated style which was fashionable in art, building, music, etc. in Europe during the 17th century）

20. the weird cowboys-and-Indians fetish of the West Germans or the aberrant French hunger for old Jerry Lewis films：西德人对"牛仔与印第安人"的古怪崇拜,或法国人对老的杰瑞·刘易斯电影的反常渴求。fetish：迷恋（obsession）；Jerry Lewis：杰瑞·刘易斯（1926— ）,美国喜剧演员,电影制片人,作家和导演,被称为"喜剧之王"

21. mania：狂热（craze）。

22. dawn on sb.：become known or understood by sb.

23. Sometimes they'd run old eroded newsreels as filler on the local station：有时他们会把一些残破的旧新闻片作为本地台的补白节目。

24. a static-ridden Hollywood baritone：充满静电的好莱坞男中音

25. putter：spend time moving about a place slowly doing unimportant activities that need little effort

26. Nash：纳什汽车

27. uninhibited technophiles：无拘无束的新技术爱好者。technophile：新技术爱好者（a person who is enthusiastic about new technology）

28. odds and ends：零星杂物（small articles of various kinds, without much value）

29. the movie marquees ribbed to radiate some mysterious energy：饰着条纹以放射神秘能量的影院遮帐

30. the dime stores faced with fluted aluminum：店面覆盖着有凹槽的铝片的小杂货店

31. perhaps with a curlicue of decorative trim：也许带着一条花体饰纹。curlicue：花体（a decorative twisted pattern, such as one made with a pen）

32. Which made a certain kind of sense：这是有些道理的

33. elaborate props：精美的道具

34. glossy：光面照片,在本文中指的是这些照片:"带翅雕像","一打弗兰克·洛伊德·赖特的约翰逊制蜡楼的照片",《惊奇故事》杂志的封面","一张速写"

35. one of Paul's spray-paint pulp utopias：一个由保罗喷绘出来的乌托邦

36. white togas and Lucite sandals：穿白色的托加袍和透明树脂凉鞋。toga:托加袍,古罗马男子穿的宽松罩袍

37. one sketch of a particularly grandiose prop-driven airliner：一张一架特别夸张的由螺旋桨驱动的班机的速写。grandiose：夸张的（foolishly grand）

38. like a fat symmetrical boomerang：就像一个大而对称的飞去来器。boomerang：澳大利亚土著居民用以捕猎、抛出后可飞回的飞去来镖

39. squash courts：壁球场

40. populist：平民主义者（a person who claims to believe in the wisdom and judgment of ordinary people, esp. in political matters）

41. trying to suffuse a really dull-looking rocker with charisma：想给一个真的看起来呆傻的摇滚乐手增添一些非凡的个人魅力。suffuse：cover.

42. and this poor guy strained my Nikon's credibility：这可怜的家伙几乎耗尽了我那架尼康相机的全部可信度。strain：使用……到极限（use sth. to the greatest possible degree）

43. the sublime artiness：极度的附庸风雅

44. ephemeral：lasting only a short time

45. extruded：pushed or forced out by pressure

46. strip：a narrow piece of land or water

47. erecting raygun emplacements in white stucco：竖起了由白色灰泥制成的射线炮位。emplacement：炮位（a special position prepared for a heavy gun or other piece of usually military equipment to stand on）

48. Lots of them featured superfluous central towers ringed with those strange radiator flanges that were a signature motif of the style：多数加油站都由一个多余的中心塔楼唱主角，一些奇异的散热凸缘环绕在周围，形成一种颇具风格的标志图样。ringed with：被……环绕（encircled with）；flange：（机械等的）凸缘；signature：标记的，标志的（serving to identify or distinguish a person，group，etc）；motif：基本图案（a single or repeated pattern）

49. I shot one in San Jose：我拍下了一个圣何塞的加油站。San Jose：圣何塞，美国加州西部城市

50. lathing：板条（尤指木板条）

51. convoluted：弯曲的，旋绕的（twisted，curved）

52. tune in to：探索；沉浸于；埋首于

53. beached submarines：上岸的潜水艇

54. sect：教派

55. slipstream：尾流（a stream of air driven backwards by an aircraft engine）

56. burnished：磨光的，抛光擦亮的（polished）

57. pit：使留下凹痕

58. thrumming its way east with an elephantine grace：带着大象般的优雅轰隆隆地向东驶去

59. rivet：铆钉

60. with an extensive line：与……有广泛的联系

294

61. pterodactyl: 翼指龙(a flying animal that lived many millions of years ago)

62. contactee: 接触者

63. the loonier reaches: 更疯狂的部分。loony: 疯狂的(insane); reaches: level, area.

64. quill: 套管轴

65. blanket: 一揽子的(covering or intended to cover a large class of things)

66. basilisk: 蛇怪(an imaginary snakelike creature, whose breath and look were thought to be able to kill)

67. score: 真相(the facts of an situation)

68. crackpot: 古怪的(strange)

69. you've taken your share of drugs: 你吸过毒。

70. to weave animated holograms of Egyptian hieroglyphs into the fabric of your jeans: 把埃及象形文字的立体动画织进你的牛仔裤

71. fish: 掏出,摸出

72. severed: 被割断的

73. hubcap: 汽车的毂盖(a metal covering over the center of the wheel of a motor vehicle)

74. Caddy: 茶叶罐,茶叶盒

75. telescoping: 可伸缩的

76. poking up: 伸出

77. burp: 打嗝

78. lapse into: 陷入(fall, slip, or sink into)

79. 'The Bionic Man' and all those 'Star Trek' reruns:《超级电子人》以及所有那些重播的《星际迷航》

80. She is clued into the main vein: 她被引入了主流。

81. polygraph: 测谎仪(lie detector)

82. classy: 时髦的,高级的(fashionable and of high class)

83. semiotic：符号的

84. sci-fi imagery：科幻意象

85. the Jules Verne airships：儒勒·凡尔纳的飞船。Jules Verne：儒勒·凡尔纳(1828—1905)，法国小说家，现代科幻小说的奠基人，主要作品有《格兰特船长的儿女》、《海底两万里》、《从地球到月球》、《神秘岛》、《八十天环游地球》等

86. a chartered plane：包租的飞机。charter：包租(hire or rent out a plane, train, bus, etc. for a special use)

87. a cattle-mutilation rumor：一个屠宰牛群的传闻。mutilate：肢解,使残废

88. shaving kit：剃须盒。kit：成套工具(a set of articles or tools needed for a particular purpose or job)

89. amphetamine：安非他命(a drug used esp. formerly in medicine and, esp. illegally, by people wanting excitement)

90. the spectral, luminous vegetation：诡异而闪亮的植物。spectral：鬼怪(似)的,幽灵(似的)(of or like a spectre)

91. in a tight, lopsided orbit：沿着一个紧密倾斜的轨道

92. infrared：红外线的

93. shreds：碎片(small narrow pieces torn or roughly cut off)

94. flying oil refineries：飞行的油罐车

95. solvent：有偿付能力的(having enough money to pay all money owed)

96. rattlesnakes and cannibal hippies：响尾蛇和食人嬉皮士

97. brothel：妓院

98. my eyeballs felt gritty in their sockets：我的眼球在眼眶里好像沾满了沙粒。gritty：沾满沙粒的

99. *Metropolis* and *Things to Come*：《大都会》和《未来的事》,奥地利裔美籍无声电影导演 Fritz Lang(1890—1976)的科幻影片

100. to zeppelin docks and mad neon spires：直到飞艇码头和疯狂的霓虹尖顶那里。zeppelin：(第一次世界大战时德国人使用的一种大

型飞艇)其柏林飞艇(a large airship used by the Germans in the First World War)

101. scale model：比例模型(exactly the same in all details, but much smaller)

102. gleaming ziggurat steps：闪闪发光的金字神塔台阶。ziggurat：金字神塔(a temple tower of the ancient Mesopotamian valley and Iran, having the form of a terraced pyramid of successively receding stories or levels)

103. running mercury：流动的水银

104. quicksilver：水银(mercury)

105. blimp：小型飞艇(a small airship)

106. gyrocopter：自旋翼飞机

107. the mileage meter：里程表

108. dashboard = dash：(汽车的)仪表板

109. ashtray：烟灰缸

110. Amphetamine psychosis：安非他命综合征。psychosis：精神病(a serious disorder of the mind that may produce character changes and makes one lose touch with reality)

111. an aluminum avocado with a central shark-fin rudder jutting up from its spine：像一个铝制的鳄梨,从其脊椎中央突起一个鲨鱼鳍般的舵

112. Tucson：土桑市,位于美国亚利桑那州(the largest city in southern Arizona and the second largest in the state)

113. the finite bounds of fossil fuel：化石燃料的有限性。bounds：限度,止境(limits)

114. I imagined them thronging the plazas of white marble：我想象他们蜂拥在白色大理石的广场上。throng：蜂拥至(某处)

115. floodlit：用泛光灯照明的

116. His words were bright and hollow as the pitch in some Chamber of

Commerce brochure：他的言辞充满希望,但空洞无物,就像某些商会小册子里的广告。pitch：广告(a sales talk, often one in which the salesperson tries to convince the buyer of the need for his or her product)

117. wafer：圆片

118. *frisson*：震颤(尤指接触到惊险的或被禁止的事所引起的一阵快感)

119. I'm letting you in on a trade secret：我要透露给你一个商业秘密。let sb. in on sth.：把……透露给某人

120. If it keeps the saucer people off my back, it can keep these Art Deco futuroids off yours：如果它能把飞碟人从我背后赶跑,那它也就能把那些装饰艺术未来派从你背后赶走。Art Deco：装饰艺术,最早起源于上世纪二三十年代的法国,迅速流行于建筑、珠宝、家具、衣饰等的设计中。装饰艺术应用于建筑风格,往往突出外立面竖向线条的使用,常外挂面砖、天然石材等。同时,其建筑装饰会尝试新鲜元素的使用,如钢铁、玻璃等,不拘一格,旨在追求单个建筑作品的个性与不可复制性(a popular international design movement from 1925 until 1939, affecting the decorative arts such as architecture, interior design, and industrial design, as well as the visual arts such as fashion, painting, the graphic arts and film)

121. I considered putting a collect call through to London：我考虑打一个对方付费的电话到伦敦。put a collect call through：make a phone call to be paid for by the receiver

122. a protracted season：一个延长的季节

123. when the road fanned out like an origami trick and left me swerving through a dozen minilanes of whizzing chrome teardrops with shark fins：当时那路面像日本折纸一样呈扇面张开,逼我突然转弯穿越了一打微型车道,装有鲨鱼鳍的镀铬水滴正飕飕地在车道上飞驰。whizz：飕飕地飞驰(move very fast, often making a noisy sound

as if rushing through the air)

124. patio decks: 露台甲板

125. riffling through them like a deck of cards: 像洗牌一样翻阅它们。
    riffle through: 很快地翻阅(turn over papers, pages, etc. quickly
    with one's finger); deck: 一副纸牌(a set of playing cards)

126. air freight: 空中货运

127. Cohen's congratulatory wire was forwarded to me: 科恩的贺电转到
    了我手里。forward: 转交;转寄

128. tenuous: 纤细的,薄弱的(thin or slender in form, as a thread)

129. proprietor: 老板(an owner of a business, etc.)

130. where I could submerge myself in hard evidence of the human near-
    dystopia we live in: 在那里我可以把自己淹没在关于我们人类居
    住的这个类反乌托邦的硬证据里

Questions:

1. What slice of Americana fascinates Dialta Downes?

2. What does Gernsback Continuum mean? How does the protagonist visit
   it?

3. Why is the narrator horrified by his vision of a man and a woman from
   that other future?

4. What are "semiotic ghosts"? How can the protagonist get rid of them?

5. What does it mean to live in a "human near dystopia"?

6. What does this story have to say about the history of the future?

Don DeLillo

(*1936-*)

Don DeLillo (1936—) is one of America's leading contemporary writers and a member of the American Academy and Institute of Arts and Letters. He has published 15 novels, along with several plays and some short stories. He is regarded as the most gifted stylist in American letters today. He writes about terrorism, celebrity, writers, mathematicians, popular culture, consumerism and the crucial shaping events of America's recent history.

DeLillo was born in Bronx, New York, to Italian immigrants. He attended Fordham University in New York where he majored in communication arts, but found the city a far more exciting playground, citing its access to experimental art, jazz, and European movies, which he said in an interview "have been the major influences" on him. In 1958 he graduated from Fordham College and got a job in advertising. He began to write short stories and published his first short story "The River Jordan" in 1960. He quitted the job in advertising in 1964.

In 1971 he published his first novel *Americana*. His major works include *Great Jones Street* (1973), *Ratner's Star* (1976), *Players* (1977), *Running Dogs* (1978), *The Names* (1982), *White Noise* (1985), *Libra* (1988), *Mao II* (1991), *Underworld* (1997), *The Body Artist* (2001), *Cosmopolis* (2003), and *Falling Man* (2007). Among the many honors De Lillo has received are the National Book Award for his postmodern masterpiece *White Noise*; the Irish Times/Aer Lingus

International Fiction Prize for *Libra*; the PEN/Faulkner Award for Fiction for *Mao II*; and the Jerusalem Prize, William Dean Howells Medal, and the Riccardo Bacchelli International Award for *Underworld*. In addition in 2005 *Time* magazine included *White Noise* in their list of the 100 best English-language novels written since 1923. *Libra*, *White Noise*, and *Underworld* received high marks on a 2006 survey sponsored by *The New York Times* to name the single best work of American fiction of the last 25 years.

"The Ivory Acrobat" is a short story published in 1988. The story describes the jitters of Kyle and Edmund, two young expatriate teachers, in Athens during a period of earthquakes, and reflects DeLillo's own life in Greece. From 1979 to 1982, DeLillo stayed in Greece for 3 years, during which time he wrote *The Names*. The ivory acrobat is a "reproduction of an ivory figurine from Crete, a bull-leaper, female, her body deftly extended with tapered feet nearing the topmost point of a somersaulting curve," a gift that Edmund gives to Kyle, who is extremely nervous after the earthquakes hit Greece. She fears more severe earthquakes will strike the city and bring it to ashes. Reading "The Ivory Acrobat" can give you an insight into DeLillo's novels. The spare and elliptical style, the accurate and realistic description, the theme of coping with fear, and the jittery characters are typical of DeLillo's fiction.

The Ivory Acrobat

Don DeLillo

When it was over she stood in the crowded street and listened to the dense murmur of all those people speaking. She heard the first distant blurt of car horns on the avenue[1]. People studied each other to match reactions. She watched them search the street for faces, signs that so-and-so[2] was safe. She realized the street-lights were on and tried to recall how long her flat had been dark. Everyone was talking. She heard the same phrases repeated and stood with her arms crossed on her chest, watching a woman carry a chair to a suitable spot. The sound of blowing horns drifted through the streets. People leaving the city in radial[3] streams. Already she was thinking ahead to the next one. There's always supposed to be another, possibly many more. The card-players stood outside the café, some of them inspecting a chunk of fallen masonry[4] on the sidewalk, others looking towards the roof. Here and there a jutting face[5], a body slowly turning, searching. She wore what she'd been wearing when it started, jeans and shirt and light sweater, and it was night and winter, and funny-looking moccasins[6] she only wore indoors. The horns grew louder in a kind of cry, an animal awe. The panic god is Greek after all. She thought about it again and wasn't sure the lights had been out at all. Women stood with arms folded in the cold. She walked along the middle of the street, listening to the voices, translating phrased to herself. It was the same for everyone. They said the same things and searched for faces. The streets were narrow here and people sat in parked cars, smoking. Here and there a child running, hand-shuffling through the crowd, excited children out near midnight. She thought there might be a glow in the sky and climbed a broad stepped street that had a vantage towards the gulf[7]. She seemed to recall reading there's sometimes a light in the sky just before it happens or just after. This came under the heading of unexplained.

After a while they started going back inside. Kyle walked for three hours. She watched the cars push into major avenues that led to the mountains and the coast. Traffic-lights were dark in certain areas. The long lines of cars knotted and bent, made scant gains forward. Paralysis[8]. She thought the scene resembled some landscape in the dreaming part of us, what the city teaches us to fear. They were pressing on the horns. The noise spread along the streets and reached a final mass denial, a desolation. It subsided after a time, then began to build again. She saw people sleeping on benches and families collected in cars parked on sidewalks and median strips[9]. She recalled all the things she'd ever heard about an earthquake.

In her district the streets were almost empty now. She went into her building and took the stairs to five. The lights were on in her flat, and there were broken pieces of terracotta[10] (she only now remembered) scattered on the floor by the bookcase. Long cracks branched along the west wall. She changed into walking shoes, put on a padded ski-jacket and turned off the lights except for a lamp by the door. Then she placed herself on the sofa between a sheet and blanket, her head resting on an airline pillow. She closed her eyes and folded up, elbows at her mid-section, hands pressed together between her knees. She tried to will herself to sleep but realized she was listening intently, listening to the room. She lay in a kind of timeless drift, a mindwork spiral[11], carried on half-formed thoughts. She passed into a false sleep and then was listening again. She opened her eyes. The clock read four-forty. She heard something that sounded like sand spilling, a trickle of gritty dust between the walls of abutting structures[12]. The room began to move in a creaking sigh[13]. Louder, powerfully. She was out of bed and on her way to the door, moving slightly crouched. She opened the door and stood under the lintel[14] until the shaking stopped. She took the stairway down. No neighbours popping out of doors this time, bending arms into coats. The streets remained nearly empty and she guessed people didn't want to bother doing it again. She wandered well past daybreak. A few camp-fires burned in the parks. The horn-blowing was sporadic[15] now. She walked around her building a number of times, finally sitting on a bench near the newspaper kiosk[16]. She watched people enter the street to begin the day and she looked for something in their faces that might tell her what kind of night they'd spent. She was afraid everything would appear to be normal. She hated to think that people might easily resume the knockabout routine of frazzled Athens[17]. She didn't want to be alone in her perception that something had basically changed. The world was narrowed down to inside and outside.

She had lunch with Edmund, a colleague at the little school where she taught music to children of the international community, grades three to six. She was eager to hear how he'd reacted to the situation but first talked him into eating outdoors at a table set against the fa,cade of a busy snack-shop[18].

"We could still be killed," Edmund said, "by falling balconies. Or freeze in our chairs."

"How did you feel?"

"I thought my heart was going to jump right through my chest."

"Good. Me too."

"I fled."

"Of course."

"On my way down the stairs I had the oddest conversation with the man who lives across the hall. I mean we'd hardly said a word to each other before this. There were two dozen people barrelling down the stairs[19]. Suddenly he wanted to talk. He asked me where I work. Introduced me to his wife, who was pretty goddamn uninterested at that point in the details of my employment. He asked me how I like living in Greece."

Skies were low and grey. People called to each other on the street, chanted from passing cars. *Eksi komma eksi*[20]. They were referring to the first one, the bigger one. Six point six. Kyle had been hearing the number all morning, spoken with reverence, anxiety, grim pride, an echo along the brooding[21] streets, a form of fatalistic[22] greeting.

"Then what?" she said.

"The second one. I woke up moments before."

"You heard something."

"Like a child tossing a handful of sand against the window."

"Very good," she said.

"Then it hit."

"It hit."

"Bang. I leapt out of bed like a madman."

"Did the lights go out?"

"No."

"What about the first time?"

"I'm not sure actually."

"Good. Neither am I. Was there a glow in the sky at any point?"

"Not that I noticed."

"We could be dealing with a myth here."

"The newspapers said a power-station may have failed, causing a flash. There's confusion on this point."

"But we experienced similar things."

"It would appear," he said.

"Good. I'm glad."

She thought of him as the English Boy although he was thirty-six, divorced, apparently arthritic and not even English. But he felt the English rapture over Greek light, where all Kyle saw was chemical smoke lapping at the ruins[23]. And he had the prim[24] outdated face of a schoolboy in a formal portrait, wire-haired and pensive[25].

"Where was the epicentre[26]?" she said.

"About forty miles west of here."

"The dead?"

"Thirteen and counting."

"What will we do?"

"About what?" he said.

"Everything. All the after-shocks[27]. "

"We've had 200 already. It's expected to last many weeks. Read the papers. Months perhaps. "

"Look, Edmund. I don't want to be alone tonight. Ok?"

She lived inside a pause. She was always pausing, alone in her flat, to listen. Her hearing developed a cleanness, a discriminating rigour[28]. She sat at the small table where she ate her meals, listening. The room had a dozen sounds, mainly disturbances of tone, pressures releasing in the walls, and she followed them and waited. There was a second and safer level she reserved for street noises, the elevator rising. All the danger was inside.

A rustle. A soft sway. She crouched in the open doorway like an atomic child[29].

The tremors[30] entered her bloodstream. She listened and waited. She couldn't sleep at night and caught odd moments in daytime, dozing in an unused room at school[31]. She dreaded going home. She watched the food in her plate and sometimes stood, carefully listening, ready to go, to get outside. There must be something funny in this somewhere, a person standing motionless over her food, leaning ever so slightly towards the door, fingertips at the table edge.

Is it true that before a major quake the dogs and cats run away? She thought she'd read somewhere that people in California habitually check the personal columns in newspapers to see if the number of lost dogs has increased noticeably. Or are we dealing with a myth[32] here?

The wind made the shutters swing and bang. She listened to the edge of the room, the interfaces[33]. She heard everything. She put a tote bag[34] near the door for hasty exits—money, books, passport, letters from home. She heard the sound of the knife-sharpener's bell.

She didn't read the papers but gathered that the tremors numbered in the 800s by latest count and the dead added up to twenty now, with hotel rubble and tent cities near the epicentre and people living in open areas in parts of Athens, their buildings judged unsafe.

The card-players wore their coats indoors. She walked past the cut-back mulberry trees and through the street market and looked at the woman selling eggs and wondered what she could say to her that might make them both feel better, in her fairly decent Greek, shopping for bargains. A man held the elevator door, but she waved him off politely and took the staris. She walked into her flat, listening. The terrace canopies humped out in the wind, snapping hard[35]. She wanted her life to be epidodic[36] again, unpremediatated[37]. A foreigner anonymous[38]—soft-footed, self-informed, content to occupy herself in random observation. She wanted to talk unimportantly to grandmothers and children in the streets of her working-class district.

She rehearsed her exit mentally. So many steps from the table to the door. So many stairs to the street. She thought if she pictured it beforehand, it might go more smoothly.

The lottery man cried, "Today, today."

She tried to read through the edgy nights, the times of dull-witted terror. There were rumours that these were not after-shocks at all but warnings of some deep disquiet in the continental trench, the massing of a force that would roll across the marble-hearted city and bring it to dust[39]. She sat up and turned the pages, trying to disguise herself as someone who routinely reads for fifteen minutes before dropping into easy sleep.

It was not so bad in school, where she was ready to protect the young, to cover their bodies with her own.

The tremors lived in her skin and were part of every breath she took. She paused over her food. A rustle. An easing reedy tilt[40]. She stood and listened, alone with the shaking earth.

Edmund told her he'd bought a gift to replace the terracotta roof ornament she'd had propped against the wall above the bookcase, acanthus leaves radiating from the head of a sleep-eyed Hermes[41], shattered in the first tremor.

"You won't miss your Hermes all that much. I mean it's everywhere, isn't it?"

"That's what I liked about it."

"You can easily get another. They're piled up for sale."

"It'll only get broken," she said, "when the next one hits."

"Let's change the subject."

"There's only one subject. That's the trouble. I used to have a personality. What am I now?"

"Try to understand it's over."

"I'm down to pure dumb canine instinct[42]."

"Life is going on. People are going about their business."

"No, they're not. Not the same way. Just because they don't walk around moaning."

"There's nothing to moan about. It's finished."

"Doesn't mean they're not preoccupied. It's been less than a week. There are tremors all the time."

"Growing ever small," he said.

"Some are not so small. Some are definite attention-getters."

"Change the subject please."

They were standing just outside the school entrance, and Kyle was watching a group of children climb aboard a bus for a trip to a museum outside the city. She knew she could count on the English Boy to be exasperated[43] with her. He was dependable that way. She always knew the position he would take and could often anticipate the actual words,

308

practically moving her lips in unison with[44] his. He brought some stability to dire times[45].

"You used to be lithe[46]."

"Look at me now," she said.

"Lumbering[47]."

"I wear layers of clothing. I wear clothes and change-of-clothes simultaneously[48]. Just to be ready."

"I can't afford a change of clothes," he said.

"I can't afford the dry cleaning."

"I often wonder how this happened to me."

"I lived without a refrigerator and telephone and radio and shower-curtain and what else. I keep butter and milk on the balcony."

"You're very quiet," he said then. "Everyone says so."

"Am I? Who?"

"How old are you by the way?"

"Now that we've spent a night together, you mean?"

"Spent a night. Exactly. One night used up in huddled conversation."

"Well it helped me. It made a difference really. It was the crucial night. Not that the others have been so cosy."

"You're welcome to return, you know. I sit there thinking. A lithe young woman flying across the city into my arms."

The children waved at them from the windows, and Edmund did a wild-eyed mime of a bus driver caught in agitated traffic[49]. She watched the lightsome faces glide away.

"You have nice colour," she said.

"What does that mean?"

"Your cheeks are pink and healthy. My father used to say if I ate my vegetables I'd have rosy cheeks."

She waited for Edmund to ask, "What did your mother used to say?" Then they walked for the time that remained before afternoon classes. Edmund bought a ring of sesame bread and gave her half. He paid for things by opening his fist and letting the vendor sort among the coins. It proved to everyone that he was only passing through.

"You've heard the rumours," she said.

"Rubbish."

"The government is concealing seismic[50] data."

"There is absolutely no scientific evidence that a great quake is imminent[51]. Read the papers."

She took off the bulky jacket and swung it over her shoulder. She realized she wanted him to think she was slightly foolish, controlled by mass emotion. There was some comfort in believing the worst as long as this was the reigning persuasion[52]. But she didn't want to submit completely. She walked along wondering if she was appealing to Edmund for staunch pronouncements[53] that she could use against herself.

"Do you have an inner life?"

"I sleep," he said.

"That's not what I mean."

They ran across a stretch of avenue where cars accelerated to a racing clip[54]. It felt good to shake out of her jittery[55] skin. She kept running for half a block and then turned to watch him approach clutching his chest and moving on doddery legs[56], as if for the regalement[57] of children. He could look a little bookish even capering[58].

They approach the school building.

"I wonder what your hair would be like if you let it grow out."

"I can't afford the extra shampoo," she said.

"I can't afford a haircut at regular intervals, quite seriously."

"I lived without a piano."

310

"And this is a wretchedness[59] to compare with no refrigerator?"

"You can ask that question because you don't know me. I live without a bed. "

"Is this true?"

"I sleep on a second-hand sofa. It has the texture of a barnacled hull[60]. "

"Then why stay?" he said.

"I can't save enough to go anywhere else and I'm certainly not ready to go home. Besides I like it here. I'm sort of stranded[61] but in a more or less willing way. At least until now. The trouble with now is that we could be anywhere. The only thing that matters is where we're standing when it hits. "

He presented the gift then, lifting it out of his jacket pocket and unwrapping the sepia[62] paper with a teasing show of suspense. It was a reproduction of any ivory figurine from Crete[63], a bull-leaper, female, her body deftly extended with tapered feet nearing the topmost point of a somersaulting curve[64]. Edmund explained that the young woman was in the act of vaulting over the horns of a charging bull[65]. This was a familiar scene in Minoan[66] art, found in frescoes[67], bronzes, clay seals, gold signet[68] rings, ceremonial cups. Most often a young man, sometimes a woman gripping a bull's horns and swinging up and over, propelled by the animal's head-jerk[69]. He told her the original ivory figure was broken in half in 1926 and asked her if she wanted to know how this happened.

"Don't tell me. I want to guess. "

"An earthquake. But the restoration was routine. "

Kyle took the figure in her hand.

"A bull coming at full gallop[70]? Is this possible?"

"I'm not inclined to question what was possible 3,600 years ago. "

"I don't know the Minoans," she said. "Were they that far back?"

311

"Yes, and farther than that, much farther."

"Maybe if the bull was firmly tethered[71]."

"It's never shown that way," he said. "It's shown big and fierce and running and bucking[72]."

"Do we have to believe something happened exactly the way it was shown by artists?"

"No. But I believe it. And even though this particular leaper isn't accompanied by a bull, we know from her position that this is what she's doing."

"She's bull-leaping."

"Yes."

"And she will live to tell it."

"She has lived. She is living. That's why I got this for you really. I want her to remind you of your hidden litheness."

"But You're the acrobat," Kyle said. "You're the loose-jointed one, performing in the streets."

"To remind you of your fluent buoyant[73] former self."

"You're the jumper and heel-clicker."

"My joints ache like hell actually."

"Look at the veins in her hand and arm."

"I got it cheap in the flea market."

"That makes me feel much better."

"It's definitely you," he said. "It must be you. Do we agree on this? Just look and feel. It's your magical true self, mass-produced."

Kyle laughed.

"Lean and supple and young," he said. "Throbbing with inner life."

She laughed. Then the school bell rang and they went inside.

She stood in the middle of the room, dressed except for shoes, slowly buttoning her blouse. She paused. She worked the button through the

312

slit[74]. Then she stood on the wood floor, listening.

They were now saying twenty-five dead, thousands homeless. Some people had abandoned undamaged buildings, preferring the ragged safety of life outdoors. Kyle could easily see how that might happen. She had the first passable night's sleep but continued to stay off elevators and out of movie theatres. The wind knocked loose objects off the back balconies. She listened and waited. She visualized her exit from the room.

Sulphur fell from the factory skies, staining the pavement, and a teacher at the school said it was sand blown north from Libya on one of those lovely desert winds.

She sat on the sofa in pyjamas and socks reading a book on local flora. A blankt covered her legs. A half-filled glass of water sat on the end table[75]. Her eyes wandered from the page. It was two minutes before midnight. She paused, looking off towards the middle distance. Then she heard it coming, an earth-roar, a power moving on the air. She sat for a long second, deeply thoughtful, before throwing off the blanket. The moment burst around her. She rushed to the door and opened it, half aware of rattling lampshades and something wet. She gripped the edges of the door-frame and faced into the room. Things were jumping up and down. She formed the categorical thought: *This one is the biggest yet.* The room was more or less a blur. There was a sense that it was on the verge of splintering[76]. She felt the effect in her legs this time, a kind of hollowing out, a soft surrender to some illness. It was hard to believe, hard to believe it was lasting so long. She pushed her hands against the door-frame, searching for a calmness in herself. She could almost see a picture of her mind, a vague grey oval, floating over the room. The shaking would not stop. There was an anger in it, a hammering demand[77]. Her face showed the crumpled effort of a heavy lifter[78]. It wasn't easy to know what was happening around her. She couldn't see things in the normal way.

313

She could only see herself, bright-skinned, waiting for the room to fold over her[79].

Then it ended and she pulled some clothes over her pyjamas and took the stairway down. She moved fast. She ran across the small lobby, brushing past a man[80] lighting a cigarette at the door. People were coming into the street. She went half a block and stopped at the edge of a large group. She was breathing hard and her arms hung limp[81]. Her first clear thought was that she'd have to go back inside sooner or later. She listened to the voices fall around her. She wanted to hear someone say this very thing, that the cruelty existed in time, that they were all unprotected in the drive of time. She told a woman she thought a water-pipe had broken in her flat and the woman closed her eyes and rocked her heavy head. When will it all end? She told the woman she'd forgotten to grab her tote bag on her way out the door despite days of careful planning and she tried to give the story a rueful nuance[82], making it funny and faintly self-mocking. There must be something funny we can cling to. They stood there rocking their heads.

All up and down the street there were people lighting cigarettes. It was eight days since the first tremor, eight days and one hour.

She walked most of the night. At three a. m. she stopped in the square in front of the Olympic Stadium. There were parked cars and scores of people and she studied the faces and stood listening. Traffic moved slowly past. There was a curious double mood, a lonely reflectiveness[83] at the centre of all the talk, a sense that people were half-absent from the eager seeking of company. She started walking again.

Eating breakfast in her flat at nine o'clock she felt the first sizeable[84] after-shock. The room leaned heavily. She rose from the table, eyes wet, and opened the door and crouched there, holding a buttered roll[85].

Wrong. The last one was not the biggest on the Richter[86]. It was only six point two.

And she found out it hadn't lasted longer than the others. This was a mass illusion, according to the word at school.

And the water she'd seen or felt had not come from a broken pipe but from a toppled drinking-glass on the table by the sofa.

And why did they keep occurring at night?

And where was the English Boy?

The drinking-glass was intact but her paperback book on plant life was wet and furrowed.

She took the stairs up and down.

She kept the tote bag ready at the door.

She was deprived of sentiments, pretensions, expectations, textures[87].

The pitiless thing was time, threat of advancing time.

She was deprived of presumptions, persuasions, complications, lies, every braided arrangement that made it possible to live[88].

Stay out of movies and crowded halls. She was down to categories of sound, to self-admonishments and endless inner scrutinies[89].

She paused, alone, to listen.

She pictured her sensible exit from the room.

She looked for something in people's faces that might tell her their experience was just like hers, down to the smallest strangest turn of thought.

There must be something funny in this somewhere that we can use to get us through the night.

She heard everything.

She took catnaps[90] at school.

She was deprived of the city itself. We could be anywhere, any lost corner of Ohio.

She dreamed of a mayfly pond skimmed with fallen blossoms[91].

Take the stairs everywhere. Take a table near the exit in cafés and tavernas.

The card-players sat in hanging smoke, making necessary motions only, somebrely guarding their cards.

She learned that Edmund was in the north with friends, peering into monasteries[92].

She heard the surge[93] of motorcycles on the hill.

She inspected the cracks in the west and spoke to the landlord, who closed his eyes and rocked his heavy head.

The wind caused a rustling somewhere very near.

She sat up at night with her book of water-stiffened pages, trying to read, trying to escape the feeling that she was being carried helplessy towards some pitching instant[94] in time.

The acanthus is a spreading perennial[95].

And everything in the world is either inside or outside.

She came across the figurine one day inside a desk drawer at school, lying among cough-drops and paper-clips, in an office used as a teachers' lounge. She didn't even remember putting it there and felt the familiar clashing agencies of shame and defensiveness working in her blood—a body heat rising against the reproach of forgotten things. She picked it up, finding something remarkable in the leaper's clean and open motions, in the detailed tension of forearms and hands. Shouldn't something so old have a formal bearing, a stiffness of figure? This was easy-flowing work. But beyond this surprise, there was little to know. She didn't know the Minoans. She wasn't even sure what the things was made of, what kind of lightweight imiation ivory. It occurred to her that she'd left the figure in the desk because she didn't know what to do with it, how to underpin or prop it[96]. The body was alone in space, with no supports, no fixed position, and seemed best suited to the palm of the hand.

316

She stood in the small room, listening.

Edmund had said the figure was like her. She studied it, trying to extract the sparest recogintion[97]. A girl in a loincloth and wristbands[98], double-necklaced, suspended over the horns of a running bull. The act, the leap itself, might be vaudeville[99] or sacred terror. There were themes and secrets and storied lore in this six-inch figure that Kyle could not begin to guess at. She turned the object in her hand. All the facile parallels fell away[100]. Lithe, young, buoyant, modern; rumbling bulls and quaking earth. There was nothing that might connect her to the mind inside the work, an ivory-carver, 1600 B. C. , moved by forces remote from her. She remembered the old earthen Hermes, flower-crowned, looking out at her from a knowable past, some shared theatre of being. The Mnioans were outside all this. Narrow-waisted, graceful, other-minded—lost across vales of language and magic, across dream cosmologies[101]. This was the piece's little mystery. It was a thing in opposition, defining what she was not, marking the limits of the self. She closed her fist around it firmly and thought she could feel it beat against her skin with a soft and periodic pulse, an earthliness[102].

She was motionless, with tilted head, listening. Buses rolled past, sending diesel fumes through seams in the window frame[103]. She looked towards a corner of the room, concentrating tightly. She listened and waited.

Her self-awareness ended where the acrobat began. Once she realized this, she put the object in her pocket and took it everywhere.

Notes:

1. the first distant blurt of car horns on the avenue: 大街上汽车喇叭远远传来的第一声鸣响。blurt: 脱口而出的话,这里指汽车喇叭突然发出的鸣响。avenue: 城市的大街,林荫道(a broad street in a twon,

sometimes having trees on each side)

2. so-and-so：某某人（someone）

3. radial：辐射状的

4. a chunk of fallen masonry：一大块建筑物上掉落的石头

5. a jutting face：向外探的头。jut：使伸出

6. moccasin：软帮鞋（a simple shoe made of soft leather）

7. a broad stepped street that had a vantage towards the gulf：一条宽阔的有阶梯的街道，可以通往海湾

8. made scant gains forward. Paralysis：几乎没有怎么向前移动。瘫痪了。scant：hardly enough

9. median strip：中央分隔带，安全岛

10. terracotta：赤陶（hard reddish brown baked clay）

11. a mindwork spiral：心里想的事越来越多。spiral：螺旋式上升或下降

12. a trickle of gritty dust between the walls of abutting structures：毗连的建筑物墙体间的沙尘慢慢滑落。trickle：细流（a thin slow flow or movement）

13. in a creaking sigh：嘎吱一声

14. lintel：（门、窗上的）过梁（a piece of stone or wood across the top of a window or door, forming part of the frame）

15. sporadic：偶尔发生的（happening irregularly）

16. newspaper kiosk：报亭

17. resume the knockabout routine of frazzled Athens：恢复精疲力竭的雅典那喧闹的日常生活

18. the fa, cade of a busy snack-shop：一家生意兴隆的快餐店的正面。fa, cade：the front of a building.

19. barrelling down the stairs：飞奔下楼梯。barrel：飞奔（move at high speed）

20. *Eksi komma eksi*：Greek, meaning 6.6. "eksi" is six.

21. brooding：causing a feeling of fear

22. fatalistic：宿命的（relating to or implying fatalism）

23. chemical smoke lapping at the ruins：在废墟上冒出化学浓烟

24. prim：端正的（stiffly neat）

25. wire-haired and pensive：头发粗粗的,有点忧郁

26. epicentre：震中（a point, directly above the true center of an earthquake, from which its shock waves appear to spread）

27. after-shock：余震

28. a discriminating rigour：一种在辨别声音上的精确。rigour：精确（careful accuracy）

29. A rustle. A soft sway. She crouched in the open doorway like an atomic child：一阵沙沙声,一次轻微的晃动。她像个小孩一样蜷伏在敞开的门口。atomic：extremely small

30. tremor：大地的轻微震动（a shaking movement of the ground）

31. caught odd moments in daytime, dozing in an unused room at school：白天抓住零散的片刻时间在学校一间无人使用的房间打个盹

32. myth：无根据的观念（a widely believed but false story or idea）

33. interface：交界处,边缘区域

34. a tote bag：a shopping bag.

35. The terrace canopies humped out in the wind, snapping hard：阳台上的雨篷被风掀开了,发出噼噼啪啪的声音。

36. epidodic：插曲般的（made up of separate and usually loosely connected parts）

37. unpremediatated：非预先计划的（unplanned beforehand）

38. anonymous：无名的（with name unknown）

39. but warnings of some deep disquiet in the continental trench, the massing of a force that would roll across the marble-hearted city and bring it to dust：而是大陆深沟某种不安宁的警告,一种力量正在积聚,它将穿越以大理石为中心的城市,使它化为灰烬

40. An easing reedy tilt：一片尖刻而和缓的倾斜声。reedy：thin and high.

41. acanthus leaves radiating from the head of a sleep-eyed Hermes：从一个睡眼蒙眬的赫尔墨斯像的头部呈辐射状伸展出的叶形装饰。Hermes：赫尔墨斯,希腊神话中的众神使者,并为掌管疆界、道路、商业以及科学发明、辩才、幸运、灵巧之神,也是盗贼、赌徒的保护神

42. I'm down to pure dumb canine instinct：我只剩下完全愚蠢的狗的本能。

43. exasperated：恼怒的(extremely annoyed)

44. in unison with：与……同时(at the same time with)

45. He brought some stability to dire times：他给可怕的日子带来了稳定感。dire：terrible.

46. lithe：灵活柔软的(able to bend and move easily and gracefully)

47. lumbering：笨重的,动作迟缓的(moving clumsily or heavily, esp. from great weight or size)

48. simultaneously：at the same time

49. and Edmund did a wild-eyed mime of a bus driver caught in agitated traffic：埃德蒙两眼圆睁地模仿一个被困在焦急不安的车辆行人中的公共汽车驾驶员。

50. seismic：地震的(of earthquakes)

51. imminent：临近的,逼近的(which is going to happen very soon)

52. the reigning persuasion：盛行的见解

53. staunch pronouncements：坚定的看法

54. cars accelerated to a racing clip：汽车加速到比赛的速度。clip：速度(pace, rate)

55. jittery：神经过敏的(nervous, very tense)

56. clutching his chest and moving on doddery legs：紧抓胸口,蹒跚而行。doddery：weak, shaky, and slow

57. regalement: entertainment

58. capering: 快活地跳跃(jumping about in a happy playful manner)

59. wretchedness: unhappiness, unluckiness

60. It has the texture of a barnacled hull: 它有藤壶壳的质感

61. stranded: 一筹莫展的(left in a helpless situation)

62. sepia: 深褐色,乌贼墨色

63. a reproduction of any ivory figurine from Crete: 来自克里特岛的一尊象牙小雕像的复制品。Crete: 希腊的克里特岛(the largest of the Greek islands, the center of the Minoan civilization, the oldest Greek and European civilization)

64. a bull-leaper, female, her body deftly extended with tapered feet nearing the topmost point of a somersaulting curve: 一个跳牛者,女性,她的身体灵巧地伸展着,尖细的双脚接近筋斗弧线的最高点。(Bull-leaping is thought to have been a key ritual in the religion of the Minoan civilization on Bronze Age Crete. As in the case of other Mediterranean civilizations, the bull was the subject of veneration and worship. This ritual consists of an acrobatic leap over a bull; when the leaper grasps the bull's horns, the bull will violently jerk his head upwards giving the leaper the momentum necessary to perform somersaults and other acrobatic tricks or stunts.)

65. in the act of vaulting over the horns of a charging bull: 正跃过一头进攻的公牛的牛角

66. Minoan: 古希腊克里特岛的弥诺斯文明(约公元前 3000 年—前 1450 年),是一种青铜时期的文明。米诺斯文明的一个突出特点是他们对女性神祇的崇拜。出土的壁画和女祭司雕塑显示了男人和妇女参与同一个体育项目(通常是跳牛),因而一些考古学家相信米诺斯社会中男人和女人有着相同的地位。甚至继承权有可能是母系的。

67. frescoe: (湿)壁画

68. signet：图章,私章(常刻在戒指上面)

69. propelled by the animal's head-jerk：由公牛的头急拉所推动。propel：推动,推进(move, drive, or push forward)

70. at full gallop：飞快地,急速地

71. tether：用绳子拴住(fasten an animal with a rope or chain so that it is free to move within a limited area)

72. bucking：jumping up with all four feet off the ground

73. buoyant：cheerful, happy

74. slit：a long narrow cut or opening

75. end table：(放在沙发等旁的)茶几

76. on the verge of splintering：快要裂成碎片。splinter：裂成碎片(break into small sharp-pointed pieces)

77. a hammering demand：一种强烈的要求

78. the crumpled effort of a heavy lifter：一个举重运动员崩溃的努力。crumpled：崩溃的,垮掉的(collapsed)

79. waiting for the room to fold over her：等着房间倒在她身上

80. brushing past a man：从一个男人身边掠过

81. her arms hung limp：她的双臂无力地垂着。limp：无力的(lacking strength)

82. a rueful nuance：一种引人同情的细微差别。rueful：causing sorrow or pity

83. reflectiveness：沉思(thoughtfulness)

84. sizeable：相当大的(fairly large)

85. holding a buttered roll：手里拿着一个涂了黄油的面包卷

86. Richter：里氏(震级)

87. She was deprived of sentiments, pretensions, expectations, textures：她被剥夺了情感、伪装、希望和神韵。

88. She was deprived of presumptions, persuasions, complications, lies, every braided arrangement that made it possible to live：她被剥夺了

傲慢、信念、纠葛、谎言,以及使生存成为可能的每一个交叉缠绕的安排。

89. She was down to categories of sound, to self-admonishments and endless inner scrutinies:她现在所做的只是对声音分类、进行自我告诫和无休止的内心审查。

90. catnap:瞌睡(a short, light nap)

91. a mayfly pond skimmed with fallen blossoms:落花掠过水面的蜉蝣池塘。mayfly:蜉蝣(an insect with large clear wings and a threadlike tail);blossom:花(the flower of a tree or bush, esp. one that produces fruit)

92. peering into monasteries:凝视修道院。monastery:修道院,寺院(a building in which monks live)

93. surge:浪涛般的轰鸣声

94. pitching instant:击中的瞬间

95. The acanthus is a spreading perennial:老鼠筋是一种分布广的多年生植物。perennial:多年生植物(a plant that lives for more than two years)

96. how to underpin or prop it:怎样在下面加个底座支撑它或把它固定在某个位置。underpin:在下面加基础以支撑(support from below, e. g. , by means of a solid piece of material)

97. trying to extract the sparest recogintion:试图找到一点点自己的影子。extract:设法获得(obtain);recognition:认识,认出(the fact of knowing someone or something)

98. A girl in a loincloth and wristbands:一个围着腰布、戴着护腕的女孩

99. vaudeville:歌舞杂耍表演

100. All the facile parallels fell away:所有浅薄的比较消失了。facile:浅薄的(shallow, superficial);parallel:比较

101. lost across vales of language and magic, across dream cosmologies:在穿越语言和魔法之谷,穿越理想的宇宙理论中消失了

102. earthliness: 世俗,凡俗(worldliness)

103. sending diesel fumes through seams in the window frame: 使柴油车排出的难闻气味透过窗户的缝隙进入了房间

Questions:

1. What does "it" refer to in the sentence "When it was over she stood in the crowded street ..." (Para. 1)? How do people react to it?

2. How do you understand Kyle's "pure dumb canine instinct"?

3. How does the writer describe the aftermath of the earthquake?

4. How do you interpret the title of the story? Why does Edmund give Kyle the figurine?

5. What is the theme of the story?

Amy Tan

(1952-)

Amy Tan (1952—) is a famous Chinese American author. She was born in Oakland, California. Both of her parents were Chinese immigrants. Her father emigrated to the United States in 1947 while her mother, Daisy, went to the States in 1949, leaving behind 3 daughters from a previous marriage. Her father was an electrical engineer and a Baptist minister. While Amy Tan was still in her teens, both her father and her sixteen-year-old brother died of brain cancers. Tan grew up in the San Francisco Bay Area, graduated from high school in Montreux, Switzerland, and received both her bachelor's and master's degrees in English and Linguistics from San Jose State University. She enrolled as a doctoral student in linguistics at the University of California, Berkeley. But she left her doctoral program before completing her degree. Before she began to write fiction in 1985, she worked as a consultant to programs for disabled children, sat on numerous boards of directorships that required "minority" representation, and did freelance technical writing.

In 1989 Amy Tan published her first novel *The Joy Luck Club*, which recounts the family stories of four modern Chinese-American women. It was widely hailed for its depiction of the Chinese-American experience of the late 20th century. The novel received enthusiastic reviews and stayed on the New York Times best-seller list for nine months. It has been translated in 17 languages, including Chinese. In 1993 *The Joy Luck Club* was made into a commercially successful film. Her subsequent novel,

325

The Kitchen God's Wife (1991), confirmed her reputation and enjoyed excellent sales. Since then Amy Tan has published two books for children, *The Moon Lady* (1992) and *The Chinese Siamese Cat* (1994); three novels *The Hundred Secret Senses* (1995), *The Bonesetter's Daughter* (2001), and *Saving Fish From Drowning* (2005); and a collection of non-fiction essays, *The Opposite of Fate: A Book of Musings* (2003).

Tan's novels often explore the mother-daughter relationships. *The Joy Luck Club*, *The Kitchen God's Wife*, and *The Bonesetter's Daughter* all center around the love and antagonism between Chinese immigrant mothers and their American daughters. In real life Tan and her mother experienced similar emotional turmoil. Daisy Tan had high expectations for her daughter. Amy recalls that as a child she was expected to grow up to be a neurosurgeon by profession with the "hobby" of concert pianist. She also remembers her mother's disappointment when she changed her undergraduate major from premed to English. The character Mother in her novels is often modelled on her own mother. Tan writes about her mother's intent, passion, imagery of speech, and her nature of thought. Tan grew up with her mother's broken English which has influenced her writing as well as her life. She spoke to her mother differently using her mother's broken English while she spoke to other people with perfect English. Her essay, "Mother Tongue", which also deals with the mother and daughter relationship, was chosen for Best American Essays in 1991 and has been widely anthologized. In this essay Tan talks about her mother's broken English and her influence on her.

"Two Kinds" is the last story in the second of four sections of *The Joy Luck Club*. Tan intended the book to be read as a loose collection of interrelated stories, but it is often referred to as a novel. Like all the other stories in the book, "Two Kinds" is concerned with the complex relationships between mothers and daughters. In this story, the narrator, Jing-Mei, resists her mother's desire to make her into a prodigy and

Two Kinds

Amy Tan

My mother believed you could be anything you wanted to be in America. You could open a restaurant. You could work for the government and get good retirement. You could buy a house with almost no money down[1]. You could become rich. You could become instantly famous.

"Of course you can be prodigy[2], too," my mother told me when I was nine. "You can be best anything. What does Auntie Lindo know? Her daughter, she is only best tricky."

America was where all my mother's hopes lay. She had come here in 1949 after losing everything in China: her mother and father, her family home, her first husband, and two daughters, twin baby girls. But she never looked back with regret. There were so many ways for things to get better.

We didn't immediately pick the right kind of prodigy. At first my mother thought I could be a Chinese Shirley Temple[3]. We'd watch Shirley's old movies on TV as though they were training films. My mother would poke my arm and say, "Ni kan"—You watch. And I would see Shirley tapping her feet, or singing a sailor song, or pursing her lips into a very round O while saying, "Oh my goodness."

"Ni kan," said my mother as Shirley's eyes flooded with tears. "You already know how. Don't need talent for crying!"

Soon after my mother got this idea about Shirley Temple, she took me to a beauty training school in the Mission district[4] and put me in the hands of a student who could barely hold the scissors without shaking. Instead of

327

getting big fat curls, I emerged with an uneven mass of crinkly black fuzz[5].

My mother dragged me off to the bathroom and tried to wet down my hair.

"You look like Negro Chinese," she lamented, as if I had done this on purpose.

The instructor of the beauty training school had to lop off these soggy clumps to make my hair even again[6]. "Peter Pan[7] is very popular these days," the instructor assured my mother. I now had hair the length of a boy's, with straight-across bangs that hung at a slant two inches above my eyebrows. I liked the haircut and it made me actually look forward to my future fame.

In fact, in the beginning, I was just as excited as my mother, maybe even more so. I pictured this prodigy part of me as many different images, trying each one on for size[8]. I was a dainty ballerina girl[9] standing by the curtains, waiting to hear the right music that would send me floating on my tiptoes. I was like the Christ child lifted out of the straw manger[10], crying with holy indignity. I was Cinderella stepping from her pumpkin carriage with sparkly cartoon music filling the air.

In all of my imaginings, I was filled with a sense that I would soon become *perfect*. My mother and father would adore me. I would be beyond reproach. I would never feel the need to sulk[11] for anything.

But sometimes the prodigy in me became impatient. "If you don't hurry up and get me out of here, I'm disappearing for good," it warned. "And then you'll always be nothing."

Every night after dinner, my mother and I would sit at the Formica kitchen table. She would present new tests, taking her examples from stories of amazing children she had read in *Ripley's Believe It or Not*[12], or *Good Housekeeping*, *Reader's Digest*, and a dozen other magazines she kept in a pile in our bathroom. My mother got these magazines from people whose houses she cleaned. And since she cleaned many houses each week,

328

we had a great assortment. She would look through them all, searching for stories about remarkable children.

The first night she brought out a story about a three-year-old boy who knew the capitals of all the states and even most of the European countries. A teacher was quoted as saying the little boy could also pronounce the names of the foreign cities correctly.

"What is the capital of Finland?" my mother asked me, looking at the magazine story.

All I knew was the capital of California, because Sacramento was the name of the street we lived on in Chinatown. "Nairobi!" I guessed, saying the most foreign word I could think of. She checked to see if that was possibly one way to pronounce "Helsinki" before showing me the answer.

The tests got harder—multiplying numbers in my head, finding the queen of hearts in a deck of cards, trying to stand on my head without using my hands, predicting the daily temperatures in Los Angeles, New York, and London.

One night I had to look at a page from the Bible for three minutes and then report everything I could remember. "Now Jehoshaphat[13] had riches and honor in abundance and . . . that's all I remember, Ma," I said.

After seeing my mother's disappointed face once again, something inside of me began to die. I hated the tests, the raised hopes and failed expectations. Before going to bed that night, I looked in the mirror above the bathroom sink and when I saw only my face staring back—and that it would always be this ordinary face—I began to cry. Such a sad, ugly girl! I made high-pitched noises like a crazed animal, trying to scratch out the face in the mirror.

And then I saw what seemed to be the prodigy side of me—because I had never seen that face before. I looked at my reflection, blinking so I could see more clearly. The girl staring back at me was angry, powerful.

329

This girl and I were the same. I had new thoughts, willful thoughts, or rather thoughts filled with lots of won'ts. I won't let her change me, I promised myself. I won't be what I'm not.

So now on nights when my mother presented her tests, I performed listlessly[14], my head propped on one arm. I pretended to be bored. And I was. I got so bored. I started counting the bellows of the foghorns out on the bay[15] while my mother drilled me in other areas. The sound was comforting and reminded me of the cow jumping over the moon. And the next day, I played a game with myself, seeing if my mother would give up on me before eight bellows. After a while I usually counted only one, maybe two bellows at most. At last she was beginning to give up hope.

Two or three months had gone by without any mention of my being a prodigy again. And then one day my mother was watching *The Ed Sullivan Show*[16] on TV. The TV was old and the sound kept shorting out. Every time my mother got halfway up from the sofa to adjust the set, the sound would go back on and Ed would be talking. As soon as she sat down, Ed would go silent again. She got up, the TV broke into loud piano music. She sat down. Silence. Up and down, back and forth, quiet and loud. It was like a stiff embraceless dance between her and the TV set. Finally she stood by the set with her hand on the sound dial.

She seemed entranced by the music, a little frenzied piano piece with this mesmerizing quality, sort of quick passages and then teasing lilting one before it returned to the quick playful parts[17].

"*Ni kan*," my mother said, calling me over with hurried hand gestures. "Look here."

I could see why my mother was fascinated by the music. It was being pounded out by a little Chinese girl, about nine years old, with a Peter Pan haircut. The girl had the sauciness[18] of a Shirley Temple. She was proudly modest like a proper Chinese child. And she also did this fancy sweep of a

330

curtsy, so that the fluffy skirt of her white dress cascaded slowly to the floor like the petals of a large carnation[19].

In spite of these warning signs, I wasn't worried. Our family had no piano and we couldn't afford to buy one, let alone reams of sheet music and piano lessons. So I could be generous in my comments when my mother bad-mouthed the little girl on TV.

"Play note right, but doesn't sound good! No singing sound," complained my mother.

"What are you picking on her for?" I said carelessly. "She's pretty good. Maybe she's not the best, but she's trying hard." I knew almost immediately I would be sorry I said that.

"Just like you," she said. "Not the best. Because you not trying." She gave a little huff as she let go of the sound dial and sat down on the sofa.

The little Chinese girl sat down also to play an encore of "Anitra's Dance" by Grieg[20]. I remember the song, because later on I had to learn how to play it.

Three days after watching *The Ed Sullivan Show*, my mother told me what my schedule would be for piano lessons and piano practice. She had talked to Mr. Chong, who lived on the first floor of our apartment building. Mr. Chong was a retired piano teacher and my mother had traded housecleaning services for weekly lessons and a piano for me to practice on every day, two hours a day, from four until six.

When my mother told me this, I felt as though I had been sent to hell. I whined and then kicked my foot a little when I couldn't stand it anymore.

"Why don't you like me the way I am? I'm not a genius! I can't play the piano. And even if I could, I wouldn't go on TV if you paid me a million dollars!" I cried.

My mother slapped me. "Who ask you be genius?" she shouted. "Only ask you be your best. For you sake. You think I want you be genius? Hnnh! What for! Who ask you!"

"So ungrateful," I heard her mutter in Chinese. "If she had as much talent as she has temper, she would be famous now."

Mr. Chong, whom I secretly nicknamed Old Chong, was very strange, always tapping his fingers to the silent music of an invisible orchestra. He looked ancient in my eyes. He had lost most of the hair on top of his head and he wore thick glasses and had eyes that always looked tired and sleepy. But he must have been younger than I thought, since he lived with his mother and was not yet married.

I met Old Lady Chong once and that was enough. She had this peculiar smell like a baby that had done something in its pants. And her fingers felt like a dead person's, like an old peach I once found in the back of the refrigerator; the skin just slid off the meat when I picked it up.

I soon found out why Old Chong had retired from teaching piano. He was deaf. "Like Beethoven!" he shouted to me. "We're both listening only in our head!" And he would start to conduct his frantic silent sonatas.

Our lessons went like this. He would open the book and point to different things, explaining their purpose: "Key! Treble! Bass! No sharps or flats! So this is C major! Listen now and play after me!"

And then he would play the C scale a few times, a simple chord, and then, as if inspired by an old, unreachable itch, he gradually added more notes and running trills and a pounding bass until the music was really something quite grand.

I would play after him, the simple scale, the simple chord, and then I just played some nonsense that sounded like a cat running up and down on top of garbage cans. Old Chong smiled and applauded and then said, "Very good! But now you must learn to keep time!"

332

So that's how I discovered that Old Chong's eyes were too slow to keep up with the wrong notes I was playing. He went through the motions in half-time. To help me keep rhythm, he stood behind me, pushing down on my right shoulder for every beat. He balanced pennies on top of my wrists so I would keep them still as I slowly played scales and arpeggios[21]. He had me curve my hand around an apple and keep that shape when playing chords. He marched stiffly to show me how to make each finger dance up and down, staccato[22] like an obedient little soldier.

He taught me all these things, and that was how I also learned I could be lazy and get away with mistakes, lots of mistakes. If I hit the wrong notes because I hadn't practiced enough, I never corrected myself. I just kept playing in rhythm. And Old Chong kept conducting his own private reverie.

So maybe I never really gave myself a fair chance. I did pick up the basics pretty quickly, and I might have become a good pianist at that young age. But I was so determined not to try, not to be anybody different that I learned to play only the most ear-splitting preludes, the most discordant hymns.

Over the next year, I practiced like this, dutifully in my own way. And then one day I heard my mother and her friend Lindo Jong both talking in a loud bragging tone of voice so others could hear. It was after church, and I was leaning against the brick wall wearing a dress with stiff white petticoats. Auntie Lindo's daughter, Waverly, who was about my age, was standing farther down the wall about five feet away. We had grown up together and shared all the closeness of two sisters squabbling over crayons and dolls. In other words, for the most part, we hated each other. I thought she was snotty[23]. Waverly Jong had gained a certain amount of fame as "China town's Littlest Chinese Chess Champion".

"She bring home too many trophy," lamented Auntie Lindo that

333

Sunday. "All day she play chess. All day I have no time do nothing but dust off her winnings." She threw a scolding look at Waverly, who pretended not to see her.

"You lucky you don't have this problem," said Auntie Lindo with a sigh to my mother.

And my mother squared her shoulders and bragged: "Our problem worser than yours. If we ask Jing-Mei wash dish, she hear nothing but music. It's like you can't stop this natural talent."

And right then, I was determined to put a stop to her foolish pride.

A few weeks later, Old Chong and my mother conspired to have me play in a talent show which would be held in the church hall. By then, my parents had saved up enough to buy me a secondhand piano, a black Wurlitzer spinet with a scarred bench. It was the showpiece of our living room.

For the talent show, I was to play a piece called "Pleading Child" from Schumann's *Scenes from Childhood*. It was a simple, moody piece that sounded more difficult than it was. I was supposed to memorize the whole thing, playing the repeat parts twice to make the piece sound longer. But I dawdled[24] over it, playing a few bars[25] and then cheating, looking up to see what notes followed. I never really listened to what I was playing. I daydreamed about being somewhere else, about being someone else.

The part I liked to practice best was the fancy curtsy: right foot out, touch the rose on the carpet with a pointed foot, sweep to the side, left leg bends, look up and smile.

My parents invited all the couples from the Joy Luck Club to witness my debut[26]. Auntie Lindo and Uncle Tin were there. Waverly and her two older brothers had also come. The first two rows were filled with children both younger and older than I was. The little ones got to go first. They recited simple nursery rhymes, squawked out tunes on miniature violins, twirled Hula Hoops, pranced in pink ballet tutus[27], and when they bowed or curtsied, the audience would sigh in unison[28], "Awww," and then clap enthusiastically.

When my turn came, I was very confident. I remember my childish excitement. It was as if I knew, without a doubt, that the prodigy side of me really did exist. I had no fear whatsoever, no nervousness. I remember thinking to myself, This is it! This is it! I looked out over the audience, at my mother's blank face, my father's yawn, Auntie Lindo's stiff-lipped smile, Waverly's sulky expression. I had on a white dress layered with sheets of lace, and a pink bow in my Peter Pan haircut. As I sat down I envisioned people jumping to their feet and Ed Sullivan rushing up to introduce me to everyone on TV.

And I started to play. It was so beautiful. I was so caught up in how lovely I looked that at first I didn't worry how I would sound. So it was a surprise to me when I hit the first wrong note and I realized something didn't sound quite right. And then I hit another and another followed that. A chill started at the top of my head and began to trickle down[29]. Yet I couldn't stop playing, as though my hands were bewitched. I kept thinking my fingers would adjust themselves back, like a train switching to the right track. I played this strange jumble through two repeats, the sour notes staying with me all the way to the end.

When I stood up, I discovered my legs were shaking. Maybe I had just been nervous and the audience, like Old Chong, had seen me go through the right motions and had not heard anything wrong at all. I swept my right foot out, went down on my knee, looked up and smiled. The room was quiet, except for Old Chong, who was beaming and shouting, "Bravo! Bravo! Well done!" But then I saw my mother's face, her stricken face. The audience clapped weakly, and as I walked back to my chair, with my whole face quivering as I tried not to cry, I heard a little boy whisper to his mother, "that's awful," and the mother whispered back, "Well, she certainly tried."

And now I realized how many people were in the audience, the whole world it seemed. I was aware of eyes burning into my back. I felt the shame of my mother and father as they sat stiffly throughout the rest of the show.

We could have escaped during intermission. Pride and some strange sense of honor must have anchored my parents to their chairs. And so we watched it all: the eighteen-year-old boy with a fake mustache who did a magic show and jungled flaming hoops while riding a unicycle. The breasted girl with white makeup who sang from *Madama Butterfly* and got honorable mention. And the eleven-year-old boy who won first prize playing a tricky violin song that sounded like a busy bee.

After the show, the Hsus, the Jongs, and the St. Clairs from the Joy Luck Club came up to my mother and father.

"Lots of talented kids," Auntie Lindo said vaguely, smiling broadly.

"That was somethin' else," said my father, and I wondered if he was referring to me in a humorous way, or whether he even remembered what I had done.

Waverly looked at me and shrugged her shoulders. "You aren't genius like me," she said matter-of-factly. And if I hadn't felt so bad, I would have pulled her braids and punched her stomach.

But my mother's expression was what devastated me: a quiet, blank look that said she had lost everything. I felt the same way, and it seemed as if everybody were now coming up, like gawkers[30] at the scene of an accident, to see what parts were actually missing. When we got on the bus to go home, my father was humming the busy-bee tune and my mother was silent. I kept thinking she wanted to wait until we got home before shouting at me. But when my father unlocked the door to our apartment, my mother walked in and then went to the back, into the bedroom. No accusations. No blame. And in a way, I felt disappointed. I had been waiting for her to start shouting, so I could shout back and cry and blame her for all my misery.

I assumed my talent-show fiasco[31] meant I never had to play the piano again. But two days later, after school, my mother came out of the kitchen and saw me watching TV.

"Four clock," she reminded me as if it were any other day. I was stunned, as though she were asking me to go through the talent-show torture again. I wedged myself more tightly in front of the TV.

"Turn off TV," she called from the kitchen five minutes later.

I didn't budge. And then I decided. I didn't have to do what my mother said anymore. I wasn't her slave. This wasn't China. I had listened to her before and look what happened. She was the stupid one.

She came out from the kitchen and stood in the arched entryway of the living room. "Four clock," she said once again, louder.

"I'm not going to play anymore," I said nonchalantly. "Why should I? I'm not a genius."

She walked over and stood in front of the TV. I saw her chest was heaving up and down in an angry way.

"No!" I said, and I now felt stronger, as if my true self had finally emerged. So this was what had been inside me all along.

"No! I won't!" I screamed.

She yanked me by the arm, pulled me off the floor, snapped off the TV. She was frighteningly strong, half pulling, half carrying me toward the piano as I kicked the throw rugs under my feet. She lifted me up and onto the hard bench. I was sobbing by now, looking at her bitterly. Her chest was heaving even more and her mouth was open, smiling crazily as if she were pleased I was crying.

"You want me to be someone that I'm not!" I sobbed. "I'll never be the kind of daughter you want me to be!"

"Only two kinds of daughters," she shouted in Chinese. "Those who are obedient and those who follow their own mind! Only one kind of daughter can live in this house. Obedient daughter!"

"Then I wish I wasn't your daughter. I wish you weren't my mother," I shouted. As I said these things I got scared. It felt like worms and toads and slimy things crawling out of my chest, but it also felt good, as if this awful side of me had surfaced, at last.

"Too late change this," said my mother shrilly.

And I could sense her anger rising to its breaking point. I wanted to see it spill over. And that's when I remembered the babies she had lost in China, the ones we never talked about. "Then I wish I'd never been born!" I shouted. "I wish I were dead! Like them."

It was as if I had said the magic words. Alakazam! —and her face went blank, her mouth closed, her arms went slack, and she backed out of the room, stunned, as if she were blowing away like a small brown leaf, thin, brittle, lifeless.

It was not the only disappointment my mother felt in me. In the years that followed, I failed her so many times, each time asserting my own will, my right to fall short of expectations. I didn't get straight As[32]. I didn't become class president. I didn't get into Stanford. I dropped out of college.

For unlike my mother, I did not believe I could be anything I wanted to be. I could only be me.

And for all those years, we never talked about the disaster at the recital[33] or my terrible accusations afterward at the piano bench. All that remained unchecked, like a betrayal that was now unspeakable. So I never found a way to ask her why she had hoped for something so large that

338

failure was inevitable.

And even worse, I never asked her what frightened me the most: Why had she given up hope?

For after our struggle at the piano, she never mentioned my playing again. The lessons stopped. The lid to the piano was closed, shutting out the dust, my misery, and her dreams.

So she surprised me. A few years ago, she offered to give me the piano, for my thirtieth birthday. I had not played in all those years. I saw the offer as a sign of forgiveness, a tremendous burden removed.

"Are you sure?" I asked shyly. "I mean, won't you and Dad miss it?"

"No, this your piano," she said firmly. "Always your piano. You only one can play."

"Well, I probably can't play anymore," I said. "It's been years."

"You pick up fast," said my mother, as if she knew this was certain. "You have natural talent. You could been genius if you want to."

"No I couldn't."

"You just not trying," said my mother. And she was neither angry nor sad. She said it as if to announce a fact that could never be disproved. "Take it," she said.

But I didn't at first. It was enough that she had offered it to me. And after that, every time I saw it in my parents' living room, standing in front of the bay windows, it made me feel proud, as if it were a shiny trophy I had won back.

Last week I sent a tuner over to my parents' apartment and had the piano reconditioned, for purely sentimental reasons. My mother had died a few months before and I had been getting things in order for my father, a little bit at a time. I put the jewelry in special silk pouches. The sweaters she had knitted in yellow, pink, bright orange—all the colors I hated—I put those in moth-proof boxes. I found some old Chinese silk dresses, the kind with little slits up the sides. I rubbed the old silk against my skin, then wrapped them in tissue and decided to take them home with me.

After I had the piano tuned, I opened the lid and touched the keys. I sounded even richer than I remembered. Really, it was a very good piano. Inside the bench were the same exercise notes with handwritten scales, the same secondhand music books with their covers held together with yellow tape.

I opened up the Schumann book to the dark little piece I had played at the recital. It was on the left-hand side of the page, "Pleading Child". It looked more difficult than I remembered. I played a few bars, surprised at how easily the notes came back to me.

And for the first time, or so it seemed, I noticed the piece on the right-hand side. It was called "Perfectly Contented". I tried to play this one as well. It had a lighter melody but the same flowing rhythm and turned out to be quite easy. "Pleading Child" was shorter but slower; "Perfectly Contented" was longer, but faster. And after I played them both a few times, I realized they were two halves of the same song.

Notes:

1. with almost no money down: 几乎不要首付。down: 作首付款 (as a down payment)

2. prodigy: 天才 (a person who has unusual and very noticeable abilities)

3. Shirley Temple: 美国童星秀兰 · 邓波儿 (an American child actress, popular in the 1930s)

4. Mission district: a San Francisco neighborhood

5. an uneven mass of crinkly black fuzz: 一头乱蓬蓬的黑色小卷毛。crinkly: curly; fuzz: a mass of soft thin hair

6. had to lop off these soggy clumps to make my hair even again: 为了把

我的头发弄整齐,不得不剪掉这一团团湿乎乎的卷发。lop off：剪掉(trim off, cut off)；soggy：湿透(completely wet)；clump：团(a lump or mass)

7. Peter Pan：小飞侠彼得·潘,是英国著名作家杰姆·巴里(1860—1937)创作的童话剧中的人物,是个不肯长大的男孩。1953 年,迪斯尼公司出品了动画版的《小飞侠》影片,之后被拍成不同版本的电影,颇受欢迎。

8. I pictured this prodigy part of me as many different images, trying each one on for size：我把自己想象成不同类型的天才,看看哪个最适合我。

9. a dainty ballerina girl：一个娇小可爱跳芭蕾舞的女孩。ballerina：a femal ballet dancer.

10. the straw manger：铺着稻草的马槽

11. sulk：生闷气(be silently bad-tempered, esp. for an unimportant reason)

12. Ripley's Believe It or Not：a newspaper column about amazing facts and events, popular since 1918.

13. Jehoshaphat：约沙法(《圣经》中的人物)

14. listlessly：无精打采地(spiritlessly)

15. the bellows of the foghorns out on the bay：海湾上面雾号发出的鸣叫声

16. Ed Sullivan Show：a TV variety show, popular in the 1950s.

17. She seemed entranced by the music, a little frenzied piano piece ... before it returned to the quick playful parts：她似乎被这音乐吸引住了,这是一支充满激情、令人着迷的钢琴小曲,乐曲有几节是快节奏的,接着几节是欢快跳动的,然后又回到快节奏的嬉戏部分。entrance：吸引(fascinate)；passage：乐曲的一节(a section of a musical work)

18. sauciness：粗鲁的,傲慢的(impolite, insolent)

19. And she also did this fancy sweep of a curtsy ... cascaded slowly to the floor like the petals of a large carnation：她也行了一个花哨潇洒的屈膝礼,她那白色蓬松的裙子慢慢地垂落到地上,好像一大朵康乃馨的花瓣。cascade：瀑布似的落下

20. to play an encore of "Anitra's Dance" by Grieg：弹奏格里格的《阿尼特拉舞曲》,作为加演曲目。encore：(在演出结束时)加演的节目

21. arpeggios：琶音(the rapid playing of a musical chord, from the lowest note to the highest)

22. staccato：断续地,不连贯地(disconnectedly)

23. snotty：傲慢的(trying to act as if one is important)

24. dawdle：do something very slowly

25. bar：(乐曲中的)一小节

26. debut：初次登台(a first public appearance)

27. squawked out tunes on miniature violins, twirled Hula Hoops, pranced in pink ballet tutus：用微型小提琴拉出又响又粗的调子,跳呼啦圈,穿着粉色的芭蕾舞短裙蹦蹦跳跳。tutu：芭蕾舞短裙(a short skirt made of many folds of stiffened material worn by women ballet dancers)

28. in unison：at the same time and in the same way

29. A chill started at the top of my head and began to trickle down：一股凉气从头顶开始,然后一点点传到全身。

30. gawker：a person who stare stupidly or with astonishment

31. fiasco：a complete failure

32. I didn't get straight As：我没有获得全优成绩。

33. recital：a muscial or dance entertainment given by one or more performers

Questions:

1. What is the conflict between the mother and daughter? What leads to it?
2. Do you think this kind of story can also happen in China? Explain.
3. Is Old Chong a good teacher or bad teacher? How does he help Jing-Mei?
4. What role does the piano serve as in the story? Does it have any symbolic meaning?
5. Compare the relationship between Jing-Mei and her mother and that between Dee and her mother in Alice Walker's "Everyday Use", and discuss their differences.
6. How do "Pleading Child" and "Perfectly Contented" have a double meaning in the story? What does the last sentence of the story mean?
7. Discuss the theme of the story.

References

常耀信.《美国文学简史》. 天津：南开大学出版社,1991.

李公昭.《20世纪美国文学导论》. 西安：西安交通大学出版社,2000.

刘海平,王守仁.《新编美国文学史》. 上海：上海外语教育出版社,
2002.

王守仁,赵宇.《英美小说》. 南京：南京大学出版社,1997.

王佐良,刘承沛.《美国短篇小说选》. 北京：商务印书馆,1982.

杨仁敬.《20世纪美国文学史》. 青岛：青岛出版社,2000.

杨仁敬等.《美国后现代派短篇小说选》. 青岛：青岛出版社,2004.

朱原等译.《朗文当代高级英语词典：英英、英汉双解》. 北京：商务印
书馆,1998.

Cleanth, Brooks, Lewis, R. W., and Warren, Robert Penn, eds. *American Literature: The Makers and the Making*. New York: St. Martin's Press, 1973.

Dalgish, Gerard M. *Random House Webster's Dictionary of American English*. Beijing: Foreign Language Teaching and Research Press, 1997.

Geyh, Paula, Fred G. Leebron, Andrew Levy. *Postmodern American Fiction: A Norton Anthology*. New York: W. W. Norton & Company, Inc., 1998.

Hart, J. D. *The Oxford Companion to American Literature*. Beijing: Foreign Language Teaching and Research Press, 2005.

The Holy Bible: New International Version. East Brunswick, NJ: International Bible Society, 1984.

Keillor, Garrison, and Katrina Kenison. *The Best American Short Stories* 1998. Boston: Houghton Mifflin, 1998.

Merriam-Webster's Collegiate Dictionary. Massachusetts: Merriam-Webster Incorporated, 2003.

Oates, Joyce Carol. *The Oxford Book of American Short Stories.* Oxford: Oxford University Press, 1992.

Alice Walker Wikipedia, the Free Encyclopedia. < http://en.wikipedia. org/wiki/Alice_Walker >

Amy Tan Wikipedia, the Free Encyclopedia. < http://en.wikipedia. org/wiki/Amy_Tan >

John Cheever Wikipedia, the Free Encyclopedia. < http://en.wikipedia. org/wiki/John_Cheever >

John Updike Wikipedia, the Free Encyclopedia. < http://en.wikipedia. org/wiki/John_Updike >

O. Henry Wikipedia, the Free Encyclopedia. < http://en.wikipedia. org/wiki/O._Henry >

William Gibson Wikipedia, the Free Encyclopedia. < http://en. wikipedia.org/wiki/William_Gibson >

后　记

《美国短篇小说选读》终于付梓了。

这是一本为非英语专业本科生编写的教材,是我多年教学和研究的结晶。几年前,厦门大学推行教学改革,鼓励教师为本科生开设选修课。我是研究美国文学的,打算结合自己的专业开一门校选课——"美国短篇小说"。有的同事听说后有些为我担心——"现在的学生喜欢选一些与经济有关的课程,会有学生来选你的课吗?"在文学被边缘化的时代,这种担心不无道理。但是我也知道,很多国内外的著名高校都非常重视培养学生的人文素养,为理工类学生开设了文学、艺术等课程。厦门大学也很重视学生人文素养的培养,也有一些教师开过英语文学类的选修课,如詹树魁教授的"莎士比亚戏剧"和李美华教授的"美国20世纪小说",据说效果都不错。

课前我心里有过担心:要是来的学生很少,怎么办呢? 第一次走进教室,我发现竟然有那么多学生来听课,一颗悬着的心落地了。一个学期上完,学生的反馈都不错。于是我接着上了第二轮、第三轮,效果都很好。我认为"美国短篇小说"课程的成功主要有以下几个原因。首先是课程的切入点。我选择文化作为切入点,通过小说教文化。因此该课程能让学生更多地了解美国文化和不同时期的美国社会生活。其次是课程的趣味性。小说有故事情节和人物描写。短篇小说篇幅短,学生能够在短时间内读完一篇小说,获得对小说故事情节完整的了解。最后是原汁原味的英语。我一直认为,要学好英语,一定要多阅读,而且要多读原著。我所选的小说都出自名家之手,文笔优美,语言规范,风格各异,是学习地道英语的很好素材。学生通过阅读这些短篇小说,能扩大词汇量,增强语感,提高英语的阅读水平和文学欣赏水平。

本书是根据我的"美国短篇小说"课程的讲义整理和补充而成的。

考虑到读者主要是理工科类本科生,我对小说中出现的难词和有些文化现象做了很详细的中英文注释,希望尽量减少阅读的困难。每篇小说后面都附有 3~6 个与小说内容有关的思考题,可供课堂讨论之用,以加深对小说的理解和欣赏。

在此书的编写过程中,我的导师杨仁敬教授给予很多鼓励和帮助。看了本书目录后,他建议增加欧·亨利的小说《麦琪的礼物》,同时还建议增加一些科幻小说。他还提供了一些宝贵的资料,让我得以顺利完成本书的编写。他还在百忙中为本书作序,给予充分的肯定、热情的鼓励和谆谆的教诲。在此谨向他表示特别的感谢。还要感谢选修我的"美国短篇小说"课程的学生,"教学相长",是他们给我信心,给我启发,帮助我不断地完善课程。我的丈夫潘勤奋先生也给了我很多鼓励和支持,这使本书能够顺利出版,在此也向他表示感谢。

由于本人水平有限,经验不足,书中错误和缺点在所难免,请读者谅解,也请同行赐教。

范小玫
2009 年 1 月

图书在版编目(CIP)数据

美国短篇小说选读/范小玫编著.—厦门:厦门大学出版社,2009.2
(2022.1重印)
ISBN 978-7-5615-3191-4

Ⅰ.美…　Ⅱ.范…　Ⅲ.①英语-阅读教学-高等学校-教材②短篇小
说-文学欣赏-美国　Ⅳ.H319.4:I

中国版本图书馆 CIP 数据核字(2009)第 025840 号

厦门大学出版社出版发行

(地址:厦门市软件园二期望海路 39 号　邮编:361008)

http://www.xmupress.com

xmup @ public.xm.fj.cn

厦门集大印刷有限公司

2009 年 2 月第 1 版　2022 年 1 月第 4 次印刷

开本:880×1230　1/32　印张:11　插页:2

字数:300 千字

定价:35.00 元

本书如有印装质量问题请直接寄承印厂调换